THE MANAGEMENT *of* IMPROVEMENT

Concepts, Organization, and Strategy

Reinhold Industrial Engineering and Management Sciences Textbook Series

CONSULTING EDITOR: Professor Robert N. Lehrer
School of Industrial Engineering
Georgia Institute of Technology

Analytic Models for Managerial and Engineering Economics, *by Herbert E. Schweyer*

Management of Improvement: Concepts, Organization, and Strategy, *by Robert N. Lehrer*

Project Management with CPM and PERT, *by Joseph J. Moder and Cecil R. Phillips*

IN PREPARATION

Introduction to Digital Computer Applications, *by Andrew G. Favret*

Management of Research and Development, *by Albert Rubenstein and Peter Norden*

Systems Engineering: Analysis and Design of Production Systems, *by Salah E. Elmaghraby*

THE MANAGEMENT *of* IMPROVEMENT

Concepts, Organization, and Strategy

ROBERT N. LEHRER
Associate Director and Professor
School of Industrial Engineering
Georgia Institute of Technology
Atlanta, Georgia

NEW YORK
REINHOLD PUBLISHING CORPORATION
CHAPMAN & HALL LTD., LONDON

Library of Congress Catalog Card Number: 64-8547

Printed in the United States of America

To

The women of my life

MAGGIE

PATSY

JOAN

PREFACE

THE MAIN objective of this book is to draw attention to the process of improvement within organizations, and to advance the proposition that improvement can be systematically pursued and achieved—the process of improvement can be managed.

The original title selected by the author was *The Management of Improvement: An Introduction to Industrial Engineering, Operations Research and Management Science.* It seems more appropriate that the subtitle be changed to its present form—*Concepts, Organization and Strategy*—for the presentations that follow are not as much an introduction to the three activities as they are an attempt to illustrate the need for and approaches to achieving continual improvement within organizations. All three activities are intimately involved with improvement endeavors, and when combined they do represent a valuable resource that can broadly serve an organization in its quest for improvement.

There are many approaches to improvement. Some are primarily concerned with obtaining improvement in the efficiency of using direct labor. Some are primarily concerned with the application of new technology. Some concentrate upon the mathematical analysis of managerial decision making. We are interested in all of these approaches to improvement plus many others. Our interest is directed toward a broad-gage and organization-wide improvement function which is not limited to any set of problem-solving techniques nor to any particular problem areas. The goal is to achieve improvement where it is needed—and to continually achieve improvement throughout an organization.

A unified approach to improvement within an organization must be problem-oriented. It must be based upon a critical analysis of the needs and opportunities for improvement, and the development of approaches to cultivating improvement in response to these needs and opportunities. Such an approach draws upon a broad range of problem-solving tools and attempts to combine the methodologies and techniques of all approaches to the development of improvement, with a generous borrowing from industrial engineering, operations research, and management science at the very least. From this point of view, the materials that follow are an introduction to these three areas of specialization. However, the concepts of improvement, organization of improvement efforts, and changing strategies of pursuing and achieving improvement will predominate.

The general philosophy of improvement that will be treated throughout the book might be summarized as "the problem is the boss." The nature of the problem should determine what approaches to its solution are appropriate, and how technology and techniques of analysis can be used effectively. The approach must be problem-oriented, flexible, and always concerned with seeking out opportunities for improving the efficiency with which an organization operates. Technology and specialized approaches to improvement are viewed as resources to be exploited, as appropriate, in our quest for improvement.

There should be little question that improvement is a desirable goal. Past success has been closely associated with improvement. Future success will be dependent upon it. But, improvement does not just happen. It is the result of desire and pursuit—and it can be achieved in fair measure by formally recognizing that it should be pursued and achieved, and by organizing for it. These points will be presented and demonstrated in a variety of ways. The experience of many individuals and organizations will be drawn upon and summarized in some form or another. The author is most appreciative of these sources of inspiration and examples. Some are acknowledged directly in the text material, but others are not. Omission is not intended to imply lack of consideration.

It is impossible to thank the many individuals—students, academic associates, professional colleagues and people from industry, both here and abroad—who have in one way or another contributed to the development of the materials which follow. However, special thanks are due to Drs. Andrew Schultz, Jr., and Raymond Villers for their review of the preliminary manuscript and for many very helpful suggestions. It is unfortunate that the author has not been able to follow through with all of them. Shortcomings of the book are clearly the author's responsibility. Perhaps these can be overcome in future writings.

ROBERT N. LEHRER

Atlanta, Georgia
September, 1964

CONTENTS

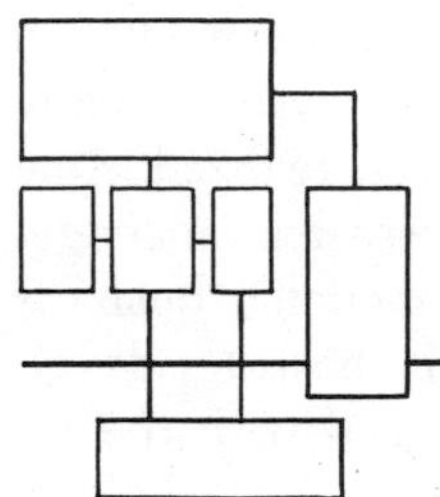

CHAPTER 1

CAN IMPROVEMENT BE MANAGED?

MANAGEMENT personnel responsible for the direction and operation of the many organizations so vital to our economic and social systems are becoming increasingly aware of the need for better and more effective solutions to their problems. They recognize that their problems are becoming ever more complex because of the boom in technology, the maturing of our social system, and a keener competition for achieving personal, organizational, national, and global objectives. Pressure for improving the effectiveness of management has sharpened the approaches to management in general, and has given a great stimulus to the development of organized approaches to achieving improvement.

Science and technology are being used more and more to provide better ways to achieve organizational objectives and to solve management problems. Research and development are becoming a significant part of our economic activity. Computers are being used to speed engineering and scientific calculations, to control processes and inventories, and to provide essential information for management decision. Operations research is being used to solve complex design and operational problems. Management science is being used to achieve solution to complex management problems. Industrial engineering is being used to achieve further improvement in the efficiency of using manpower, materials, and facilities.

To say the least, there has emerged a wide variety of approaches to improving the efficiency of management and the activities for which management is responsible. All of these approaches have been beneficial, but they all fall far short of the need. Improvement must be *managed.* The fragmentary approaches must be brought together.

Fortunately, there are encouraging indications that improvement can be effectively managed and that a unified approach to systematically striving for, developing, and using improvements can be realized. One approach is through an amalgamation of operations research, management science, *traditional* industrial engineering, and functional business or management specialties. This combination provides the basis for developing an organization-wide improvement function, charged with the responsibility for encouraging and assisting the organization as a whole to systematically and continually improve. This theme will be the main one in the remainder of the book.

APPROACH AND ORGANIZATION

A variety of specific approaches to improvement endeavors will be presented. These examples have been selected to represent situations of some particular significance to the solving of problems associated with developing an effective improvement function. The reader can learn from the experience of others, and if perceptive he can detect causes and effects that will guide him in the successful *improvement* of improvement endeavors within any organization and in the development of a broader improvement function serving his entire organization. These specific examples are presented within a matrix of introductory, background, and supplementary material. The general organization is as follows.

BACKGROUND

In Chapters 2 and 3 the nature of management, the management cycle, levels of management, and the emergence of science and engineering as aids to more effective management are discussed. After indicating the growing importance of engineering and science as means of helping management improve its effectiveness, the nature and characteristics of science, management, and engineering are discussed and compared.

The background of our present high level of material well-being is discussed, and the concept of *three* industrial revolutions is presented. These are viewed as being responsible for past achievement. The concept of an organized improvement function as a means of assuring continual improvement and advancement is presented. Various approaches to improvement are discussed, and their shortcomings assessed. A unified approach, combining the better aspects of *traditional* industrial engineering, operations research, and management science, is advocated and equated to the basis of a broad-gage improvement function. The aspirations of *modern* industrial engineering, representing this amalgamation, are examined and related to the improvement function.

THE IMPROVEMENT FUNCTION

In Chapter 4 a specific example is presented, picturing what one company expects of an improvement function activity and what it actually gets.

OPERATIONS RESEARCH

Chapters 5 through 10 discuss operations research, what it is, its main characteristics, and problems associated with its effective use as an improvement approach. One version of operations research represents an application of science to management problems. The success of this application depends largely upon how effectively *engineering* has been incorporated into it.

SYSTEMS

Chapters 11, 12, and 13 are devoted to an expansion of the systems approach in improvement endeavors. The concepts of full-range management improvement, systems simplification, and systems validation are presented. Examples of the analysis and design of systems for producing and systems for managing are also presented illustrating the effective use of technology in developing such systems.

INTRODUCTION OF CHANGE AND IMPROVEMENT

Chapters 14 and 15 are concerned with the problems of introducing a new function within an organization and the human problems that assist or impede the development of improvement.

EXAMPLES OF IMPROVEMENT FUNCTION ACTIVITIES

Chapters 16 through 21 are devoted to examples of improvement function activities, within widely differing types of organizations and under a variety of conditions. They have been selected to illustrate various aspects of the problem of achieving continual improvement in a systematic manner. They range from starting improvement efforts in a very modest manner, to approaches that are mature and include sophisticated methodologies, to problems of managing or administering an improvement function. The examples are not intended to be a complete coverage of improvement endeavors, but to indicate the viability of the improvement function concept under differing circumstances, requirements, and handicaps.

CONSOLIDATION AND GENERALIZATION

Chapters 22 and 23 are devoted to a restatement of some of the problems, characteristics, and theoretical bases of *modern* industrial engineering and their consequences relative to the improvement function in application and the education of personnel for specialization in improvement function activities.

KEY POINTS

Chapter 24 is devoted to a consolidation and restatement of some key points and concepts which have been presented and developed within the previous text material.

SUMMARY

Although great strides have been made in the improvement of the functioning of the many organizations so vital to our economic and social systems, the obligations of the period within which we live make it critically important that we continue to improve the efficiency of all organizations—and to *increase* the rate of improvement. This is true for small organizations as well as large organizations and also for very large organizations representing the functioning of our social and economic values. If we achieve increased efficiency—the elimination of needless waste—we can more nearly do the things that we as individuals and as a society believe should be done. The case for improved efficiency is a pervasive one. It is an imperative.

How can efficiency be improved? There have been a variety of approaches. We will examine some of these briefly and some of them in detail. We will select several, combine them, and broaden their scope in an attempt to develop a more effective approach to cultivating continual improvement.

How can improvement be managed? There are many ways. First, it must be pursued in a systematic way where it is really needed. Secondly, it must be achieved. Thirdly, it must be put to effective use. This can and must be done, and done in a manner fully consistent with our moral and social values.

The material that follows amplifies these thoughts. While reading it one should keep in mind the objectives and approach of the book and its underlying philosophy.

1. Approaches to improvement should serve the entire organization, as a whole and in all its parts as related to the whole.
2. Improvement is a management responsibility. In a sense all individuals within an organization are managers. However, the heaviest obligations for improvement efforts are at the top.
3. Improvement can be achieved by:
   - management improvement
   - better systems for managing
   - better systems relative to those being managed, including
     - improved design of products and services
     - improved design of operations
     - improved design of processes
     - improved design of systems of operation.
4. Improvement can be achieved by management helping themselves.
5. Improvement can be achieved by staff support and assistance.
6. Improvement can be achieved by exploitation of science and technology —and experience and common sense—in the areas of:
   - systems being managed
   - systems for managing
   - the "art" of managing.
7. The efficiency of the process of improvement can be improved by:
   - retaining those aspects of existing approaches that have proven to be of value
   - improving the effectiveness and utility of available approaches by modification and adaptation
   - by devising new, broader, and more effective approaches.
8. Any organization can increase its rate of improvement by establishing "improvement function" responsibilities as one of the basic functional parts of the organization. This function is charged with the responsibility for assisting, guiding, and supporting the quest for improvement by:
   - helping to determine what areas within the organization need improvement
   - helping to devise strategies and tactics for achieving the desired improvements
   - helping to achieve useful and lasting application of improvement
   - providing strong guidance for the continual and systematic quest for and achievement of improvement throughout the organization.

Improvement can be managed!

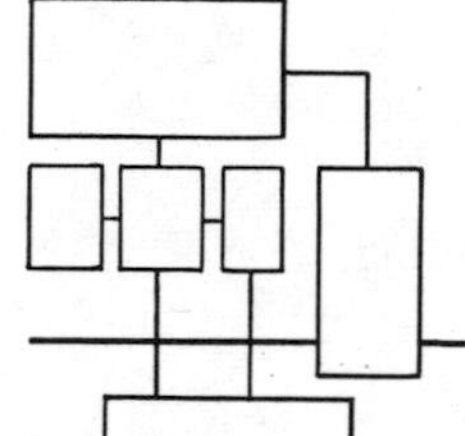

CHAPTER 2

MANAGEMENT: The Growing Importance of Science and Engineering

MANAGEMENT has been aptly described by Lawrence A. Appley, President of the American Management Association, as the process of getting things done through others.[1] This definition is accurate, but deceptively simple. Management is a highly complex function and one of considerable importance to the effective operation of every organization and to our country. The manager is an organizer, a director of other people's activities, a planner, a salesman, a decision-maker, an expediter, and much more. His basic responsibilities are to plan for achieving some specific result, to organize to achieve these results, to see that the necessary actions for achievement are taken, to monitor and evaluate these activities, to take corrective action where necessary, and to achieve the desired results in an *efficient* manner. Thus, in rather brutal language (but not intended to be derogatory) the manager is an exploiter of resources for achieving a desired result. This desired result may be the production of a product, the rendering of a governmental, social, or public service, or the securing of national defense.

The manager exploits the resources at his disposal to achieve results and benefits in a manner that is regarded by those who evaluate his performance as efficient. In private industry the criterion for evaluation may be largely based upon profits. In other organizations the results may be evaluated in terms of accomplishments relative to anticipated results and costs. In all legitimate organizations results are evaluated, at least in part, by social and political values in addition to values more closely associated with the economic and legal systems. These values are highly individualistic, depending on the manager and his organization and upon the environment. What may be regarded as outstandingly good management in one organization at a particular time may be quite unsatisfactory in another organization or different time period.

Even so, there seems to be a common denominator for guiding management, which allows flexibility for tailoring actions to the needs of the specific situation. This is implicit in the management cycle consisting of

1. Planning,
2. Organization,
3. Execution, and
4. Evaluation and corrective action.

This cycle is repeated in any management activity. It is in keeping with the Appley definition of management and applies equally well, but in a slightly different manner, to the various levels of management. The cycle, along with the definition, implies the critical role of management—the leadership and direction (or guidance) of other people's endeavors on behalf of the objectives of an "organization."

The way in which the cycle is implemented will vary with the level of management. Top management is primarily concerned with the over-all operation of their organization, the general guidance of total organizational endeavors, and the formulation of basic policy to give direction to the total activity. Middle management is mainly concerned with translation of basic policy into operational policy, plans, and actions. The third level of management, supervision, is usually regarded as the direct link between the management hierarchy and the "producing" part of the organization. Supervision (the first-line supervisor or foreman) is responsible for getting results—to see that the formulated plans are executed.

In all parts of the management cycle, and at all levels, management has the overriding obligation to achieve results—*and* to do this in an efficient manner.

History is illuminated by individuals possessing a gift for leadership and a keen insight into the fundamentals of effective management. For example, more than 150 years ago Napoleon Bonaparte stated that "people are like digits, the higher their position the greater is their value." Management has only recently recognized the fundamental importance of this concept relative to providing an opportunity and challenge for each individual to work to the upper levels of his abilities and thus to better achieve personal and organizational objectives. But, it has only been during the last half century that the management process and its systematic improvement have become the subject of concentrated attention.

SCIENTIFIC MANAGEMENT

The evolution of the art of management has been very gradual, with considerable progress having been made since the start of the scientific management movement in the early 1900's.[2] This movement, even though usually regarded as passe, has had a profound effect upon the keen interest in management improvement that has passed through a *scientific* management phase to the more recent management *sciences* phase. During this period, of approximately 50 years, there has been an up and down and an up in the realization that management and science have close bonds. The original concept, based upon the application of the scientific or engineering approach to the problems of management, was that all these problems could be solved by rational and scientific analysis. Pervasive principles would be discovered, and in a short period all problems of management would be solvable by routine application of categorized fundamental principles. These aspirations never became a reality. The complexity of management and of human behavior was vastly underestimated. The power of science was vastly overestimated. Even so, the scientific management movement accomplished astonishing results. It served to focus attention upon the development of the *art* of management —and subsequently laid the foundations for a healthy combination of art and science as contributors to more effective management.

At present, there is no question concerning the impact of engineering and science upon the management process. We live in an era of growing technological complexity, which influences all our lives. Management is greatly influenced both by the growing technical aspects of the endeavors they must manage and the general environment of a "technological" society—and also by the impact *upon* the management function of the application of technology *to* the management function. Computers, operations research, and management science all tend to complicate the lives of management personnel, but they also represent opportunities for extending and improving the effectiveness of management.

The importance of engineering and science to management has passed through several phases, which can be approximated as follows: (1) The industrial revolution created the technology (or the start of it) that is the basis of modern industry. (2) Problems associated with the effective and economical use (that is, the exploitation) of this technology resulted in attempts to apply the essence of the genesis of technology (the scientific or engineering method) to the improvement of the *management* of these problems. (3) Later, and until quite recently, science and technology have been associated primarily with new product and process development. (4) Recently, science and technology have been redirected toward solution of the problems that have arisen from (or as a consequence of) these developments. This has resulted in the evolution of a combination of art and science *within* the management function. The end result is that management is inextricably involved with science and engineering. The modern manager is forced to be involved with these technical areas, for they are important components of many of the problems with which he must contend—directly and indirectly. Because he must operate within an increasingly technical environment—both in his own organization and the larger social system—he must develop a better understanding of engineering and science if he hopes to do his job effectively, and if he hopes to effectively utilize the skills and abilities of engineering and scientific personnel within his organization.

Some of the ways in which science and engineering can be exploited by management to help them do a more effective job of managing will be presented in subsequent chapters. At the present time it will be useful to set the stage for a better appreciation of how this exploitation can be accomplished. This requires the development of an understanding of the similarities and differences among management, engineering, and science. It is important for the manager to know the characteristics and peculiarities of the engineer and scientist so that he can utilize the knowledge, skills, and abilities of these individuals to help him and his organization. It is also important for the engineer and scientist interested in helping management to obtain a better understanding of the problems of management and the ways in which science and engineering can better serve their organizations. These three groups—management, engineering, and science—are basically quite different, and effective collaboration to achieve mutual organizational objectives requires accommodation and understanding.[3]

SCIENCE

The basic characteristic of science is implicit in the origin of the word —from the Latin *Sciencia,* which means *knowing*. Science has been principally concerned with the quest for knowing—for understanding the phenomena of the world within which we live. The scientist is motivated by his curiosity without any particular regard to the practical utility of what he learns. Many scientists spend their entire lifetime seeking new knowledge and understanding that will represent their contribution to a more complete understanding of the world. The scientist, in his quest for knowledge and understanding, is searching for fundamental truth on as broad a basis as he can possibly achieve it. The dream of many scientists is to discover a universal truth—one that has the broadest possible application in explaining the phenomena of nature and man. This is seldom achieved; but it represents the "spirit" of science, and it exerts a profound influence upon the behavior of the scientist. These individuals, in their quest for knowing, rely heavily upon the so-called scientific method:

1. Intuition in speculating what fundamental truth may be.
2. Formulation of hypotheses.
3. Controlled experimentation to test the viability of speculations (or hypotheses).
4. Generalization of the experimental results to implications within a much broader sphere.
5. Open examination, verification, and evaluation of what they have done by the world-wide community of scientists.

Nowhere in the spirit of science is there any implication of practical application of knowledge. This is left to others—mainly the engineer, who is the middleman vendor of science. The scientist is the fountainhead of expanding knowledge, which is available to others for translation into practical application.

MANAGEMENT

The nature of management has previously been outlined. The management man is an individual of action who is primarily concerned with getting practical results and getting them now. He is preoccupied by the successful operation of his organization. His interest in science is in how it can help his organization better to achieve its objectives. Management has interest in the pure scientist only to the extent that they expect some practical results to emerge from the scientist's endeavors. In a few organizations, the scientist is allowed to be a pure scientist—to pursue his quest for knowledge without regard to the practical implications of his work. This is the exception. In most organizations, the scientist is expected to perform as an "applied" scientist—to devote his efforts to the solution of problems regarded by management as being of practical utility to the organization.

Management cannot afford the luxury of seeking knowledge for knowledge's sake. They must achieve practical results, and within very short time limits. The manager must keep things going—he must make decisions even though he may have insufficient information upon which to base his judgments. Even when science and engineering support his judgments, he must wed the technical knowledge with his intuitive and broader understanding of operational insights, policy restraints, organizational needs, and economic-social-political requirements. He may be quite impatient with the naiveté of science within his own sphere of responsibility and also considerably in awe of science where it is beyond his understanding.

In basic characteristics, objectives, mode of behavior, and in function the manager and the scientist are on opposite poles. They need each other in our modern society, but collaboration in a profitable manner is difficult and filled with potential conflicts and frustrations. A middle ground is essential and has traditionally been associated with engineering.

ENGINEERING

The engineer has often been characterized as an individual who can do for one dollar what any fool can do for two. The role of engineering is to draw upon technical knowledge (science) and intuition—the resources of nature and of human nature—to benefit mankind. This statement may seem somewhat altruistic. Engineering is concerned with the practical solution of problems having some technical content. The main characteristic of engineering is design (that is, practical problem solution). The effectiveness of engineering is usually evaluated in terms of satisfactory results obtained at a reasonable cost. The engineer, in a sense, fills the void between management and science. He draws heavily upon science to guide him in his analysis and design work. He also draws heavily upon intuition and experience. Science, and scientific precision, are not of *primary* concern to him, for his overriding objective is to produce a workable design. When scientific understanding and theory are not available, he may proceed on an empirical basis. He uses safety factors to safeguard his designs from unforseen demands and lack of complete precision in his analysis and design work. He usually faces deadlines or schedules for the completion of his work.

The engineer, upon occasion, may assume some of the characteristics of the scientist. Lack of complete understanding of some phenomena involved in his design work may motivate him to search for better knowledge. Typically, however, the engineer's motivation is intimately associated with solving specific problems of importance to his management. These problems are usually technical in nature, require the engineer's understanding of the technology involved and his skill at systematic analysis. These problems also require the engineer's skill at blending theory and practice and are characteristically limited to less than full consideration of the complexities of human behavior and the total impact upon the organization. These broader considerations are usually reserved for management in their decisions concerning the adoption and implementation of the engineer's design.

SUMMARY

The main theme of this book centers around the management of improvement—the effective use of science and engineering by management for a more successful operation of their organizations. Science and engineering are of considerable importance to research and development, and the engineering of products and processes. However, the application of science and engineering to management processes and the problems of management will receive the major share of our attention. Solution of these problems—those related to achieving better performance within and by the organization—is not entirely a matter of concern for the scientist and the engineer. Management is most intimately involved. The manager may be his own problem solver in many cases. However, it may also be that the manager, because of limited time for problem-solving, the pressure of other duties, and the need for specialized technical knowledge, will rely upon staff help. It is this type of improvement activity that is usually associated with modern industrial engineering, operations research, and management science. These professions serve management as technical specialties, in staff capacities, in order to help solve specific problems of importance to management and the organization. These services are essentially an *engineering* function, even though managers and scientists are upon occasion directly involved. Likewise, when an engineer or a scientist is charged with a management responsibility, he can no longer function strictly as an engineer or scientist. Solving management problems requires an engineering orientation, full appreciation of the problems of management and the rendering of a service to management, and the drawing upon science and technology as useful tools to help develop practical solutions which are acceptable to management. Some of the key characteristics of management, engineering, and science are highlighted in the following list:

Science and the Scientist: Characterized by theory and "knowing."
- Application of knowledge is a remote thought.
- Problems are abstracted out of a specific context into the abstract—results are not related back only to the specific original context, but generalized to much broader areas.
- Time is of little importance.
- Makes heavy use of theory, models, and mathematical techniques.
- A seeker of "truth."
- Evaluated by the scientific acceptance of his work by the world community of his fellow scientists.
- Motivated by curiosity and desire to make a "scientific" contribution—to achieve recognition by the world community of scientists and to publish the results of his work.

Management and the Manager: Characterized by decisions and action.
- Decides on courses of action.
- Has little regard for abstractions—deals with his problems in concrete terms.
- Time is of critical importance.
- Has little use for theory, models, or mathematical techniques—wants problems solved in terms of cost and consequence evaluations.
- A man of action.
- Evaluated by the "success" of his organization.
- Motivated by desire to get results—to see his organization succeed.

Engineering and the Engineer: Characterized by design and problem-solving.
Recommends course of action for management decision.
- Problems are related to a specific and technical environment.
- Uses abstractions where useful to solve problems, but deals mainly with real world activity.
- Schedules and deadlines are important.
- Theory, models, and mathematical techniques are regarded as useful tools for analysis and design—means to an end only.
- A practical problem solver.
- Evaluated by the technical and economic success of his designs and problem solutions relative to their impact upon his organization.
- Motivated by a desire to see problems with some technical content solved in a practical way on behalf of his organization.

CONCLUSIONS

Management within all organizations is being increasingly influenced by the impact of science and engineering upon the activities which they manage and upon the process of management. Modern industrial engineering, operations research, and management science have tended to increase the emphasis upon *useful* application of engineering and science in various areas of management. This application requires a better understanding of science and engineering, and the way scientists and engineers behave, on the part of management—and it requires a better understanding on the part of engineers and scientists of their role in serving management, and how their behavior can be modified to improve the successful application of science and engineering to the problems of management. More importantly, it requires the *behavior of engineering,* and not of science, on the part of the operations researcher and the management scientist.

REFERENCES

1. Lawrence A. Appley, *Management in Action: The Art of Getting Things Done Through People,* American Management Association, New York, 1956.
2. Additional information on the development of management may be found in:
   Peter F. Drucker, *The Practice of Management,* Harper, New York, 1954.
   George Fillipetti, Industrial Management in Transition, Richard D. Irwin, Homewood, Illinois, 1953.
   Frederick Harbison and Charles A. Myers, *Management in the Industrial World: An International Analysis,* McGraw-Hill, New York, 1959.
   Harwood F. Merrill, *The Classics in Management,* American Management Association, New York, 1960.
3. The summary of characteristics of management, science, and engineering is based upon personal observation, interchange of views with friends and associates, and presentations by Dr. H. O. Davidson. See
   H. O. Davidson, "The Management, Engineering and Scientific Functions," *The Journal of Industrial Engineering,* March–April 1960, pp. 120–124.

   and a similar chapter in
   D. G. Malcolm and Alan J. Rowe (eds.), *Management Control Systems,* Wiley, New York, 1960.

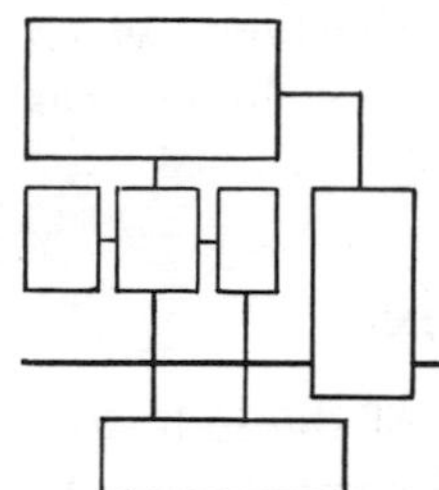

CHAPTER 3

THE IMPROVEMENT FUNCTION

In considering the improvement function it would also be worthwhile to consider the main factors that have contributed to the high level of material well-being that we currently enjoy. It is important to recognize that our material well-being has not just "happened." It results from a willful striving for achievement. Further improvement will only result from a continuation of this striving. To be sure, the events that have allowed progress in the past are history, and the continuation of improvement will require new events and new strivings to build upon past success. It is not only interesting, but fundamental that we understand at least the basics of past success as a prelude to attempting to encourage further advancement and improvement.

FIRST INDUSTRIAL REVOLUTION

The start of the fantastic economic development of the western world is usually associated with the industrial revolution, which centers about the first blooming of technology and its impact upon social and economic processes. It is usually thought to have been originated by Watt's steam engine, Arkwright's spinning jenny, and other mechanical innovations that allowed man to effectively multiply his efforts in the production of material goods. These developments, going far beyond those we have mentioned, did accomplish much in freeing man from mechanical labor and were responsible for the birth of the factory system. The factory system, and subsequent innovations of mechanical devices, did much to improve the productivity of man and free him from the drudgery of survival. New problems did emerge with the development of industrialized society, but man has benefited greatly from industrialization—which was sparked by the industrial revolution. The industrial revolution was sparked by the first blooming of technology.

SECOND INDUSTRIAL REVOLUTION

Technology has continued to blossom since the start of the industrial revolution. It is impossible to enumerate all of its accomplishments, which have had a substantial influence upon industrial and economic development and upon our daily lives. The development still continues. New products, processes of manufacture, and machinery are daily making their appearance.

It is doubtful that anyone would question the significant impact of the industrial revolution. However, it is not generally recognized that a second industrial revolution has been taking place and that its impact has been every bit as substantial as the original revolution. This second industrial revolution has been concerned with the *efficient* adaptation of technological innovations for the service of mankind. This seems to be a simple concept, but it is not frequently recognized. The effective utilization of technological innovation has been a substantial problem ever since the start of the first industrial revolution. Adam Smith formally recognized this problem as early as 1776 in his advocacy of division of labor and the economies which would result therefrom. In *Wealth of Nations* Smith discussed the subdivision of pin-making into four separate tasks rather than having the entire pin produced by one worker. Workers could develop more skill and proficiency in the execution of the individual subdivided tasks than in executing them all, and basic efficiences in the mechanical aspects of the work would result from the division of the total job into smaller components. Using this approach, ten men performing the subdivided tasks could easily produce 48,000 pins per day while an individual workman performing the entire operation could scarcely make 1000. Charles Babbage again called attention to the concept of division of labor in 1827, when he was studying problems of manufacture concerning the construction of his analytical engine, and extended the application of rational analysis and planning as aids to effective management of work activity.

Another significant contribution to the second industrial revolution was made by Eli Whitney. It is generally recognized that Whitney contributed substantially to the first industrial revolution by his invention of the cotton gin. His contributions to the second were even more important, for they resulted in the development of the fundamental concepts of mass production.

In the days prior to the American Revolution, America had not been allowed to develop a manufacturing capability. This posed many significant problems after independence had been won. It also provided a setting for free reign of man's creative intellect in devising ways to satisfy his needs, control the forces of nature, and exploit the new developments growing out of the industrial revolution. The new government's needs for muskets, and Whitney's creative approach to satisfying this need, illustrate a very significant development in the second industrial revolution. Muskets in those days were made piece-by-piece by skilled gunmakers. Each musket was an individual unit, with its own parts fitting only that gun. Skilled gunmakers were in short supply, and many muskets were needed. Whitney's approach was to produce standard parts, each and every one sufficiently similar that there would be no need to have parts fitted individually to a given gun. He visualized being able to produce the interchangeable parts by "tooling-up" for the work—using tooling and fixtures to help achieve the necessary accuracy. Progress was slow. His sponsors became increasingly impatient as Whitney spent his time building his tooling rather than producing guns. Finally, as patience was almost exhausted, parts were being produced rapidly and complete assemblies were available in large number. The preinvestment of labor in tooling that allowed rapid production of interchangeable parts resulted in improved quality, production at a rapid rate once the tooling was completed, and production at greatly reduced costs.

Whitney had developed the basis of mass production that was to allow the development of American industrial and economic might more than a century later. Further refinement of the concepts of mass production was eagerly pursued in the early 1900's by Henry Ford, who combined the Whitney fundamentals with progressive assembly using mechanical devices to bring the work to the worker.

Another aspect of the second industrial revolution also concerned the importance of economics in engineering and production. These developments, when combined with those previously mentioned, resulted in a coordinated approach to the rationalization of work efforts and provided management with systematic tools for doing a more effective job of *managing*.

In a presentation to the American Society of Mechanical Engineers in 1879, Mr. Henry Towne of the Yale and Towne Company stressed the role of the engineer as an economist. He had observed in his own factory that skilled locksmiths spent 12% of their working day in opening and closing vices to facilitate their skilled work. It seemed to Mr. Towne that this was a gross waste of skilled manpower, for opening and closing vices contributed nothing to production and did not demand any of the skills associated with the locksmith's trade. Other examples of inefficiency were also cited. It seemed that the speaker was attempting to develop a thesis that lack of organization and orderly planning of production work resulted in waste and inefficiency. A systematic analysis of work and of the problems of managing were likely to yield substantial economies and allow technology to better serve mankind. The engineer should be concerned with these problems.

It seems likely that a young engineer by the name of Fredrick W. Taylor was inspired by Mr. Towne's message. He had recently progressed into a position of substantial management responsibility, and his prior experience as a worker led him to be very interested in what engineering could do to help management *manage* more effectively. He recognized that workers determined *how* work was to be done, *what* procedures would be used, and *how rapidly* results would be accomplished. Management did not really *manage.* Great inefficiencies existed in industry, primarily because of management's lack of concern with systematic procedures for planning and managing the work activities for which they were responsible.

Taylor applied engineering logic and methodology to the analysis of the problems of management. One of his early questions was "what is a fair day's work?" His quest for an answer developed the techniques of time study, which allowed management to preplan production activity according to performance standards representing reasonably efficient methods for executing work and at performance levels representing a fair application of energy and dexterity.

Many other contributions to the effective utilization of the technology of the first industrial revolution stem from the work of Taylor and individuals who were sparked by his innovations. The Taylor system of rationalization and systematic approach to solving problems led to the scientific management movement, which was based on the assumption that the problems of management would all yield to the engineer's approach—the application of science—and that a set of governing principles would emerge—a science of management. Unfortunately, the problems were far too complex, the available science far too immature, and the expectations of a science of management with precise governing laws far too naive.

Even so, rationalization did an effective job of serving the needs for the exploitation of technology at that time. Taylor's concepts and those of men following him (such as the Gilbreths, Gantt, Emerson, Cooke, etc.), combined with the concepts developed by Whitney and Ford, allowed America to achieve a position of industrial and economic might during the early part of the twentieth century.

The scientific management movement resulted in keen interest in various problems of management. The need for accounting and cost data for managerial control, the significance of human problems created by industrial life, the application of psychology to the problems of industry and management, and the need to study the art of management were all in some measure influenced and stimulated by it. Industrial engineering is a direct outgrowth of it.

It should not be inferred that the second industrial revolution has run its course. It is still an active force and will be discussed, but not by name, in material to follow.

THIRD INDUSTRIAL REVOLUTION

The development of computers—machines that "think"—and automation is frequently referred to as the second industrial revolution. The implication is that the first industrial revolution resulted in the development of machines that relieve man of routine physical drudgery, while the second resulted in the development of machines that relieve him from routine mental drudgery. This structuring of terminology has certain appeal, but it ignores the importance of what we have called the second industrial revolution—the result of man's ingenuity to *effectively* utilize the technology at his disposal. It also neglects the broad nature of the third industrial revolution, which encompasses computers and automation —and much more.

The third industrial revolution is the result of a new boom in science *and* its useful application to the problems of man. Computers are a significant part of this development, but many other breakthroughs have also occurred. The developments have been greatly stimulated by World War II and by the challenges of defense and space exploration. Some examples of the new technology would include advances in automatic control, microminiaturization, development of atomic energy, exotic metals to perform in an outer space environment, a host of developments in solid state physics, in addition to the development of computers and automation. All of these developments are a new brand of technology, which is heavily dependent upon the results of the other industrial revolutions for effective application. These very problems of *effective* utilization of the new technology have stimulated a further development of the second industrial revolution and a parallel development in the third.

Operations research, the use of the research method to analyze operational problems, has been one of the results of attempting to develop ways to effectively solve the problems of exploiting the new technology. This can be regarded as the development of an *additional* technology—encompassing operations research techniques and methods. The scientific management movement has been revived, in a more realistic structure, as the management science movement. A quest for better understanding of a wide variety of human and management problems, extending to all human endeavor, has resulted in new knowledge and understanding, which management scientists are exploiting as aids for analyzing real world management problems. A vast new area of knowledge has thus been made available to the engineer for his translation into useful applications.

The growing complexity of problems associated with our society, economy, and technology—both old and new—has been strong encouragement to the development of more effective ways to deal with these problems. Operations research, management science, and engineering are all responding to the challenge. The third industrial revolution is well underway—creating new technology—and creating new approaches and technologies to help solve the problems of effective exploitation of technology.

THE IMPROVEMENT FUNCTION

The industrial revolutions have allowed man to make substantial progress in controlling nature for his benefit. In some cases they have allowed him to become more human and to better solve problems resulting from development of technology and the problems of interpersonal relations. In many cases, the developments have caused a more realistic appreciation of the limitations of science and technology and the role of faith in the conduct of human affairs. Many problems still remain unsolved.

One of the significant problems that has been approached, but not entirely solved, has to do with the ever more effective exploitation of science and technology for the benefit of mankind. Material well-being is prerequisite to the solution of many significant problems of a nontechnical nature. Material well-being can only be achieved by efficiency in the expenditure of human effort—both physical and mental—and by effective development and application of technology.

It is of growing importance that we better solve the problems of efficiency in the conduct of our affairs. This is particularly true within our many organizations—production, government, service, research, etc.

One approach to accomplishing this is to make a concerted effort to continue to achieve improvement. This can be done by utilizing developments associated with all three industrial revolutions, with particular emphasis upon effective use of operations research, management science, and engineering, and by an organized approach to the development *and* management of an improvement function within our organizations.

APPROACHES TO ORGANIZED IMPROVEMENT

An improvement function within an organization should permeate the entire organization. It may be formally organized as one or more departments, perhaps designated by a descriptive name, or it may be incorporated within existing staff departments. It requires a sincere determination on the part of all individuals to strive for improvement, an overt recognition of the importance of betterment by incorporation of the improvement objective within the primary responsibilities of all personnel, particularly in management and supervisory positions, and continuing direction and modification of approach in order to respond to the dynamic requirements of an organization. For full effectiveness it demands a highly competent staff to render encouragement, stimulation, direction, and assistance to management and supervisory personnel. It also requires of this staff the skill and ability to develop recognition of improvement opportunities, to develop strategic approaches to the opportunities, and to execute broad studies that are beyond the time or technical abilities of the managers and supervisors.

There have been many approaches to improvement within organizations. Most of these have been of genuine value but few have been sufficiently broad to satisfy the needs for a true improvement function involving the entire organization. They have been primarily confined to one aspect of the total problem. For example, controllership tends to concentrate on cost and financial analyses. Industrial relations is limited to human relations and related problems. Traditional industrial engineering tends to concentrate upon manufacturing problems. The functional specialist in marketing, administration, office management, etc., seldom has the inclination or ability to view the total scope of an organization. All of these approaches, although of some benefit, are much too confined to satisfy the needs of a true improvement function.

There have been attempts to develop a broad improvement function within many organizations. Some have been outstandingly successful. Many have failed. The successes and failures have been greatly influenced by the presence or lack of the following key factors:

1. Management support and vision relative to the improvement function—usually originating with top management and then spreading enthusiastically to all other levels.
2. A dynamic, flexible, and responsive function—proceeding according to the needs of the organization and the serving of those needs at the appropriate time.
3. Keen awareness of the strategy of improvement endeavors—using appropriate strategies for detecting needs and for satisfying them. A breadth of vision and competency, and also a narrowness and depth within a wide variety of specialized activities, is essential.
4. Personnel participating in the improvement function with technical competency in both the broad and the narrow problem areas, and a nontechnical competency to achieve harmonious endeavors in pursuit of improvement.
5. A dual approach: (a) strengthening of the manager's position and the line organization, and (b) effective staff support to further strengthen the manager's position by extending and expanding the skills at his disposal.
6. An exploitation of science and technology for management's use.
7. Practice of the concept of dual management responsibility; (a) to accomplish results from the activity for which the manager is responsible, and (b) to continually pursue *and achieve* improvement in accomplishing these results.

The scientific management movement represented an approach to developing a broad improvement function. But, as previously mentioned, the scientific management movement has died. Emerging from it, however, have been a number of narrower improvement specialties, including industrial engineering (in the traditional sense), the functional specialties (such as personnel, office systems and procedures, controllership, purchasing, etc.), and more recently operations research and management science. All of these approaches, while in themselves narrow, provide an excellent basis for unification and broadening into the desired improvement function. Before discussing this combination and expansion, we should briefly consider the characteristics of these three improvement approaches.

TRADITIONAL INDUSTRIAL ENGINEERING

Industrial engineering is a direct outgrowth of the scientific management movement. Although never visualized as a narrow activity, a substantial portion of its application has been confined to the manufacturing area and to the use of time study and wage incentives. There have been notable exceptions, and some of these will be discussed subsequently. But the *traditional* role of industrial engineering is typified by one executive's outlining of its activities for a seminar presentation to a group of Indian industrialists:[1]

INDUSTRIAL ENGINEERING

1. Organization Structure:
   Importance of middle management—delegation of responsibility coupled with authority to act.
2. Functions:
   Process engineering—work standards, measurement, and methods—plant layout and materials handling—product design—machine and tool design.
3. Equipment, Machines, and Tools:
   Basic equipment economics—obsolete versus depreciated machines—jigs and fixtures—upgrading old equipment—material handling at machine—maximizing operator effectiveness—equipment balance—idle equipment utilization—tool crib procedure.
4. Materials and Material Handling:
   Handling means and costs analyzed—straight line flow—flexibility of space—Buy/Make decisions—role of specifications and vendor relations.
5. Quality Control:
   Specifications and clarity of instructions—first piece and in-process inspection—Statistical Q.C.—reporting to show trends—Material Review Board (MRB) procedure—motivating workers toward quality.
6. Maintenance:
   Preventative versus corrective—procedures to insure continuity—spare parts—standby equipment.
7. Procedures and Relations with Coordinating Departments:
   Flow charting of quote and order action—coordination with other departments.
8. Motivating the Engineer:
   Recognition of efforts—authorship—professional identification—night schools and correspondence courses—job evaluation—periodic reviews.
9. Creativity:
   Mental approach to problem solving—flexible, imaginative attack—means of avoiding mental inertia.

Although these activities are narrow compared with a broad improvement function, they have helped improve the efficiency of manufacturing activities. Many of these approaches have also been successfully applied to nonmanufacturing activities.

FUNCTIONAL SPECIALISTS

The birth of the scientific management movement brought with it a hope that science could aid management in solving all problems. During its development it was recognized that this was an impossibility. As it died, the original aspirations were channeled into narrower problem areas where management could benefit from the application of science and the systematic development of knowledge, understanding, and a codification of experience. A number of functional specialities developed, including management and administration, controllership, industrial engineering, personnel administration, quality control, marketing, purchasing, systems and procedures, etc. Each of these specialities concentrated upon a more limited array of problems than visualized by a unified scientific management. They borrowed approaches and techniques for solving their own specific problems and devised new problem-solving approaches. In a way, these functional specialities were a fragmentation of the broad spirit of scientific management. They developed in a narrow and confined way—just as industrial engineering (the main current of scientific management aspirations) became increasingly confined to manufacturing activities.

OPERATIONS RESEARCH AND MANAGEMENT SCIENCE

The developments of operations research and the rebirth of the spirit of scientific management as management science are developments of the third industrial revolution. They are principally the scientist's approach to solving management problems. They have contributed new approaches and techniques for solving complex problems and translation of the concepts of science to the solving of business problems.

The original concept of operations research was the researching of operational problems by individuals not familiar with the problems. A detached, scientific approach was the essence. Mathematical analyses and models were the *sine qua non.* The operations researcher would make an abstract analysis and recommend a course of action. He was a scientist, not to be involved in the practical problems of translating recommendations into cost and consequences or actions necessary for implementation of recommendations. These were problems for management.

This analysis of the behavior, or mentality, of the early operations researcher is perhaps just a bit harsh, but it is based upon the facts. In view of the discussion of the roles and modes of behavior of the scientist, the engineer, and the manager, this is understandable—for the early O.R. practitioner (and still many at the present time) regarded himself and behaved as a "scientist." This is all well and good—within limits. There is a place for the O.R. scientist, but the needs of a broad improvement function are tied to the role of the "engineer," translating and exploiting science for the benefit of management.

The management science movement stemmed from operations research, and incorporates it, but in a slightly broader manner. Early O.R. people were primarily concerned with military problems. Management-oriented people were displeased with the imposed limitation to the military problem area in professional meetings, publications, and structuring of the professional society. They organized a management sciences society, which attracted many individuals of diverse backgrounds interested in solving management-type problems. Many of these individuals are scientists by training, motivation, and behavior. They have made substantial contributions, but the need for an engineering approach still is in evidence.

A UNIFIED APPROACH

The needs of a broad improvement function clearly are not met by the three approaches outlined, nor by any other with which the author is familiar. However, the synthesis of the three represents an attractive possibility. This synthesis is being attempted by a recasting of *traditional* industrial engineering. There have been some encouraging results, but the metamorphosis is far from complete. Even so, the aspirations of *modern* industrial engineering are most encouraging and do offer hope for the emergence of a solid development of a broad improvement function.

The *modern* industrial engineering approach has been selected as the most promising avenue to achieving what is needed for the improvement function with due caution and with considerable reservation. The modern developments in management, business administration, and industrial administration education are very encouraging—as are the educational approaches in operations research, the various management sciences, and systems engineering. But, the only group that has attempted to approach the challenge of meeting the needs of the broad improvement function has been industrial engineering. The objectives have been established; some individuals identifying themselves with industrial engineering have met the challenge, and some have not. But the aspirations are clearly demonstrated. It remains to be seen if they will be fully realized.

We will frequently use the term industrial engineering in materials that follow. It should be recognized that this terminology is being used both in terms of the aspirations for this endeavor and as a synonym for the improvement function. As individuals who do not claim affiliation with industrial engineering can contribute to the improvement function, they are identified with it. As industrial engineers can contribute to the improvement functions, they will be identified with it. I do not attempt to define, dictate, nor direct what any professional group must be, but only to develop the theme of an improvement function—and the contributions to it of science, engineering, and management.

ENGINEERING, SCIENCE, OR MANAGEMENT?

As discussed in the previous chapter, engineering, science, and management have differing roles and differing modes of behavior. The needs of a broad improvement function affect and are affected by all three. The predominant needs emerge in the areas of management and engineering. Management is in the key role. Science must be converted, in an engineering manner, in order to satisfy the needs of management.

The behavioral and intellectual role of engineering is pervasive in this matter, since problems of improvement are heavily dependent upon technology for their solution. The general method of engineering, a systematic analysis and design to meet practical requirements, is intimately associated with improvement. Engineering has traditionally been the middleman vendor of science—translating theory into useful application. The engineer is accustomed to working within constraints of economy, time, and his specific environment in developing practicable answers to problems. But, the role of engineering goes far beyond this. Many problems of improvement involve technical processes—and their solution requires a technical ability.

The case for engineering is a strong one. However, nonengineers can also participate in this venture. Many of these individuals behave as engineers and contribute in their own fashion to the general engineering process that is involved in improvement activities. Also, there are some parts of the improvement function that are essentially nontechnical, where the engineering base of methodology is not critical.

We should also recognize that engineering, while the middleman vendor of science to management, has certain deficiencies and liabilities. Engineering has only recently become conscious of the critical importance of systems and of the human, informational, managerial, and organizational aspects, which are critical components in addition to the physical. The dedication of engineering as an agency of service to management in dealing with more than just technical factors is quite new to a large segment of engineering, for most engineers have not been accustomed to dealing with the broad problems of total improvement endeavors.

MODERN INDUSTRIAL ENGINEERING

Modern industrial engineering is a blending of traditional industrial engineering, operations research, and management science. It has emerged gradually over a period of years, with a very substantial development since the founding of the American Institute of Industrial Engineers in 1948. This organization has accomplished much in providing direction for the healthy growth and modernization of traditional industrial engineering. One of its endeavors, starting in 1955 and continuing for 5 years, was to sponsor a series of symposia where leading representatives from industry, government, consulting and academic institutions, representing industrial engineering and other professional specialties, considered the problems of the changing nature of industrial engineering in an attempt to provide guidance in the healthy modernization and growth of the profession. An abstracting of the summary report of these symposia will help define the aspirations of this professional group.[2]

The Emerging Role of Industrial Engineering

A Summary Report of Industrial Engineering Symposia Sponsored by the American Institute of Industrial Engineers

edited by **AUSTIN WESTON**

Secretary, AIIE Long Range Planning Committee

. . .

THE DEFINITION OF INDUSTRIAL ENGINEERING

Industrial engineering is concerned with the design, improvement, and installation of integrated systems of men, materials, and equipment. It draws upon specialized knowledge and skill in the mathematical, physical, and social sciences, together with the principles and methods of engineering analysis and design, to specify, predict, and evaluate the results to be obtained from such systems.

. . .

Interpretation for Management. The industrial engineer makes an engineering contribution to achieving management's objective, primarily that of optimizing the gains and minimizing the risks of an enterprise. He assists every level of management by originating and developing operating plans, programs and controls which will permit the increasingly effective use of human and economic resources.

This is accomplished through stimulating and working with other staff and line departments in such fields as:

making location and site, layout and handling plans.
designing organization and operating procedures.
designing controls for organization functions.
designing tools and equipment, work processes and methods.
designing compensation plans.
determining the most economic way of procurement and use of materials.
analysis and evaluation of data and other information required for these planning tasks.
conducting research in these areas.

. . .

Interpretation for Engineers and Other Staff Groups. The industrial engineering approach is a unique application of engineering design and analysis techniques. The industrial engineer's consideration of people, the design of systems involving people, and the manner by which human performance is analyzed requires a fundamental, analytical approach that is essentially different from other engineering disciplines.

The contribution of the industrial engineer is in the management decision-making process. The problems existing in this area deal with the optimum utilization of men, materials, equipment, and energy to achieve the purpose of an organization. The organization may be an individual department of a company, a hospital, an entire corporation, or any other group organized to produce a product, perform a service, or carry out a function. The managers of the organization need factual information arranged to define alternatives and consequences, to help them recognize and solve existing problems. The industrial engineer collects, analyzes, and arranges this information in such a way as to fulfill this management need, as well as searching for better ways to do the job. The industrial engineer operates in two major areas, the design of new systems and the maintenance and improvement of existing systems.

To summarize, in his work the industrial engineer:

1. Identifies problems, gathers facts, and appraises difficulties.
2. Visualizes solutions and designs, develops or improves systems.
3. Searches out requirements for quality, quantity, cost, and timing.
4. Makes economic analyses and justifies their results.
5. Specifies, constructs, installs and, sometimes, initially operates these systems.
6. Devises methods of controlling and evaluating the performance of systems.
7. Develops acceptance by and secures cooperation of those who operate such systems.

The industrial engineer is distinguished from other engineers in that he:

1. Places increased emphasis on the integration of the human being into the system.
2. Concerns himself with the total problem.
3. Predicts and interprets the economic results.
4. Makes greater utilization of the contributions of the social sciences than do other engineers.

Interpretation for the General Public (With Special Emphasis for High School Students). The industrial engineer is concerned with the design of industrial enterprises or other types of organizations existing for a worthwhile purpose, and the planning or blueprinting of the combination of men, equipment, and materials necessary to produce most effectively desired goods or services. The industrial engineer differs from other engineers in the degree that his fundamental concern is with operations that result from both physical and human forces, and are measured in both physical and economic terms. Therefore, he is educated not only in the engineering methods of analysis and design which stem from mathematics and the physical sciences, but also is concerned with psychology, physiology, sociology, economics, costs, and human relations.

He may be dealing in the automation of the manufacturing process, in the development of methods of handling materials, in the development of procedures to control production, or to measure performance of any type of work. He frequently serves as management's advisor in the solution of special problems.

In doing his job he comes in contact with all functions of an organization and employees at all levels. He must be able to deal, not only with the technical aspects of his problems, but also the human. Philosophically, he is devoted to the ideal of helping the nation to use most effectively its physical facilities and human talents for production of goods and services.

. . .

EXAMPLES OF MODERN INDUSTRIAL ENGINEERING

Analysis and Design of an Airlines Reservations System

by **WARREN ALBERTS**
United Air Lines

The operation of an airline, both from a profit and passenger service standpoint, is extremely dependent upon the speed and accuracy with which it handles and controls the space it has for sale.

United Air Lines' management, in 1955, decided on an over-all analysis of the company's reservation function, including the possible design of a system which would take care of its projected needs through 1965. The system at that time employed over 2000 people, cost approximately $12,000,000 a year to operate, and was handling up to 50,000 transactions a day. This system could be visualized as a large information processing complex covering some 80 stations spread throughout the country.

The industrial engineering department of United Air Lines undertook the direction of this study. A study team was given the assignment to:

1. Analyze the entire system.
2. Isolate the basic problems.
3. Measure the key variables and project the system and its requirements 10 years into the future.

To help the team concentrate on developing requirements, their initial goal was set as the development of a functional specification.

This first phase took approximately a year to complete. Basic problems such as time lags, exposure to human error, divided responsibility, and the inability of people within the system to audit their work, were highlighted. Problems susceptible to short range solutions were turned over to operating groups and an interim system, utilizing IBM Ramac computers at Denver connected to transceivers in the largest reservations offices, was installed.

The functional specifications which contained volumes and desired service levels in very specific terms soon pointed up the limitations of existing electronic hardware and communications networks.

A second phase, that of system design and translation of the functional specification into a technical one, was undertaken. Stanford Research Institute was called in as a consultant to evaluate existing technology and help specify a realistic system. Concurrent with the development of technical specifications, a complete economic analysis of existing manpower and machine costs, along with the value of meeting specific design requirements, was made.

This system study, which spanned a period of two years, finally resulted in the procurement by United of a highly advanced electronic reservations system which will not only meet its specifications, but also make an important contribution to profit and increased productivity. The study also pointed up the need to consolidate certain functions basic to the system which previously had been spread out among several departments. These organizational changes were made.

The project dramatically highlighted the importance of taking an over-all industrial engineering approach to the analysis and design of complex systems which involve both technical and human aspects. An important point in the approach taken is the development of system requirements which manufacturers are asked to meet as opposed to the current practice of trying to adopt and integrate existing hardware to meet business needs. The results, both in satisfying the company's requirements and in improving productivity, point up the value of allocating industrial engineering effort to the research and development of business systems.

Design of a Synthetic Detergent Production and Distribution System

by **RICHARD FORBERG**
Procter and Gamble Company

A system to produce and distribute synthetic detergents was presented as a whole. The major information flows and the product flow were indicated graphically.

The system was divided into subsystems, each of which was a major project area. The work on the subsystem for production scheduling and inventory control was presented as a typical project. This study team developed a production scheduling procedure which considered all the significant costs and reduced the time lags in decision making. Installation of the improved system involved simulation, parallel runs, and limited scale tests.

Another subsystem discussed briefly was the mechanized material handling of packaged, finished product. Equipment components for such systems have become commercially available. Designing an integrated system to perform over a wide range of expected levels of consumer demand and modifications of product mix required a total system approach. The use of the Monte Carlo method of simulation to test alternative designs was outlined.

A third subsystem involved the processing of customer orders on electronic data-processing equipment. Orders were taken on mark-sense cards by salesmen. A system to process all subsequent paper work necessary for shipment, accounts receivable, sales analysis, and product inventories was under design.

The key role of the Industrial Engineering Division in system design on these separate projects and for coordination at the corporate level was emphasized.

Mechanization of a Finishing Operation

by **GEORGE GUSTAT**
Eastman Kodak Company

An industry was pictured that had successfully employed industrial engineering for many years. It has used ideas such as measured work, cost control, quality control and scheduling to strongly aid the organization. In an economic climate of rising input costs, industrial engineering had contributed to holding the costs to such a level that it was unnecessary to raise sales prices. However, an expanding market demanded an accelerated growth in production. This, coupled with technological complexity, required that planning be shifted from a 5 year basis to projections of 10 and 15 years. The conventional methods of industrial engineering then being employed were no longer adequate.

A team was used to assess the situation aggressively. A large number of new ideas were presented and scheduled to be worked out and installed in the next 10 years on a scheduled priority basis. These suggestions ranged from very minor ones to complete revisions of the productive system.

One of these ideas was presented to demonstrate the development of this improvement scheme. In this case, large quantities of product were being inspected in a rigorous manner to get a product with a low defect rate. To attack this potential problem more effectively, it became necessary for the industrial engineer to form a part of a specialized team. It was emphasized that an industrial engineer concerned only with restricted techniques would have had little success with this problem, requiring as it does technical knowledge from other fields. Since the present operation was profitable, there was a considerable tendency to multiply the existing types of facility to meet the new demands. A complex machine was developed to replace the human inspection and handling previously employed. The evolutionary development, testing, installation, and redesign were continued over an extended period with a follow-up of industrial engineering techniques applicable to a man-machine work unit of high value. Now, the new machine produced a systems scheduling problem for the industrial engineers that required a more sophisticated solution.

The success of this productive equipment influenced the expansion plans. Here it was noted that each progressive and needed change in the system caused more changes involving more coordination and planning in the over-all system. In summary, the over-all economic influences and pressures cause industrial engineering to become oriented toward an expansive, dynamic improvement program. The narrow and admittedly static concepts of thinking previously used were now being directed toward a broader and more progressive view of the system and the larger potentials for use of resources.

Organization for Systems Design

by **L. T. OHMART**
Armstrong Cork Company

The modern national trend in industrial engineering has continued to emphasize systems engineering. This has resulted from the realization that industrial engineering problems cannot be completely divorced and isolated from their environment. For the industrial engineer to properly function, it is necessary that he become less specialized and have a good command of the broader industrial engineering functions.

To better serve the needs of making and marketing a competitive product an interesting organizational change was reported. Specialization was de-emphasized and individuals with broad scope and background were assigned to areas of functional responsibility. These individuals were grouped into a developmental team that had successive responsibilities as a new product was developed and marketed.

A case study was presented showing the accelerated and coordinated stages employed as a floor backing was successfully moved from research to production. The group of broadly oriented personnel composed a small, coordinated team that now employed various specialists as internal consultants. As the product progressively developed on a time scale, each responsible member of the team could draw on specialists to assist him in accomplishing his part of the mission. The team members were generally drawn from production, research, project engineering, and industrial engineering.

Successful experience in this organization has shown that if systems engineering work is to be effective, responsible staff people must know and respect what effects their actions will have on other parts of the organization. If the industrial engineer is to participate in this system, he should develop a perspective that enables him to look at any problem as an integral part of the whole system.

This orientation of thinking had also been demonstrated to be excellent training for handling emergency systems problems.

KEY POINTS

From these case studies, what conclusions can be drawn concerning some of the major and distinguishing general aspects of industrial engineering?

1. The concept of opportunity-oriented solutions to problems.
2. The concept of industrial engineering as a continuum for all management levels.
3. The concept of the emerging role of the industrial engineer in a dynamic profession of engineering.
4. The concept of industrial engineering as a research, developmental, and creative staff function.
5. The recognition of the similarities of the industrial engineering systems concepts with those of other branches of engineering. A recognition of some of the distinguishing differences, such as the emphasis on the human component, economic orientation, degree of predictability and probabilistic nature of problems.
6. A recognition of the inadequacies of information about communication from the viewpoints of man-to-man, man-to-machine, or machine-to-machine transfers. Systems design is, of course, critically dependent upon knowledge of this type.
7. A recognition that both the practicing and academic industrial engineer is broadening his intellectual scope as he views and practices industrial engineering.

TOOLS AND TECHNIQUES FOR SYSTEMS DESIGN, AND THEIR USE

. . .

Since the industrial engineer is concerned with the design, improvement, and installation of systems involving men, materials, and equipment, he must have fundamental training in mathematics, physics, chemistry, and in the engineering sciences. The treatment of the human component of the system requires knowledge of the behavior, motivation, capabilities, and limitations of people. Knowledge derived from training in the social sciences, as psychology and sociology, is necessary to predict and describe the variations in the performance of men, equipment and processes and the environmental factors affecting them. The industrial engineer makes extensive use of probability and mathematical statistics. A wide variety of special tools and techniques are used in the analysis and design of complex integrated systems. Among these are methods of linear and dynamic programming, gaming theory, digital and analog simulation techniques, control theory, computer applications, and many others associated with recent developments, as well as such tools as process charts, methods analysis, and others long associated with industrial engineering activities.

The evaluation of both systems and components requires familiarity with various branches of economics and with the techniques of modern decision theory. Tools used in setting standards for and in measuring the performance of men, equipment, and systems range from work sampling, micromotion and time study to synthetic time standards. Since he works closely with management, the industrial engineer must be familiar with management principles and organization theory. He must have the experience, skills, and knowledge necessary to design, analyze, and evaluate systems used by management for control of cost, production, and quality. Because he deals with people at every level of the organization and because his work directly affects the activities of these people, the industrial engineer must have the special skills necessary to convey his ideas and results by verbal, written, and visual methods. This problem of efficient communication is becoming more important as our requirement for more frequent change increases.

How does an industrial engineer use these tools and techniques when he first contacts the reality of the problem area? In the initial or *survey phase* he utilizes visual observation and preliminary data samples to design subsequent approaches and determine the scope of his analysis. He would include a review of records that are available for an existing activity and a check for similarities to existing activities if the design is new. From these he would begin to develop a conceptual model of the area under investigation and to comprehend directions in which improvements may be made. The whole process of design through which the industrial engineer may subsequently go is carried out in a rough conceptual way in this first approach.

Next the industrial engineer must usually design a method of *obtaining additional information.* Normally, this will require the selection of suitable units of measure and the design of data collection or the use of experimental statistics to design such procedures.

The third phase is *modeling,* putting measurement into a form representing some important aspects of the situation. Many tools and techniques are useful in this phase: job standards, process charts, flow diagrams, layout models, simulation programs, or a wide variety of mathematical formulations.

What techniques are available for *manipulating the model* that has been constructed? The simplest manipulative activities are those which the industrial engineer recognizes in the "why" approach of work simplification, as used with a job description, process flow chart, or plant layout. For other models, appropriate manipulations are chosen: for example, Monte Carlo methods in process simulation. In addition to the manipulative techniques, the industrial engineer uses his creative imagination and experience to develop a range of alternative solutions to the problem.

These phases are part of a repetitious, cyclical process which may be repeated several times to evolve a design which meets the final design criteria, and which may also be analyzed by the critical processes or decisions of management.

THE INDUSTRIAL ENGINEERING PROCESS

The combination of activities referred to immediately above can be considered a part of the industrial engineering "process." This process can be charted to facilitate its understanding and discussion (Fig. 3-1). The chart is intended to graphically illustrate these activities and to classify them as either operating, engineering, or research. The boxes across the top represent the engineering activities in the industrial engineering process. Across the bottom are the "operating" activities which have often characterized the industrial engineering department in a company. As has been noted, the trend is away from such narrow use of the term "industrial engineering" by management. Up the left side is illustrated the research activities, the refinement of existing techniques, the development of new techniques and problem solving tools, and the transfer of techniques from other areas of endeavor. The relation to management and the objectives of the organization are also noted.

. . .

AREAS OF OPPORTUNITY FOR THE FUTURE

The industrial engineering concept has been defined and explained. The unique aspect of this branch of engineering, systems design, has been defined and illustrated by case examples. The tools and techniques of the industrial engineer and the manner of their use by him have been examined.

. . .

. . . In addition to his traditional role in work measurement, cost studies, plant layout, etc., management now looks upon the industrial engineer as one concerned with:

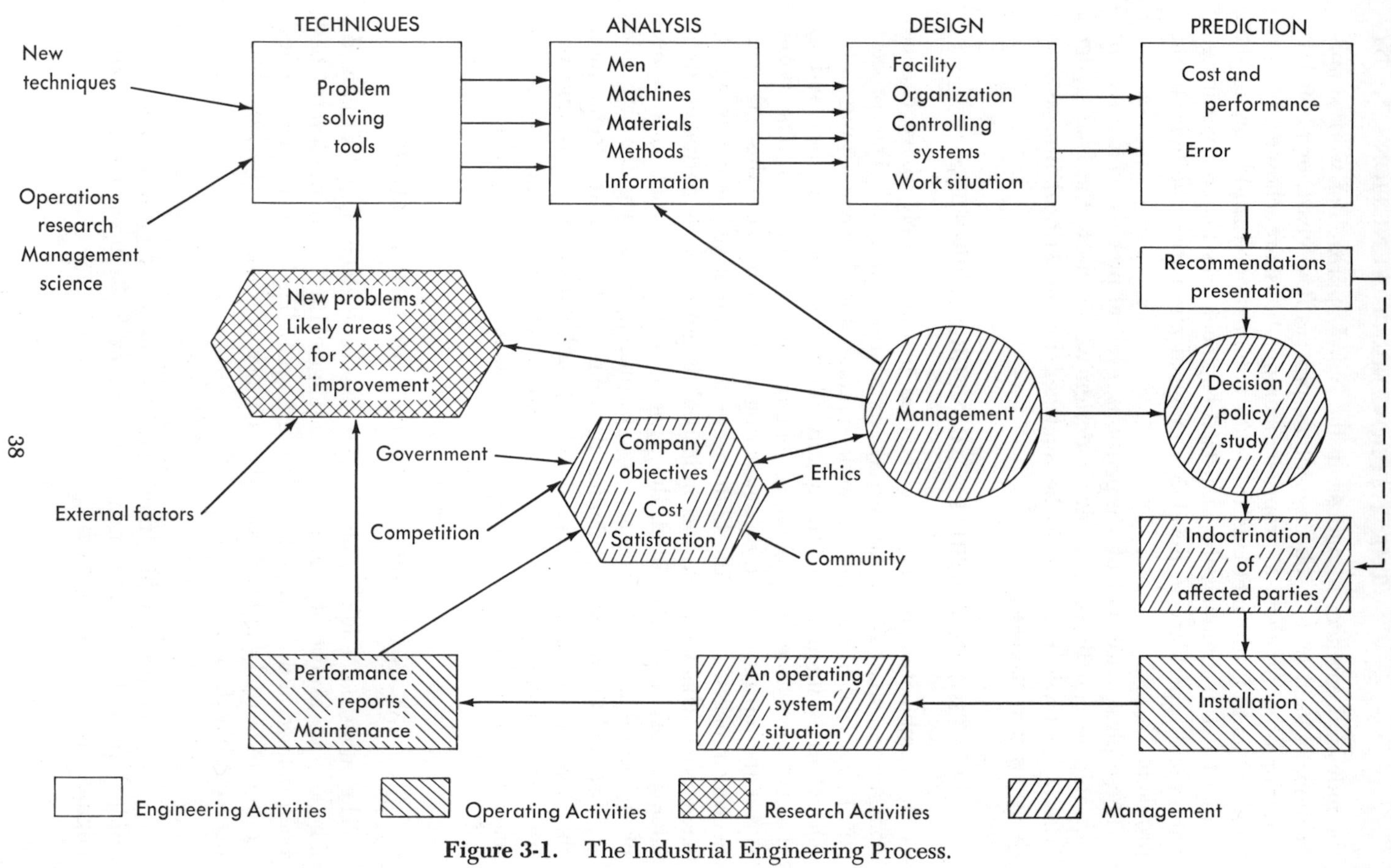

Figure 3-1. The Industrial Engineering Process.

1. Analyzing, developing, and implementing an entirely new system consistent with modern decision methods and computer technology.
2. Improving the performance and output of an existing system of men, machines, materials, and information regardless of whether it is in the manufacturing function (where most industrial engineering activities have sprung up and are concentrated) or in the budgetary, legal, or sales function.
3. Improving the design of existing controlling systems.

Further, three trends in the pattern of the industrial engineer's activities were noted. The first trend is a shift in emphasis from action after the fact to action before the fact on the part of the industrial engineer, i.e., a shift from controlling or helping to control what exists to the task of *designing* improvements or innovations. Thus, in addition to the opportunity to develop solutions for a given problem, management is giving the industrial engineer opportunity to diagnose the basic problem and to search out new solutions.

The second trend observed is the use of the industrial engineer in a more creative role in support of dynamic modern business. In implementing the concepts of science and engineering, management is faced with many problems of an application and acceptance nature. The industrial engineer is turning from the routine operation of various controlling systems to the task of speeding the installation of new . . . technologies and the timely acceptance of change by those affected. Support of such research and development activities by industrial engineering analysis is producing much needed reduction in installation time for new products and processes, as well as new systems of management.

The third trend lies in the increasing development of factual and unbiased solutions based on an increased ability to measure, understand, and manipulate systems. The industrial engineer has a significant role in the use of operations research and system analysis for such studies. In addition to such study, the industrial engineer is concerned with more than merely being responsible for the development of such solutions. He also lays the foundation for ultimate acceptance at the very outset of his work; he should keep up the promotion and stimulation of interest during his work; and he should complete his work with a presentation which utilizes the skills necessary to secure the full understanding needed for a decision to accept and implement.

The major areas where the industrial engineer can directly serve management in key staff-role were identified:

1. Establishment, clarification, and modification of company objectives. The definition of mission and direction of a company as well as its components.

2. Design of an organization or a system of human physical resources used to accomplish these objectives.
3. Recommendations concerning the allocation of the resources that have been organized, whether they be staff, operating, or line. This allocation must not only be initially determined but must be kept continually in balance. Here management is looking for an engineering approach in the determination of where their dollars, their human, or their physical resources can be invested for the greatest return.
4. Design of the basic system by which these resources are utilized. Included here is not only the operational system by which these resources distribute or provide goods and services, but also the staff system which serves the operational system. The same types of operational improvement are possible in functional areas outside of the traditional manufacturing area—for example, sales and research and development control.
5. Design of control systems for these resources. The systems by which the planning, scheduling, or co-ordinating of resources is done represents an important area for company improvement and is a challenging design opportunity.
6. The evaluation of results achieved in the performance toward objectives, i.e., the realization from the investment in human, physical, or money resources as measured by the satisfaction of human and management wants. Such evaluation, though difficult, provides conclusions which when fed back close the loop described in sections 1 through 5. If the realization obtained is not satisfactory, the industrial engineer is asked to reexamine the organization, objectives, allocations, resources, use, control, and realization. This full circuit can be generally applied to any type of organized human activity—industry or government, product or service producing.

In these areas management is looking to an industrial engineer more and more as an individual who can step back far enough from the day-to-day operations to observe objectively the system by which the company is run rather than as a specialist in a particular area. Further, management looks to an industrial engineer to assist in interpreting what he has seen and experienced to the other people in the organization.

THE RELATION OF INDUSTRIAL ENGINEERING AND MANAGEMENT

. . .

. . . Industrial engineering employs engineering thinking, principles, and methodology. It also uses the knowledge from other fields, particularly the physical and social sciences and mathematics. The mission of the engineer is "design," that of management is direction of "operations."

Where the industrial engineer serves management, he can perform many managerial tasks. However, these can only be in the service and auxiliary phases of management—i.e., in planning, in review, and in management research and development. In the "operations" section of management the engineer, as an engineer, is a stranger. Some engineers have become effective managers in management's main area, that of operations. Before this could occur, these persons had to develop special personal traits and gain experience and knowledge beyond that acquired in engineering. The reverse movement (where managers have become engineers) has only rarely occurred in the past and is less likely to do so in the future.

A dramatic change has taken place in the industrial engineering profession. Emphasis is now being placed on action before the fact rather than after. Greater attention is now being given to the creative role in support of dynamic modern business. And most importantly, the industrial engineer is now teaming with others to stress the scientific, the economic, and the management aspects of an organization.

. . .

It is evident from the foregoing material that modernization and broadening of industrial engineering is in progress. Developments of modern engineering, operations research, and management science have been substantial in their influence upon the changes taking place within this profession. The traditional approaches and techniques for serving management and for improving productivity have been retained—but they have been supplemented and reoriented by newer developments. The aspirations implicit in the symposia reports are far from universal in their practical translation to every day industrial engineering activities, but they do represent an attractive foundation for the development of broad-gage improvement functions.

REFERENCES

1. D. Wendell Fentress, Director of Research and Development, Flexonics Division of Calumet & Hecla, Inc., 300 East Devon Ave., Bartlett, Ill.
2. Austin Weston (ed.), "The Emerging Role of Industrial Engineering: A Summary Report of Industrial Engineering Symposia Sponsored by the American Institute of Industrial Engineers," *The Journal of Industrial Engineering*, March–April 1961 (part 2).

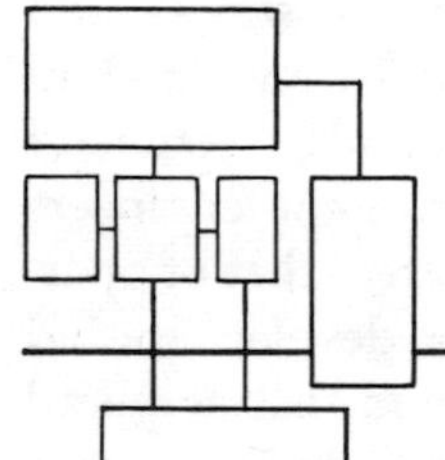

CHAPTER 4

IMPROVEMENT FUNCTION: What One Company Expects, and What It Gets

INDUSTRIAL engineering was defined and described in the previous chapter. This definition can be simplified and interpreted as follows:

The industrial engineer is:
1. A problem solver, and
2. A management advisor.

He deals with the problems of:
1. Systems for producing,
2. Systems for managing.

He serves as a translator and exploiter of science, to serve his management and his organization by assisting them in better achieving their objectives.*

* It has been suggested that the interpretation of industrial engineering might include a third problem area: 3. *Systems for controlling* (*financial, sales, production, technical, etc.*) This would serve to stress the importance of management control systems, which deserves to be stressed. The listing of only two problem areas is intended to include systems for controlling within 2. *Systems for managing*. Also included in *Systems for managing* are systems for *enabling* and *facilitating*. These latter two words imply management by leadership rather than by dictate and control in its narrow meaning.

This definition and the interpretation both tend to describe key aspects of the improvement function and may be related directly to it. But, it is necessary to keep in mind the comments we have previously made concerning the improvement function. Improvement efforts should be directed to areas and problems within an organization where improvement is needed and where improvement efforts have a good potential "payoff." The needs of the total organization should always be paramount. The improvement function should *permeate* the entire organization—both line and staff. Strategy—in determining where improvements are needed, how they can be developed, what the timing should be, and how they can best be implemented—is of critical importance.

LEVELS OF IMPROVEMENT EFFORT

The development of appropriate strategies for implementing improvement activities can be aided greatly by recognition of three levels of endeavor.*

1. Achieving better performance from the *present* systems of producing and managing.
2. Achieving better performance by *modification* of present systems to improve their "potential" for performance.
3. Achieving better performance by designing substantially *new,* or entirely new, *systems* with greater capacity for performance.

The systems being dealt with may be broad systems (the entire company, basic policies, managerial planning and control, production facilities, the information system), more confined or functional systems (a product line, a wage and salary control system, a division or department, a transportation or materials handling system), or subsystems and components. Different techniques and problem-solving tools are associated with improvement activities at various levels. The skills of the personnel involved with the improvement activities vary with the level of endeavor. The time required to solve problems, the amount of manpower and its cost vary with the level. The potential payoff may also vary considerably. The point to remember is that the needs of the organization will determine what activities the improvement function should be involved with at any particular time. The level of endeavor will greatly influence the requirements for implementing the efforts.

* The author is not entirely certain where he first encountered this particular structuring of levels of improvement endeavor. However, he is certain that the use of this concept as a guide for improvement activities and the dramatically successful results achieved by the industrial engineering programs at United Air Lines have greatly impressed him. Mr. Warren Alberts perhaps should receive credit for its origination.

THE COMPANY

Industrial engineering activities have long been associated with manufacturing industries, particularly in metal processing. Outstanding results have also been achieved in other types of organizations, including both manufacturing and nonmanufacturing industries. It has only been recently that chemical and process industries have become interested in industrial engineering. Part of this newly created interest is due to the broadened scope of the profession, and part to the great success in using industrial engineering by a few organizations such as International Minerals & Chemical Corporation.

IMC is a growing company in the mining and chemical processing industry. Its president and chief executive officer is an aggressive, progressive, and highly successful manager—an ex-industrial engineering consultant. He introduced internal industrial engineering consulting services when he first joined the company in 1947 and has aggressively, but cautiously expanded this area of influence. Operations research studies were initiated in 1950 with the assistance of external consultants to obtain better planning and balance in phosphate mining. The industrial engineering activities were subsequently expanded to encompass O.R. as well as a broad range of services to management. Today, the total industrial engineering activities approach an organization-wide improvement function. It is organized as the Industrial Engineering–Operations Research Division reporting to the vice-president of plans at the corporate level and as industrial engineering departments or functions within all of its seventy-two plant operations. At the major plant locations the industrial engineering manager reports to the plant manager or operations manager.

WHAT IT EXPECTS

The expectations for the improvement function within IMC are reflected by comments made by the director of the Industrial Engineering–Operations Research Division when talking about what industry expects of industrial engineers:[1]

1. Assist management in increasing the productivity of human and productive resources.
2. Assist management in cost reduction.
3. Develop management information flow systems.
4. Conduct organizational studies and design new organizational systems.

5. Develop data processing and computer control systems.
6. Coordinate development of corporate maintenance policies and programs.
7. Develop communications and reporting systems.
8. Formulate and recommend corporate inventory management policies and procedures.
9. Initiate, develop, and recommend corporate equipment replacement policies.
10. Assist management in developing long range planning strategies.
11. Develop production planning and scheduling procedures.
12. Establish engineered standards of performance for management control.
13. Determine and recommend the optimum usage of plant, equipment, and office facilities.
14. Verify economic feasibility of capital expenditure requests.
15. Conduct manufacturing and office methods surveys.
16. Conduct facility location studies.
17. Identify and solve distribution problems.
18. Perform functional counterpart audits.
19. Furnish liaison services between division management and outside consultants.
20. Provide assistance to all levels of management in solving problems requiring statistical and applied mathematical analysis.
21. Assist management in decision making through the use of computers or through the development of mathematical models simulating complex business problems.
22. Coordinate studies involving line and staff functions crossing divisional lines.
23. Assist management in formulating and developing corporate policies and procedures.
24. Develop and recommend production and quality control programs.

All levels of management, and all areas of activity, should be served by the improvement function. Mathewson states that industrial engineering must work with the following functions:[2]

1. *Top Management.* Assist management in designing strategic long range plans for decision making through the use of computers and the development of mathematical and statistical models simulating alternative courses of action.
2. *Operations.* Conduct research studies of all operating problems to increase productivity, reduce costs, increase production, improve quality and recoveries and optimize profits.

3. *Technical.* Work with technical groups to see that instrumentation, computer controls, human engineering, system design and work analysis concepts are followed in facilities and machinery design, placement, usage, and standardization of equipment.
4. *Marketing.* Provide assistance in analyzing complex pricing and marketing systems through the use of mathematics, statistics, and computers to develop alternative courses of action.
5. *Finance.* Develop the systems used to control labor, materials, and expenses. Design improved financial information flow systems to work in conjunction with programmed computers.
6. *Industrial Relations.* Keep industrial relations management informed on matters that affect employee relations. Matters pertaining to training, incentive compensation, working conditions, or organizational design changes should be carefully coordinated.
7. *Purchasing.* Provide assistance in evaluating optimum material specifications, establishing economic order quantities and order points, and developing methods and procedures to provide best service for least cost.
8. *Transportation.* Provide assistance in evaluating alternative distribution patterns to determine the optimum plans in meeting customer requirements, particularly where advanced techniques are feasible.
9. *Maintenance.* Work closely with maintenance management to reduce maintenance costs and improve production output.
10. *Production and Quality Control.* Provide assistance to achieve maximum utilization of equipment, materials, tools, and products to achieve optimum cost performance and high quality standards and assure excellent customer service.

This listing of services expected of the improvement function is very broad but not all-inclusive. The listing is intended to encompass the entire organization, and to serve all of management.

WHAT IT GETS

The expectations that are implicit in the previous listing are quite substantial. All levels of management are to be served—with a wide variety of assistance, ranging from traditional industrial engineering to management science and operations research. The results are indicated by the following yearly report to IMC management personnel by the Industrial Engineering–Operations Research Division.

OPERATIONS RESEARCH INDUSTRIAL ENGINEERING

1961-62

Report To Management

INTERNATIONAL MINERALS & CHEMICAL CORPORATION

COVER: The background diagram of the cover is a portion of an arrow diagram, an initial phase of critical path scheduling. Arrow diagramming consists of circled numbers representing events, and arrows representing jobs between events. The job is described briefly and an estimated time assigned to it. The "Critical Path" is the sequence of jobs which take the longest elapsed time from the beginning of the first to the completion of the final event. (See Page 15 for more on critical path scheduling).

INTERNATIONAL MINERALS & CHEMICAL CORPORATION
ADMINISTRATIVE CENTER · OLD ORCHARD ROAD · SKOKIE, ILLINOIS

IE–OR REPORT TO MANAGEMENT 1961

REPORT TO MANAGEMENT

Broader and more diversified professional services were offered by both the divisional and corporate Industrial Engineering—Operations Research functions in 1961. Substantial cost reductions were achieved through joint efforts of IMC management and IE–OR personnel. Division and corporate IE–OR groups conducted management studies, economic evaluations, statistical programs, and provided other professional services to all levels of management. Individual contributions to trade publications, professional societies and educational institutions served to bring forth recognition to IMC and this function. Increasing interest, stronger support and greater attention given to the use of the IE–OR tools and techniques by plant and corporate management are responsible for the substantial progress made in 1961. Even greater improvements are planned for 1962.

Wider applications of IE–OR will be provided for division and corporate management in the immediate future as the result of rapid increases in technology. The ever-increasing influence of computers will be felt in data processing, process control and engineering calculations. Continued emphasis will be placed on the development of new Management Information Systems. Florida has completed the installation of the IBM 1401 Computer; the Corporate 1401 Tape Computer will be installed early in 1962. Forward thinking involves planning for even more sophisticated computer systems in the future.

In the immediate future top priority is being given to the successful and rapid startup of the Esterhazy operations. Also increasing services are being provided marketing and sales in the application of mathematical and statistical tools for the formulation of marketing and selling strategies.

With management's receptive attitude to use these new tools, great progress can be predicted for the future. Plans for the future are based upon projects contributing to accelerated profit generation and the development of new operating and planning techniques for penetration of new markets. As a service to management, IE–OR will continue to aid all facets of the company's operation: Management, Production, Sales, Marketing, Financial and Technical. IMC's IE–OR groups are dedicated in their efforts to provide greater knowledge and facts needed in the management decision-making process.

2

CORPORATE IE–OR
SERVICES TO MANAGEMENT

Broader and more diversified professional services are being offered in the Corporation by the corporate and divisional Operations Research — Industrial Engineering staffs. The following describes the major projects undertaken throughout 1961.

AGRICULTURAL CHEMICALS DIVISION OPERATIONS

$750,000 MAINTENANCE IMPROVEMENT PROGRAM UNDER WAY IN FLORIDA AND CARLSBAD

Purpose: To design a program to reduce IMC's maintenance costs by $750,000.

Results: Program presented at Banff Manager's Meeting. Detailed cost analysis made of specific production areas and suggestions offered on where reductions could be realized. Goal for first year reduction in maintenance cost set at 7%.

Comments: $750,000 cost reduction will be realized upon successful completion of MIP.

1961-62 MAINTENANCE IMPROVEMENT PROGRAM

	61-62 Planned Mtce. Cost	% of Total	61-62 Estimated Reductions
Carlsbad	$ 3,783,000	35	$ 262,500
Florida Minerals	4,020,000	37	277,500
Bonnie	2,974,000	28	210,000
TOTAL	$10,777,000	100	$ 750,000

INDUSTRIAL ENGINEERING AND OPERATIONS RESEARCH PROGRAM DESIGNED FOR CANADIAN POTASH OPERATIONS

Purpose: To develop a complete IE–OR program for Esterhazy.

Results: Plant IE–OR program was developed for preproduction and operational phases. Orientation of the chief IE is completed and program is being implemented.

Comments: IMC is the first mining company in Canada to establish an Operations Research group.

NIAGARA FALLS STUDIES RESULT IN POTENTIAL $200,000 COST REDUCTION

Purpose: To assist Niagara Falls management in a cost reduction program.

Results: Organization study, manpower analysis, materials handling and warehousing evaluation, and overtime reduction resulted in $108,600 cost reduction.

Comments: $115,400 additional potential savings outlined in Corporate IE report titled, "Niagara Falls Cost Reduction Program," issued May 19, 1961.

ESTERHAZY IN-PROCESS STORAGE AND HANDLING STUDIED

Purpose: To analyze existing Esterhazy plant facilities for storage and materials handling in order to determine revisions necessary for anticipated increased production capacity.

Results: Recommendations were made regarding load-out bin capacities, car loading and track facilities, raw-ore storage requirements and adequacy of shift bins and conveyors.

CARLSBAD PRODUCTION PLANNING AND CONTROL SYSTEM STUDIED

Purpose: To study order handling activities at Carlsbad to determine the desirability of establishing a formalized production planning and control group.

Results: Present system satisfactory; no change needed at this time.

Comments: Matter will be reconsidered when Esterhazy Potash operation becomes productive and problem of balancing production and shipments between operations arises.

AGRICULTURAL CHEMICALS DIVISION SALES

LINEAR PROGRAMMING MODEL HELPS TO SOLVE FEED INGREDIENTS PROBLEM

Purpose: To establish optimum feed formulations under varying cost situations in different locations.

Results: Pilot linear programming model formulated and solved.

NEW MANAGEMENT INFORMATION FLOW SYSTEM DESIGNED FOR AG. CHEM. SALES

Purpose: To develop integrated order handling system for the Materials Department of the Ag. Chem. Sales Division.

Results: New system installed enabling fast, accurate transmission of data from regional offices to Skokie and then to the plants and back. Orders processed faster, billing and sales control reports issued more regularly.

Comments: New system uses direct line communications between regional sales offices, Skokie and the plants through programmatic Flexowriters and punched tapes.

FINANCE DIVISION

IBM 1401 TAPE COMPUTER TO BE INSTALLED IN SKOKIE EARLY IN 1962

Purpose: To install IBM 1401 tape computer for Management Information System and scientific problem solving.

Results: A task force was organized and projects selected for initial conversion, development of the project schedule, and systems redesign for computer use.

Comments: This project is under direction of a computer installation committee composed of members of the Corporate Industrial Engineering and Accounting Departments.

PUBLIC RELATIONS DIVISION

GOF'R GROWTH PROGRAM COORDINATED THROUGH BETTER METHODS PROGRAM

Purpose: To coordinate the Gof'r Growth Program of the Public Relations Division with the existing Better Methods Plans at Carlsbad and Florida.

Results: Better Methods Coordinators at each location became key members of local Gof'r Growth Committees and assisted in the successful implementation of the Gof'r Growth Program.

LONG RANGE PLANNING DIVISION

MODEL DEVELOPED FOR PREDICTING COSTS AND REVENUES FOR A NEW AGRICULTURAL CHEMICALS PLANT

Purpose: To consolidate the information developed for the Agricultural Chemicals expansion study so that it could be used for other studies.

Results: A report, "Plant Optimization Model for a New Agricultural Chemicals Plant," was issued and sent to the corporate planning groups responsible for making studies in this area.

Comments: The Bonnie planning group requested additional copies of the report and used the information in planning their divisional long range capital needs.

MARKETING DIVISION

PROFIT IMPROVEMENT PROGRAM

Purpose: To offer customers the opportunity to train key production people in the principles of work simplification.

Results: Profit Improvement Program proposed to Marketing Division and Sales personnel of the Ag. Chem. Division and Industrial Minerals Division.

TECHNICAL DIVISION

NON-TECHNICAL POSITIONS STUDIED IN TECHNICAL DIVISION

Purpose: To study organizational requirements for non-technical positions in the Technical Division.

Results: Non-technical positions in the Skokie Research Building analyzed. Recommendations leading to actual cost savings of approximately $12,000 plus a potential of $28,000 annually were submitted to the Technical Division management.

GENERAL MANAGEMENT

NEW MANAGEMENT INCENTIVE PLANS DESIGNED

Purpose: To design new incentive plans for management personnel in the Industrial Minerals Operations and the Niagara Falls Plant.

Results: Incentive plans developed and installed.

Comments: 1. Production management incentive plans have been designed around the same basic factors used in other divisional plans (i.e., controllable unit costs, recoveries and safety). 2. Niagara Falls incentive was developed as a portion of the overall cost reduction program, which also included organizational realignments and use of a resident IE.

CURRENT MANAGEMENT INCENTIVES MAINTAINED

Purpose: To audit, review and update management incentive plans at Florida, Carlsbad, San Jose and Plant Food to reflect changing conditions.

Results: 1. Florida plan extensively overhauled. Divisional profit plan was used to help establish standards in order to relate the incentive program to the planning phases of the operation. 2. San Jose plans modified to reflect $800,000 expansion program. Preliminary review was made of the use of concentrated fermentation liquor and its impact on incentive standards. 3. Routine audits performed at Carlsbad and Plant Food. Standards were adjusted. Major change is being made at Carlsbad to reflect the planned termination of the MgO–HCl circuits.

DIVISIONAL IE–OR SERVICES TO MANAGEMENT

FLORIDA IE–OR SERVICES AGRICULTURAL CHEMICALS DIVISION

The following major projects were completed:

OPERATIONS RESEARCH TECHNIQUES ASSIST MANAGEMENT IN LONG RANGE PLANNING AND ECONOMIC ANALYSES

Purpose: To assist in the development and evaluation of long range plans for the Minerals Department.

Results: 1. Two plant strategy to meet increased minerals sales demand was developed. 2. Alternative minerals expansion plans, incorporating potential acquisitions of reserves, were evaluated. Other work involved the updating of reserve information on punched cards, maintaining a record of production coefficients, and the development of geological data for the minerals expansion group and Skokie geological personnel. 3. New and comprehensive methods of economic analysis have been used on various projects. These methods include net cash flow, discounted rate of return, present worth evaluation and incremental analysis of alternatives. They have been applied on such projects as: a. Economic analysis of holding action for present defluorinated phosphate operation in Tennessee and provision of new plant in Florida. b. Economics of relocating county road in order to acquire additional reserves under the existing right of way. c. Minerals expansion alternatives.

Comments: OR emphasis in future will be on projects with tangible savings, on computer applications and on improved quality of services to management.

WORK ANALYSIS REDUCES LABOR COSTS $115,000 DURING 1961

Purpose: To install a continuing program of work analysis for the Florida operations.

Results: 23 positions eliminated to date, resulting in total savings of $115,000 during 1961.

Comments: Work sampling of operating and maintenance activities is regularly performed. Detailed time, method, tool, equipment and layout analyses are used to determine optimum manner to perform work. Job standards, improved methods and economic automation are recommended and installed. Assistance and follow-up on implementation is furnished to operating management.

WORK ANALYSIS PROVIDES MANAGEMENT SUPPORT TO REDUCE COSTS

Purpose: To use work analysis methods to assist management in day-to-day problems.

Results: 1. Time study data developed to support management's action in eliminating jobs after liquid sulfur handling facilities were installed. $20,000 annual labor saving continued after favorable decision by arbitrator. 2. New reporting system introduced as initial step toward improved control over reporting overtime. 3. Revised interoffice mailing system recommended for transmitting data between the plant and the shipping coordinator's offices. Additional $5,000 savings resulted. 4. Better reporting and recording procedures for operating data recommended. Fourteen forms eliminated.

SUCCESS OF BETTER METHODS PROGRAM LEADING TO TRAINING OF ALL SUPERVISORY PERSONNEL

Purpose: To train all supervisory personnel at Florida under the Better Methods Plan.

Results: Significant cost reduction and safety projects already installed. $254,000 savings in 1960-61, and 68 participants completed their training.

Comments: Better Methods achieve cost reduction, safer working conditions and quality improvement. Numerous aids to self-improvement, including case problems, are utilized. All installed projects have not yet received post installation audits; hence, listed results are conservative.

Better Methods 1961-62 objectives are centered around new product installations with annual savings of $400,000 per year.

CARLSBAD IE–OR SERVICES
AGRICULTURAL CHEMICALS DIVISION

The following major projects were completed:

SHIPPING STUDY NETS $60,000

Purpose: To streamline the shipping function towards efficient utilization of crew sizes, overtime and demurrage.

Results: This study permitted an average reduction of ten persons in the shipping crew and a new record of 199 tons per man-shift. This represents an increase in efficiency and an estimated annual savings of $60,000.

Comments: Previously, 60% of the orders shipped on any one day arrived at the plant on that day or the day before. A change in the order pattern was developed in which 80% of the orders for any one day were on hand ten days in advance of the order shipment.

MINE INTELLIGENCE TECHNIQUE REDUCED DELAYS BY 50%

Purpose: To improve communications between foremen and crews and between the mine and maintenance department personnel.

Results: New intelligence technique reduced delays on one level by 50%. Estimated increase in manufacturing profits of approximately $45,000.

Comments: Operating information describing all mine conditions was made available. It is now possible to rapidly determine the status of production, maintenance, bottlenecks, repair priorities, etc.

JOB ANALYSIS IMPROVES EFFICIENCY OF TRAMP MOTOR CREW

Purpose: To study the activities of the tramp motor crew by using the job analysis technique.

Results: Reduced manpower requirements totaling approximately $16,000 per year.

Comments: Job requirements between the first and second shift crews were coordinated.

CRITICAL PATH SCHEDULING AIDS MINE MAINTENANCE SHUTDOWN SCHEDULING

Purpose: To schedule all mine maintenance schedules with minimum interruption to production.

Results: Estimated $40,000 yearly saving.

Comments: Each of the eight sections has its own critical path schedule which must be integrated into the total mine critical path schedule.

SUCCESS OF BETTER METHODS PROGRAM LEADING TO TRAINING OF ALL SUPERVISORY PERSONNEL

Purpose: To train all supervisory personnel at Carlsbad under the Better Methods Plan.

Results: Significant cost reduction and safety projects already installed. $205,550 savings in 1960-61.

STATISTICAL CONTROL LOWERS TOOL USAGE COSTS

Purpose: To study usage costs of small hand tools.

Results: Analysis and reporting technique resulting in $10,000 estimated annual saving.

Comments: By plotting such factors as type of tool used per man-shift or per ton produced, norms were established which could be used in comparing actual tool requests.

OPERATIONS ANALYSIS IN MINE RESULTS IN 140 TON-PER-SHIFT INCREASE — 18% MORE THAN BEFORE

Purpose: To analyze Panel 10 operations for possible efficiency increases.

Results: Increases from 780 tons per shift to 929. Increases from 132 tons per man to 140. Annual savings of over $40,000.

Comments: Recommendations included moving the maintenance shop, checking the power supply, operations cycling, stock-piling of ore, scheduled belt and power moves, reassignment of operators, repair priorities, lubrication scheduling and equipment status reporting.

STATISTICAL ANALYSIS REDUCES BAG PRODUCT OVERWEIGHT

Purpose: To reduce overweight in bag shipments.

Results: Product savings of about $20,000.

Comments: Statistical analysis of bagged weights over a period of time permitted the narrowing of limitations consistent with local requirements.

ESTERHAZY IE–OR SERVICES
AGRICULTURAL CHEMICALS DIVISION

The Industrial Engineering – Operations Research function of the Esterhazy operation was established during the fiscal year 1960/61. A Chief Industrial Engineer was hired to head up the department and candidates were interviewed for the other positions in the department. To provide the proper understanding of IMC's IE–OR policies, the Chief IE spent two weeks in Skokie with the Corporate IE–OR staff. This also provided the opportunity to meet key members of other corporate departments. The following major projects were undertaken.

OPERATION OF CONTINUOUS MINER STUDIED

Purpose: To participate as a member of a team used to operate and observe the new continuous miner at Carlsbad.

Results: This participation provided valuable information for the Canadian operation, since the mining at Canada will be done with continuous miners.

Comments: While in Carlsbad the IE–OR program was reviewed to provide additional background for the establishment of this function in Esterhazy.

ORGANIZATION STUDY COMPLETED

Purpose: To develop the organizational relationships of all functions in the Esterhazy operation, utilizing unique concepts in coordinating production and service activities.

Results: Working with management and Industrial Relations personnel, a new organizational plan has been developed. It is based on a concept of maintained operation and locates the responsibility for maintenance in the production department and utilizes a service-operator concept for performing production and maintenance work.

Comments: This organizational approach is designed to place responsibilities at the lowest possible level, provide flexibility in meeting operating requirements and permit lower cost operations.

SHAFT SINKING PLANNING ASSISTANCE

Purpose: To minimize time and expense in sinking shaft and effectively coordinate activities at the surface in servicing the shaft during construction.

Results: A planning and scheduling program was developed for the various activities involved in the Galloway stage. Diagrammatic activity charts were prepared and material handling studies are being continued.

Comments: A phase of the planning involved the study of setting curb rings. This analysis resulted in reducing the time of setting each ring by two hours.

JOB EVALUATION AND
STANDARD PRACTICES BEGUN

Purpose: To institute equitable job responsibilities and operating routines for all personnel in the Esterhazy operations.

Results: Job descriptions are currently being written for all jobs and positions. Assistance is being given to operating departments in preparing operating procedures. A job evaluation program utilizing point rating has been established in cooperation with the Industrial Relations Department.

Comments: This work is important to the effective coordination of all activities in the operation and is basic to the development of a sound wage and salary structure.

MANAGEMENT INFORMATION SYSTEM
DESIGNED

Purpose: To assist in the design of an overall information system to serve all phases of management.

Results: Working with division management and corporate staff, the Chief Industrial Engineer from Esterhazy contributed to the design of a management information system which encompasses the requirements of accounting, maintenance planning and control, and production management.

STATION CUTTING AND LOADOUT
INSTALLATIONS SCHEDULED

Purpose: To provide schedules for the initial cutting of stations and loadout installations.

Results: In cooperation with mine personnel, schedules and procedures are being prepared to cover all phases of the sinking operations, service and equipment installations.

TRAINING PROGRAM FORMALIZED

Purpose: To prepare supervisory and management personnel for training of staffs.

Results: Working with the Production Manager and Industrial Relations personnel, a complete training schedule has been prepared outlining time and place of sessions. Assistance has been given in organizing conference leadership training and in the selection of personnel through participation in the employee committee.

Comments: Conference leadership techniques are currently being taught at Esterhazy. These sessions will be completed by the end of December and will assist Esterhazy management to carry on individual staff training in the future.

SAN JOSE IE SERVICES
AMINO PRODUCTS DIVISION

METHODS ENGINEER POSITION CREATED

During the 1960/61 fiscal year the position of Methods Engineer was established at the San Jose operation of the Amino Products Division. An Industrial Engineer from Carlsbad was transferred to San Jose, which provided an excellent beginning for the IE program. The engineer was already knowledgeable about IMC operations and IE–OR programs, and the need for a lengthy indoctrination was thus eliminated. The following major projects were undertaken:

FINISHED AC'CENT PACKING, HANDLING & STORAGE SYSTEM REVAMPED

Purpose: To improve the methods used in the shipping area for packing, handling and storing finished goods.

Results: A recommendation was approved for the installation of a vibrator, automatic filling equipment, material handling equipment and new layout for the packing room. Not only was a substantial reduction in manpower achieved, but valuable storage space was freed for other purposes through the use of smaller drums and trailer storage of empty drums. Savings in material and labor of approximately $50,000 will result annually.

Comments: This is the first plant on the West Coast to have conveyorized a fiber drum system.

WORK SAMPLING TO REDUCE MANPOWER

Purpose: To use random sampling as aid to determining productivity levels of all personnel, including supervision and secretaries, in advance of more detailed studies of personnel assignments and work station layout.

Result: Substantial reductions in manpower can be made through realignment of work load and better utilization of available work hours.

Comments: Unique method of random sampling was employed. Each department supplied a supervisor for the study. Supervisors, in addition to performing their normal work routine, assisted the Methods Engineer in making studies and used punched cards and hand punch to collect data. Each supervisor sampled all departments.

INDESA MEXICAN IE PROGRAM
INDESA MEXICAN DEHYDRATION OPERATION

Purpose: 1. Make economic equipment evaluation study of entire plant. 2. Plan and direct construction program. 3. Conduct feasibility study of operating efficiencies of equipment and personnel. 4. Organize maintenance efforts and equipment operating procedures. 5. Establish warehouse and central equipment filing system.

Results: Developed program to optimize production capacities to increase volume from 30,000 to 100,000 pounds per day with minimum of capital. Established maintenance work order planning and inspection system. Central equipment file system was established to accommodate any maintenance, production or accounting analysis. Plant equipment was put in operating condition.

Comments: Location of operation, plus the fact that very few people were experienced, created the necessity of developing a sequential job system.

INDUSTRIAL MINERALS IE–OR SERVICES
INDUSTRIAL MINERALS DIVISION

The Corporate IE–OR group serves the Industrial Minerals Division management. Such projects as the following were undertaken:

INDUSTRIAL ENGINEERING SURVEY

Purpose: To determine the extent and manner by which a broad IE–OR activity could contribute to the attainment of divisional profit objectives.

Results: Survey started and several operations visited. Overall divisional activities being reviewed.

SIMULATION OF TRANSPORTATION COSTS FOR PRE-MIXED FOUNDRY SAND ADDITIVES

Purpose: To determine the transportation cost of shipping pre-mixed foundry sand additives to a probable market.

Results: Cost estimates of transportation were determined resulting in further study of feasibility of this procedure.

MANAGEMENT INCENTIVE PLAN

Purpose: To design an incentive plan for management personnel in the Industrial Minerals operations.

Results: Incentive plan installed as of July 1, 1961.

Comments: This incentive plan was designed around the same basic factors used in other divisional plans (i.e., controllable costs, recoveries and safety).

PROFIT IMPROVEMENT PROGRAM

Purpose: To offer customers the opportunity to train key production people in the principles of work simplification.

Results: Profit Improvement Program proposed to Marketing Division, Sales and Production personnel of Industrial Minerals Division.

PLANT FOOD IE SERVICES
PLANT FOOD DIVISION

The following major projects were undertaken by the Division Industrial Engineer of the Plant Food Division.

RAUH AND SONS OPERATIONS ANALYSIS

Purpose: To perform operations analysis of Rauh and Sons Corporation, newly acquired fertilizer operation, with annual production of approximately 150,000 tons of plant food.

Results: Recommended and instituted changes in administrative procedures, accounting system, organizational structure and plant operations. Included proposals for improvements in maintenance, materials handling, warehousing and shipping. Developed capital and profit plans with Rauh executives and designed and installed incentive system for superintendents and foremen.

NEW ACQUISITION PHASED INTO PLANT FOOD OPERATIONS

Purpose: To introduce managerial controls into Miami Plant.

Results: In newly acquired Miami Plant at Dayton, Ohio, designed and installed incentive system for superintendent, established production standards and repair and maintenance budgets.

INCENTIVE STANDARDS REVIEWED

Purpose: To audit and review Plant Food Division incentives.

Results: Updated incentive standards for Field Management and Production Supervisory Incentive Plans.

BLENDING PLANT LOCATION STUDIED

Purpose: To assist Plant Food management in locating proposed blending plant.

Results: Worked with division management in planning the location facilities and economics for blending plant anticipated to be in operation this year.

PRODUCTION MEETING HELD

Purpose: To conduct production programs for Plant Food management and supervisors.

Results: Program stimulated supervision to improve operations and generate profits through better understanding of costs, labor effectiveness, quality control, and general performance.

DRY AND LIQUID FERTILIZER EVALUATED

Purpose: To evaluate dry and liquid fertilizer companies and equipment.

Results: Conducted investigation of companies and equipment with regard to facilities for handling and distributing dry and liquid fertilizers.

LAWN AND GARDEN OPERATION INSTALLED

Purpose: To develop complete production program for new Lawn and Garden products.

Results: Lawn and Garden Department assisted through locating new building, designing a cost system and establishing packaging, handling and shipping operations.

FULL ORBIT PROGRAM AIDED

Purpose: To provide assistance to Ag. Chem. Sales in their Full Orbit program.

Results: Outlined draft for Marketing and Technical Service presentation regarding fertilizer manufacturing, costs, budgets, etc.

CURRENT & FUTURE IE–OR PROJECTS

The Corporate and Division IE–OR groups are currently working on a number of important projects which are listed below.

MANAGEMENT INFORMATION FLOW SYSTEM FOR ESTERHAZY

Working with Ag. Chem. Division Management and Esterhazy personnel, a complete Management Information Flow System is being designed to provide cost, production performance, and maintenance information within a totally integrated framework, wherein common source information is used to provide reports both for managerial and financial control. A team comprised of Canadian and Corporate Accounting and Industrial Engineering personnel has formulated the basic framework of the system, and work is now in progress to detail the various sub-systems. These efforts will be followed by the implementation phase. This project, when completed, will provide control information in a useful form and on a timely basis.

AUTOMATIC PROCESS CONTROL BY COMPUTERS

Many plant processes appear suitable for automatic control by digital or analog computers. IE–OR personnel are conducting studies to determine feasibility of such installations.

EXTENSION OF SYSTEMS BALANCE TO FLORIDA CHEMICALS

The Minerals Systems Balance techniques are being adapted to the Bonnie Chemicals operations.

OPTIMIZATION OF CARLSBAD-ESTERHAZY PRODUCTION COMPLEX

Detailed investigations will be made to determine optimal production quantities and markets for Carlsbad and Esterhazy muriates.

ANALYSIS OF WORLD MINERAL PRODUCTION AND MARKETS

Working with Marketing and the CEIR consulting organization, the IE–OR group will assist in the application of Operations Research techniques to analyze world mineral production and marketing dynamics to determine IMC's position and potential in the world markets.

INDUSTRIAL MINERALS OPERATIONS ANALYSIS

The Corporate IE–OR group has proposed to the Industrial Minerals Division that a survey of their operations be made in order to determine where IE could help reduce costs and improve profits.

AG. CHEM. DISTRIBUTION-WAREHOUSING STUDY

The future storage needs and distribution patterns for the entire Agricultural Chemicals Division are being studied for the purpose of obtaining maximum service and adequate storage at minimum costs. Cost models are being developed for several alternatives.

SCIENTIFIC MANAGEMENT FARM STUDY

IE–OR is working with the Marketing Division and Agri-Research in a project to aid farmers in integrating their resources for maximum net return. Linear programming, an OR technique, will be used in this study. Farm management consultants are gathering necessary input-output data.

UNITIZATION OF CANADIAN POTASH VENTURE

This involves the selection of a unitization plan which will maximize royalty returns from the Canadian Potash venture. Working jointly with Canadian Management, a series of unitization strategies were developed, providing areas which will maximize IMC royalty returns and, at the same time, permit flexibility in going into high grade ore areas, provide for various expansion alternatives, and create maximum assurance that new mines will fulfill requirements to qualify for certain Canadian tax benefits.

PRODUCTION EXECUTIVE INCENTIVE PLANS

As a result of a decision by the Board of Directors, the Corporate Incentive Plan for executives and key employees was changed effective July 1, 1961. New incentive plans have been designed for key production executives to measure the performance of activities under their direct control.

14

NEW MANAGEMENT TOOLS USED AT IMC IN PROBLEM SOLVING

IMC management is using the following wide range of scientific management tools in problem solving and decision making.

CPS *(Critical Path Scheduling)* NOW BEING USED EXTENSIVELY BY IMC MANAGEMENT

Management, Supervisory and Technical personnel are using CPS extensively on a highly diversified range of activities which call for sound planning and scheduling. Such jobs as large maintenance projects and major construction programs are now being controlled and managed by using arrow diagramming and critical path techniques. Typical projects involving the use of CPS include:

1. Carlsbad mine shutdowns involving eight separate sections having individual critical path schedules which are integrated into the total mine critical path schedule. This unique way of scheduling mine shutdowns has resulted in an estimated savings of $40,000.

2. Critical path scheduling has also been used to outline construction plans at the Esterhazy mine.

3. Capital expansion projects in Florida included the use of critical path scheduling. The continued use of this technique in the DAP plant construction at Bonnie has averted material shortages and labor delays. The technique was also used in preliminary planning of Noralyn projects.

SIMULATION

Systems simulation provides a method of studying complex problems by developing models of the system which can be solved with computers and various mathematical techniques to determine the behavior and optimum operation of the system. For example, the effects of new products, expansion of facilities, or changes in competitive activity can be simulated to determine ideal operating strategies.

LINEAR PROGRAMMING

Linear programming is a widely used technique for determining optimum strategies where many variables are present. Computer solutions are usually required. IE–OR personnel will continue to use linear programming where needed in the future. Typical problems susceptible to linear programming solutions include the following:

1. Analysis of world minerals production and markets.
2. Determination of product distribution patterns and warehouse locations.
3. Optimization of production and distribution in the Esterhazy-Carlsbad complex.
4. Integration of management capabilities on cash grain farms.
5. Determination of least-cost feed formulations.

OTHER IE–OR TOOLS & TECHNIQUES USED AT IMC

Computer Application
Probability Theory
Statistical Analysis
Monte Carlo Procedures
Queuing Theory
Series and Probability Functions
Work Analysis
Man and Machine Charts
Simo Charts
Gantt Charts
Nomographs
Mathematical Programming
Job Analysis and Evaluation
Standard Data
Motion Pictures
Micro-Motion Study
Breakeven Analysis
Product Analysis
Decision Theory
Game Theory
Model Building
Work Sampling
Better Methods

CONCLUSION

IE–OR PROFESSIONAL SERVICES ARE BEING PROVIDED THROUGHOUT IMC'S OPERATIONS

Industrial Engineering and Operations Research professional services are being provided to every division and in every phase of the company's operations.

In *production,* for example, maintenance, manpower deployment, better methods, work analysis and communications problems have been solved through the use of IE–OR tools.

Marketing activities continue to offer opportunities for application of IE–OR techniques. Some of these described earlier were: distribution-warehousing, world raw mineral studies, and farm management.

In the areas of *finance* and *sales,* new information flow systems have been installed. The Profit Improvement Program for our customers is an example which will assist both sales and marketing.

During the past few years, Industrial Engineering and Operations Research have become tools of *Management.* Many illustrations have been given in the previous chapters, including the IBM 1401 Computer installation, the incentive programs, the Industrial Minerals operations analysis and the Canadian Potash unitization. One of the most important projects to be implemented in the near future will be the application of computers to process control. In the future, as in the past, IMC's IE–OR staffs will continue to make available the latest technological developments to serve management.

REFERENCES

1. Morley H. Mathewson, "What Does Industry Expect of the Industrial Engineering Graduate?" *The Journal of Industrial Engineering,* May–June 1962, p. 198.
2. *Ibid.,* p. 198.

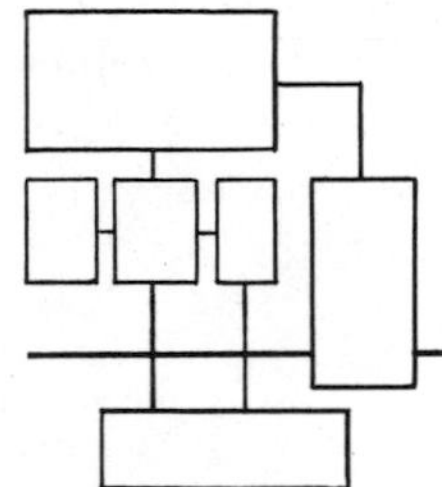

CHAPTER 5

OPERATIONS RESEARCH

One of the terms frequently used in conjunction with the application of science and engineering to management problems is operations research. This terminology had its formal origins in the military activities of World War II, but since has come to be quite closely associated with the researching of a wide variety of management and other problems in business, industry, and government.

The term operation*al* research (from which O.R. is derived) occurred during the Battle of Britain while the entire British people were literally fighting for survival. The Nazi war was pressing hard against a nation that was without much in the way of material resources, for defeat and the retreat from Dunkirk left the English with their war equipment on the beach in Europe and their military organization shattered. Manpower and equipment to defend the home isles were in extremely short supply. Many skilled personnel were forced to participate in activities quite strange to them. In addition, effective utilization of a new technological development, radar, presented sizable problems. In essence, the birth of operations research began with the assignment of teams of university-educated personnel (mainly with backgrounds in some area of science) to assist the military in solving the management problems of effectively using their limited resources. These teams had almost no understanding of military operations, but they did have the objectivity characteristics of the scientist. Their lack of familiarity with military operations necessitated a very detached search for underlying concepts that would explain what was happening. In many instances this approach led to revealing simplicity in the formulation of basic cause and effect relationships. Great faith was placed in the power of the scientific method and the research approach.

A definition of operations research is illusive and will be largely a reflection of the definer's own background. To the author, the most appropriate definition is:

> Operations research is the researching of operational problems.

This definition is not entirely satisfactory, for an interpretation of "researching" and "operational problems" still leaves much room for misunderstanding.

Operations research, even though not clearly defined, usually has associated with it several distinguishing characteristics. The most significant are usually claimed to be:

1. The research approach
2. The systems approach
3. The use of models and mathematics
4. The team approach
5. Consultive to "top management"

Each of these main features will be discussed in subsequent chapters. It should be remembered that all of these characteristics will not necessarily be found with every example of O.R. But, they tend to define the nature of O.R., or perhaps we should say they tend to illustrate the ways in which engineering and management science contribute to the solving of management problems.

DIFFERING VIEWS OF OPERATIONS RESEARCH

Just as any definition of operations research is likely to reflect the views of the definer, and is likely not to receive universal acceptance, the nature of O.R. activity is likely to differ from individual to individual or from group to group. Several schools of thought concerning the proper approach to the activity have emerged, each having their own vocal advocates.

The original operations research approach was closely associated with the application of the research approach and the use of scientific tools for the detection, analysis, and solution of operational problems. Operations research people were advisors to line management and, because of their scientific background, attempted to maintain a scientific detachment from direct involvement with operational and management activities. They would analyze and manipulate abstractions or models of the problem situation and then recommend courses of action to the manager—or, as frequently termed, the decision maker. It was entirely the responsibility of the decision maker to make and implement the decisions.

Further views in the early period were associated with the concept of solving problems within the physical limitations of the present system. This approach implied that the system could be manipulated to achieve better performance in the solution of operational problems, but that physical changes—the redesigning of the hardware of the system—were inappropriate and beyond the scope of operations research endeavor.

Although these views have persisted, they have been substantially modified to include more engineering in the solution of problems. Better performance in operations research work may be achieved by direct modification of the operational system, its components, or even by the design of entirely new systems. Operations research may also be used as a design tool by the engineer, which is somewhat of a departure from the views of the early O.R. practitioners. Much of the better O.R. work in recent years has had a heavy engineering content, and the problems of effective implementation of the results of O.R. studies have become recognized as a direct and critically important aspect.

Some O.R. groups have maintained the orientation of the scientist, and perform their work in a detached—almost isolated—manner. Problems must be formulated for them; they then apply analytical techniques and present the results to others to do something with. These O.R. scientists perform the role of a mathematical advisor or consultant to the manager and the engineer. They may also perform research in the development of new analytical techniques for solving particular types of operational problems.

Another grouping of O.R. activities is strongly influenced by the team approach. This takes the form of an interdisciplinary team, and assumes that individuals of intelligence from various academic fields, when familiar with the basic mathematical techniques associated with operations research, will be able to research operational problems successfully. A variation of this approach places great emphasis upon the philosophy of science, and usually supplements the team with at least one individual who has a strong background in philosophy, logic, and scientific methodology.

Many of the early operations research people regarded themselves as scientists, searching—not for solutions to problems, but—for general methods appropriate for handling various types of problems. Classes of models were developed for dealing with various groupings of problems. The challenge was to develop new understanding of phenomena involved in management and to develop O.R. "tools." The problems could then be solved by others.

This multiplicity of views of operations research—what it is, and how it is done—has persisted. In a way this is unfortunate, because it does lead to confusion and misunderstanding. It is also fortunate, since the differing approaches have resulted in contributions that perhaps would not have been made if a unified, single approach had developed. One of the most significant evolutions has been associated with the gradual assimilation of operations research by engineering, and a parallel changing of O.R. away from a scientific endeavor toward an engineering type of activity. This change has resulted from the realization by engineers, managers, and operations researchers that the most successful operations research work has been performed as an engineering function—with a preoccupation on the part of the operations researchers with practical solution to problems of significance to management and their organizations, drawing upon science-based knowledge, intuition, and experience.

During the Battle of Britain the operational research teams solved many significant problems, including such things as the location and use of radar for detecting aircraft and V-1 buzz rockets, the grouping and use of antiaircraft guns, the protection of convoys, the determination of where armor protection was most needed to protect aircraft, the strategy of deploying bomber squadrons, and many others. In almost all cases the operational research teams acted as staff advisors to the military managers, rendering assistance in analyzing the strategy of using available resources more efficiently. The O.R. advisors worked with the military on a joint basis, using their detached and objective approach in an attempt to understand basic cause and effect relationships. This understanding, when combined with military experience, allowed the military managers to make more meaningful and effective decisions. In many cases, the methods which O.R. people had used in their own professional field as research tools had applicability and utility in the new settings. In other cases, an unbiased and detached view of the operational situation and a factual stating of the problem, objectives, and alternatives tended to make the appropriate solution obvious.

Since the origin of operations research in the military setting of World War II, numerous industrial and business applications have been made. These extend from the solution of production scheduling to the refinement of long-range policy formulation. Several applications will be presented in subsequent chapters.

SUMMARY

Operations research as an aid for management, that is, as a means of directly implementing a broad-gage improvement function, must possess a great deal of flexibility—to the extent that its behavior and execution is determined by the opportunities and needs for improvement within an organization. What constitutes proper operations research will be dependent upon the nature of the problems encountered—by the needs of the organization. In most cases, this requirement will result in operations research work being performed as an engineering type of activity; the personnel engaged in the activity will "act like engineers."

Some of these same thoughts are reflected in comments from a former student* with undergraduate education in electrical engineering and graduate education in industrial engineering.

> "I now have 16 people in my organization, 11 of whom perform industrial O.R. work. I believe that we have found the real key to success in performing operation research. It lies in the unsophisticated approach to the numerous problems in management control; in the ability to communicate ideas and recommendations to a nontechnical customer; and in the ability to demonstrate humility by exhibiting a genuine desire to assist in improving operations. All this tempered by a rather unique way of looking at things which is intuitive with good O.R. people. In roughly one year we have gone from a one man level of support to the current 11 man level—with demonstrated savings of over $1,500,000 per year."

In previous chapters we have discussed the need for a broad-gage, organization-wide improvement function, and have suggested that a combination of *traditional* industrial engineering, management science and operations research provides a logical base for developing such activities. We have also examined the attempts of industrial engineering to modernize and to incorporate operations research and management science within its scope. The next several chapters will be devoted to a closer look at the main characteristics of O.R., in a very simplified and sketchy manner, and will gradually build to its use within the modern industrial arena. Techniques and mathematical models will not be presented except for a simple illustrative example which demonstrates the use of models as a means of abstracting key relationships from the real-world environment, and the use of such abstractions as an aid in decision making. These chapters will then be followed by materials treating the ways in which the broad range of improvement technology can be used to support broad-gage improvement functions.

* Joel M. Goodman, Lockheed Missiles & Space Company, personal correspondence.

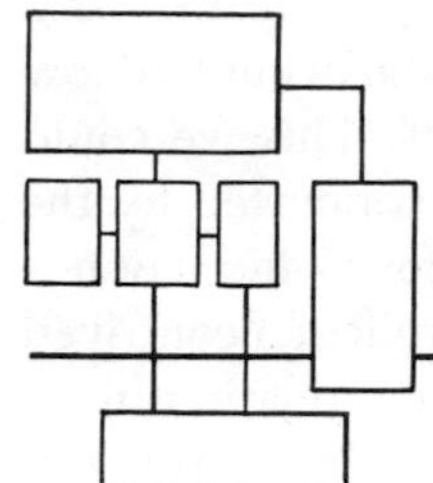

CHAPTER 6

THE RESEARCH APPROACH

THE RESEARCH APPROACH is an adaptation of the scientific method, which is usually thought of in terms of a four step process:

1. Observation
2. Hypothesis
3. Experimentation
4. Induction

These steps can be visualized as a way to approach understanding and to systematically solve problems. The same basic approach is, of course, used by more than just the scientist.

As a well-known example of the scientific method, visualize Sir Isaac Newton—enjoying a bit of relaxation in the shade of an apple tree. An apple falls and hits him on the head. This causes him to wonder why apples fall. He perhaps speculates, from this and other observations, that all (or almost all) objects fall—that they must be attracted by some force —call it the force of gravity. If this is so, he should be able to determine the nature of this force and to predict the behavior of falling objects. Thus, Newton executed steps one and two of the scientific method. Step one was observation—recognizing the phenomenon of falling objects and becoming conscious of some insight that might explain what had been observed. This then led up to step two—the explanation of the phenomenon by means of an hypothesis—the force of gravity, which causes all objects to be attracted toward the center of the earth with a force proportional to their weight. Next would be step three, experimentation, for he must attempt to substantiate (or refute) his speculation (hypothesis) about what causes the observed phenomenon. If we were involved in this experimentation, we might tote several objects up to the top of a convenient tower, and by means of a helper below, who would follow our series of signals, time the descent of various objects. This we could do, and we could rediscover that the speculations were supported by the experimental data. We would then be ready for step four—induction—reasoning from the very specific of the contrived experiment (contrived to demonstrate very specific and restricted cause and effect relationships) to the more general context of the actual goings on in the world. For

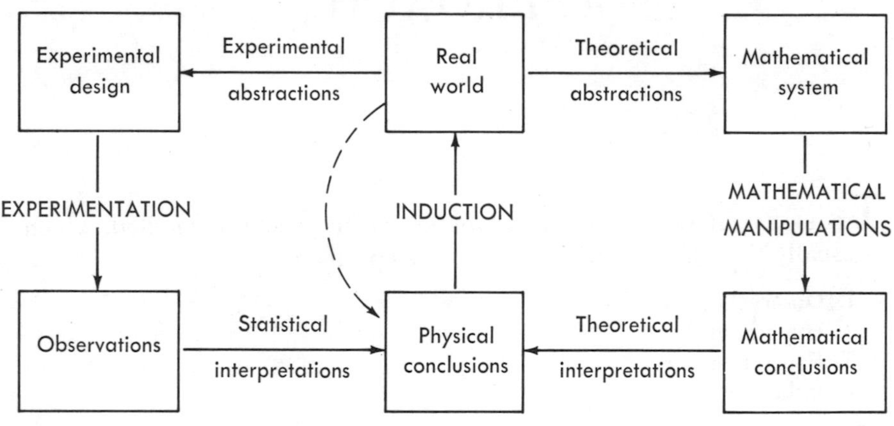

Figure 6-1

example, does our new knowledge explain why a feather floats when dropped while a lead ball descends with dispatch? Perhaps we have neglected some significant factors in contriving our experiment. We did drop several objects of various weights, and they all landed at the same time, just as predicted. That is, all except that dratted feather—so how can we explain it. The exception that proves the rule? No. Air resistance? Maybe. How can we test this speculation? What would happen if we dropped the feather in a vacuum? Oh, oh—we have gotten around to another hypothesis, based upon observation—and we are starting another cycle in the so-called scientific method.

In our quest for understanding, we might well parallel Sir Isaac's series of experiments and his use of mathematics in symbolizing the interrelationships involved in the phenomenon he sought to understand. Perhaps we would "discover" the law of gravity by our use of the scientific method if we continued. But, enough is enough. Our very simple example should have made its point and help us to understand the meaning of Fig. 6-1. This demonstrates the scientific approach—or call it the research approach—to better understanding of what is going on about us. In some cases we can theorize about what is happening and why, and call upon developed bodies of knowledge (such as mathematics) to describe the relationship—this is shown on the right side loop. In other cases, we must rely upon formal experimentation—as shown on the left side loop. In either case, we seek better understanding—by means of simplifying a real world situation into a manageable *abstraction* which allows us to manipulate and experiment with a mere shadow of reality. When we have finished our manipulations, we must then transfer back to the real world from our idealized, simplified abstractions. The manipulated shadow of reality must be related back to reality. This is shown at the lower part of the figure where the mathematical conclusions are translated into physical conclusions by means of theoretical interpretations, and the observations of experimentation are translated to physical conclusions by means of statistical interpretations. The physical conclusions must then be related to the real world situation.

The use of the research approach to solving operational problems will be further illustrated in subsequent materials, particularly in Chapter 8.

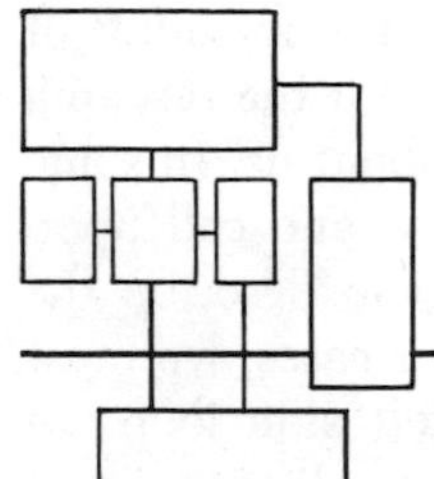

CHAPTER 7

THE SYSTEMS APPROACH

IT WOULD SEEM rather obvious that we should attempt to solve problems in such a way that their full range of consequences is anticipated and the solving of one isolated problem does not create other unwanted ones. However, human nature tends to encourage us to view our own sphere of activities as the most important and to ignore (or at least minimize) the effect of our actions as they may complicate the problems and activities of others. This is the essence of the problem of not analyzing *systems* when attempting to solve problems.

The systems approach attempts to consider the broad consequences upon the entire system of changing one part. But, in attempting to use a systems approach, we must decide what constitutes a system and also determine what measures (values, criteria) can be used to evaluate the performance of the system and its parameters.

Ideally, the ultimate system would include the universe or the galaxy. Realistically, we must be much more restrictive. In the military setting we might consider the total military effort, including all theaters of operation and allies. In business, we might consider the entire company—or perhaps one autonomous unit or division. In government, we might consider the entire community or nation. Obviously any arbitrary delineation of a system must be a compromise. But, the solution of practical problems requires compromises. Total systems can be divided into smaller systems or subsystems, which still possess the characteristics of a system, but are restricted so that they can be analyzed, problems solved, and the solutions properly related to performance of the broader system. Even where it is necessary to deal with very restricted parts of a system, the impact and consequences of change can be related to the system.

Operations research work is characterized by attempts to quantify—to measure and express relationships in quantities. Many of the criteria that are significant in O.R. work are extremely difficult to "quantize" and are almost impossible to convert to the scale of measure that constitutes an evaluation of the system performance at a higher level. Subjective evaluation must be used as a supplement to objective measures, criteria must be selected with great care, and system interaction must be assessed in both objective and subjective ways. The impact of changes within portions of a total system must be evaluated as meaningfully as possible and economical, and related to the appropriate system. It is the objective of improvement activities to achieve improvement, and hopefully, "optimization," of the system. Optimization is an illustory goal—but the search for it is of importance. Suboptimization can be fatal to effective system performance and a handicap to improvement activities.

The problems of optimization and suboptimization—the effective treatment of systems problems—has long been of concern to the industrial engineer, the operations researcher, and management. The recent developments in industrial engineering and operations research have served to highlight the importance of these concepts. The following presentation, "Systems Design—A Broader Role of Industrial Engineering," [1] reflects some of the problems associated with a narrow discharge of industrial engineering activities and suggests easy ways to remedy the situation.

Systems Design—A Broader Role of Industrial Engineering

by **WILLIAM G. BRUNER, JR.**

Associate Consultant, Arthur Young and Company

EVERY industrial engineer has at one time or another experienced the disappointment and frustration of a project that failed or a recommendation that was shelved. In some organizations, this has become customary and completed staff work is seldom achieved.

Explanations for these consequences are often vague and rarely comforting but such practices continue at a rate that seems to be increasing.

Many industrial engineers have left the field because of a lack of tangible accomplishment rather than a lack of career opportunity. Others, who stay in the field, become resigned to incomplete or untested solutions as a way of life. A few regard such an outcome as an indication of defective staff work, and try to identify how to avoid similar situations in the future.

Notwithstanding technical incompetence, which is present to a degree in industrial engineering as in any professional field, it appears that the historical environment and organization of industrial engineering tend to generate incomplete and inappropriate solutions. As background for exploring this hypothesis, let's consider a few representative case histories of industrial engineering projects that failed:

CASE HISTORIES

1. Industrial engineering develops and installs a job evaluation plan to determine appropriate rate ranges and job progressions. The plan involves relative weightings of several different factors that contribute to the total job value. The company also uses a merit rating plan developed by industrial relations to grant pay increases and select employees for promotion. Most of the workers are individually controlled in terms of production standards and a quality control program has been installed to pinpoint the source of quality problems.

   The weighting of traits in the job evaluation plan does not match that in the merit rating plan. Production performance and quality records are not used in merit rating individual employees, although quality and quantity of work comprise a large part of the rating. Personnel selection criteria are based on still another set of qualifications. As a result of this diversity, each of these controls disagrees in part with the other, thus limiting the effectiveness of them all. In particular, the rate range and progression controls are violated as often as they are complied with because of conflicts originating in the merit rating and personnel selection processes.
2. A small company hires an industrial engineer to help reduce costs and improve the profitability of their operations. His first assignment is production work measurement. He establishes time standards and installs performance reporting against them in each production department. By working with production department heads, he suc-

ceeds in improving labor performance against standards by 20%, while maintaining the same total production capability. Yet the company's income statement indicates no reduction at all in the cost of sales. The industrial engineer had overlooked the opportunity to apply labor standards in the cost accounting system. Management had changed the product mix based on historical cost data and unknowingly increased the sales volume of low-margin items and reduced the volume in a highly profitable line. Thus the impact of the industrial engineer's efforts to reduce costs was lost from the standpoint of profit improvement.

3. Based on a detailed evaluation of apparent factors within a major division of a large corporation, industrial engineering recommends, and local management adopts, a plan to substantially change manufacturing operations by modifying processing equipment and production techniques over a two-year period. The recommended program anticipates during this period a major operating loss in the division through equipment modifications resulting in reduced productivity. The loss, however, is estimated to be offset in the third year's operation and the complete modification program is expected to result in significant economic gain at the end of five years.

   After the modification program was well underway, corporate management's post-evaluation resulted in severe criticism. Although industrial engineering had considered the effect of income taxes in their economic evaluation, they failed to realize that the corporation had an income tax loss carry-forward, the benefits of which would be partially lost because of the operating losses to be sustained during the modification program. Because of the loss carry-forward effect, either a delay or a stretch-out of the modification program would have produced considerably greater economic benefit from a total, corporate point of view.

In each of these cases, the industrial engineer failed to identify and use an appropriate frame of reference in the design of the project. It is academic whether or not the failure can be attributed to the industrial engineer himself or to factors beyond his control. What really matters is that his output was not compatible with the conditions affecting the work situation. In other words, his solutions were not sufficiently "system-oriented" in the light of the real problems to be solved.

SYSTEMS-ORIENTED SOLUTION

Ironically, a system-oriented solution to a project relies on one of industrial engineering's basic tenets—the scientific method. The systems approach enlarges the scope of the first step in industrial engineering work—gathering information and identifying the problem. It seeks to trace a problem or situation upstream to its cause, as well as to identify cause-and-effect relationships along the way. A systems-oriented solution is expressed conditionally, in terms of three parameters:

Assumptions: pertinent facts assumed to exist at a particular time for a particular solution.

Boundary Conditions: limits within which a system can be expected to operate (and within which the solution is valid).

Performance Requirements: measures of effectiveness of the system, the output characteristics intended to be met.

The expression of these parameters as part of the solution qualifies the conditions under which a system is expected to operate in a certain manner. The statement of these premises not only defines the limits of the solution but also specifies what action is necessary to keep the solution valid.

The treatment of control requirements is a second basic quality of the systems approach. In any industrial operation, adequate control measures are essential for continued effective performance. The systems approach includes the control phase as part of the system itself, thereby creating a self-regulating operational environment. Machine designers employ this feedback principle in the design of automated mechanical equipment. Similarly, designers of systems using human beings must devise means of monitoring performance, comparing it with predetermined measures of effectiveness, and executing control actions to keep the system on course.

Considering each of the three hypothetical cases described, this time in a broadened systems context, let's identify and classify the missing links in these projects. In the case of the job evaluation program, the boundary conditions selected did not encompass the total problem area. In the work measurement example, both the boundary conditions and the performance requirements assumed in the study fell short of the real problem and failed to agree with management's intentions. In the case of the program to improve plant operations, a significant assumption was overlooked, thus the limits of the solution were invalid.

Each of these projects failed because of the use of an inappropriate frame of reference. But what is equally important, their frames of reference were not announced at the outset. Had the systems approach been used, the parameters of the apparent problem area would have been communicated to management first, thus enabling management to participate in the solution through endorsement or substitution of significant objectives or limitations. This is probably the most important quality of this approach—improved communications with management.

Undoubtedly, a major share of the failing of conventional industrial engineering efforts rests with the limited organizational range of its historical environment. Since its inception some 80 years ago, the function of industrial engineering has been practiced almost exclusively in production departments. With the advent of mass production techniques, the amount and cost of labor per unit of product has decreased steadily. Numerically controlled machine tools, mechanized assembly and checkout equipment, and line-flow production processes have replaced the craftsman at his bench. The typical worker in modern industry is employed in a capacity that relies more and more on his mental facilities and less and less on his prime-mover capabilities.

Just as manual skills are being replaced by intellectual skills in production, the outputs of production are being upgraded in variety and complexity. New products of radical form and function require a massive diversion of capital and management attention into nonproduction areas—product and market development, basic and applied research, and production engineering, as well as indirect and clerical functions. As a result, the bulk of human effort in industry is no longer in production, but is distributed in a broad range of functional activities.

Because of these changes, production today offers far less potential for the application of industrial engineering techniques than it once did. Not only does production now require fewer workers and a smaller share of company resource, but management of production affairs is interrelated with provisions and policies entirely outside the scope of production operations.

Looking at our three cases again in the framework of production and its parameters, we see that in each one significant considerations outside the production scope were overlooked. If the industrial engineer had not been identified so closely with production, he would have been in a better position to define the real problems and develop solutions that were compatible with company value scales.

CONCLUSION

In conclusion, the systems approach is more than a methodology to be applied whenever it fits the circumstances. It is a fundamental and basic requirement of successful staff work in any field. . . .

SUMMARY

The basic concept of the systems approach and optimization requires that great care be used in approaching problems to insure that the limits of the system being analyzed and manipulated are clearly established and defined, that the objectives of the system and of the study effort are clearly established and adequately reflected in the objectives function of the problem, and that the subject system and problem are adequately related to appropriate higher level systems.

A common concept of a system in business and industry is the individual organization—a company or corporation operating as an entity. This limitation is arbitrary and somewhat restrictive, but even so is usually much too extensive and large to be subjected to formal analysis. Most problems must be restricted to a smaller system or subsystem—a part of the whole. These problems should be approached with due regard for their interaction with the system of which they are a part. Criteria for evaluating performance of the parts should be formulated such that their relationship and interrelationship with the whole is accurate. Problems should be approached for solution on the broadest basis possible. The philosophy of the systems approach and the quest for optimization are valuable guides in formulating and pursuing improvement function activities.

REFERENCE

1. William G. Bruner, Jr., "Systems Design—A Broader Role of Industrial Engineering," *The Journal of Industrial Engineering*, March–April 1962, p. 91.

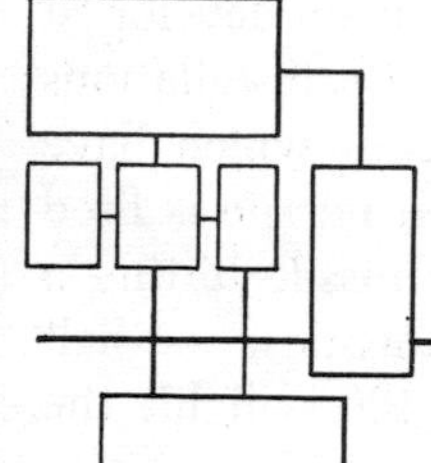

CHAPTER 8

USE OF MODELS AND MATHEMATICS

THE SCIENTIST places heavy reliance upon abstractions from the real world when he analyzes and attempts to solve problems. Many of these abstractions are formulated in mathematical terms and are called analytical or symbolic models. There are also iconic (or look-like) models such as photos, scale models, etc., and analog models that represent characteristics of a situation with some substitute means of portrayal. However, the use of analytical or mathematical models seems to be the cause of most difficulty in understanding operations research. This is unfortunate and unnecessary, for we all use abstractions, models, and mathematics (or quantitative methods) in dealing with the goings on in the real world. Keep in mind that it is reality that is of most concern to us (unless we are detached scientific theoreticians) and that the abstractions or models help us to pick out several of the most significant (we hope) aspects of the real world so that we can analyze them, manipulate them, and hopefully gain new understanding and insight. Models are greatly simplified pictures or representations of reality, but they can be quite valuable because of their simplicity and isolation from the tremendous complexity of actuality. If we have abstracted successfully, that is, if we have succeeded in selecting the really significant characteristics, perhaps we can then translate the newly gained understanding back to the actuality of the real world.

AN EXAMPLE

Consider the following situation:[1] A defense system has been developed in which various areas are protected from enemy attack by installations of missiles. These missiles have performance characteristics which have been evaluated as the average probability, p, that when a missile is fired it will hit its target. If p is 0.5, the chances of any one missile hitting a target when fired are 50%, or of a large number, say 100 missiles, one half of them can be expected to strike home, or 50 of the 100 will hit the target.

It has been proposed that the effectiveness of the defense system can be improved by the development of centralized control to supplement the individual control now being used in each missile. The present system involves individual guidance of the missiles by a self-contained system. Once the missile is fired, it seeks out the enemy target by means of its own guidance unit. If it is fired at a fleet of enemy planes or missiles, its selection of an individual target is somewhat fortuitous. If several missiles are fired at a fleet of enemy craft, it is possible that more than one of the missiles will select the same target and "over-kill" it only to, perhaps, leave other targets unselected by any missiles.

The proposed centralized control system would be developed such that each weapon would be assigned to a specific target. When fired, each missile still would be guided by its own internal guidance system, but would ignore all but its own assigned target. It has been claimed that the proposed centralized control system is technologically feasible, and that it would completely solve the problem of over- or under-killing inherent in the present scheme of strictly independent missile control. The proponents of the centralized control system are quite enthusiastic about the benefits of their system and strongly advocate its authorization. Others claim that the development of the centralized control system involves too many uncertainties, will be extremely costly, and will take quite some time to place in operation. They claim that a better defense system can be obtained by increasing the number of the present type of missiles or in improving the performance characteristics of the present missiles. In addition, a centralized control system might pose serious problems in concentrating the key component of an entire defense system such that it would be vulnerable—perhaps a single enemy hit, or sabotage, would prevent the use of the entire missile fleet.

THE MANAGEMENT PROBLEM

Let us consider the management problem that is emerging in this situation. We have mentioned a few of the significant factors involved, but there are still many others that should be considered. What are the emerging technological developments in defense systems? What is the urgency of bolstering the present defense system? How long will it take to develop a centralized control system? Is the skilled manpower required for research and development of the centralized control system available? What other activities might have to be foregone if the centralized control system is developed? How much effort and cost would be required to improve performance of the present missile? How much extra protection could be bought if the money required to develop the new control system were applied toward the purchase of additional missiles or the improvement of missile performance? What are the performance characteristics of the centralized control system as opposed to the local control arrangement?

ABSTRACTION

Even this listing of significant factors is far from complete, but it demonstrates that the problem in its true setting is quite overwhelming. Perhaps some significant facets of the over-all problem can be abstracted and manipulated in order to gain further insight.

Let p represent the performance characteristic of the missile, indicating the kill probability when a single missile is dispatched to a single target. (Note that this is not influenced by the matter of local or centralized control.)

Let m represent the number of missiles in one area.

Let t represent the number of enemy targets in an attacking force.

With local control each missile seeks out its own target. The probability that any one target will be selected by any one missile is $1/t$. If there are four enemy planes, and one missile is fired, the probability that any of the targets (planes or missiles) is selected is $\frac{1}{4}$. Obviously, some simplifying assumptions have been made—that the formation of the targets has no effect upon the missile's selection, that the enemy has not jammed the guidance system, etc. These assumptions are almost always necessary when using models and mathematics to simplify the situation sufficiently for a model to be constructed and mathematics used. Mathematics can be very powerful and complex, but its use still requires vast simplifications of reality. This is quite appropriate and permissible—as long as the assumptions are remembered and their validity reckoned with. Quite frequently, formal analysis is impossible without assumptions to accompany the simplifications.

The probability that a single target will not survive the firing of a single missile would be a combination of the performance characteristic of the missile and the probability that the missile will select any specific target. This is represented mathematically by the product of the two probabilities: $p \times 1/t = p/t$.

Stated in a converse manner, which will simplify the mathematical manipulations, the probability of survival of a single target would be the kill probability subtracted from one: $1 - (p/t)$.

The chances of killing the single enemy target, of course, will be increased by firing more than one missile. This means that the survival probability will decrease as the number of missiles fired is increased. This is expressed mathematically, for m missiles as: $[1 - (p/t)]^m$. This expression gives the probability of a single enemy target surviving the firing of m missiles under the local control scheme. For a fleet of t enemy targets, the number of targets expected to survive is obtained by multiplying the survival probability by the number of targets: $t[1 - (p/t)]^m$. The expected number of kills will, of course, be the difference between the total enemy fleet and the expected number of survivors: $t - t[1 - (p/t)]^m$ or $t\{1 - [1 - (p/t)]^m\}$. The probability of destroying the entire enemy fleet will be $1 - [1 - (p/t)]^m$, obtained by dividing the expression by t.

This rather brief mathematical development describes the total performance characteristics of the local control scheme for any number of missiles and targets and any performance characteristic of the missiles. In graphical form these relationships look like Fig. 8-1. The vertical axis is expressed as the probability of destroying the entire enemy fleet. This has been done to simplify graphical presentation, since the expected number of targets killed is related to the performance characteristic of the missile, p, the number of missile, m, the number of targets, t, and the actual size of the enemy fleet. Since these are too many variables to display on a two dimensional graph, the size of the enemy fleet is removed, and curves for various representative values of numbers of missiles and targets are plotted. This allows us to predict the probability of destroying the entire enemy fleet (expressed as a probability value ranging from 0 to 1 on the vertical axis) for any value of p on the horizontal axis and selected values of m and t.

Next, we would like to develop a similar prediction for the performance of the defense system under centralized control, where each missile is assigned to a specific target by the central control system and then is guided to that target by its own internal guidance system. The kill probability for a single target, if a single missile is assigned to it, is represented by the performance characteristic of the missile, p. The survival probability will be the difference between one (a probability value representing certainty) and the kill probability: $1 - p$. Each target is as-

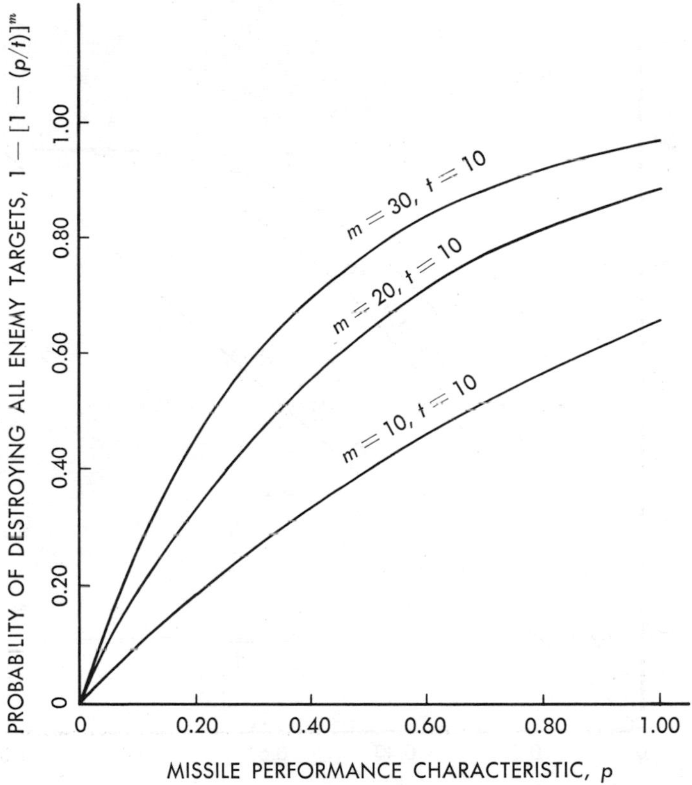

Figure 8-1. Performance Characteristics for Centralized Control.

signed m/t missiles. If there are more missiles than targets, m/t is greater than one and each target is fired upon by one or more missiles. The survival probability for a single target in the enemy fleet when fired upon by m/t missiles is a combination of the survival probability for a single target and the number of missiles assigned to it: $(1 - p)^{m/t}$. The expected number of survivors in an enemy fleet would be obtained by multiplying the survival probability for a single target by the number of targets: $t(1-p)^{m/t}$. The expected number of enemy targets to be destroyed would be the difference between the total size of the enemy fleet and the expected number of survivors: $t - [t(1-p)^{m/t}]$ or $t[1-(1-p)^{m/t}]$. The probability of destroying the entire enemy fleet will be $1-(1-p)^{m/t}$, which is obtained by dividing the expression by t.

We can now plot the performance curves for the centralized control

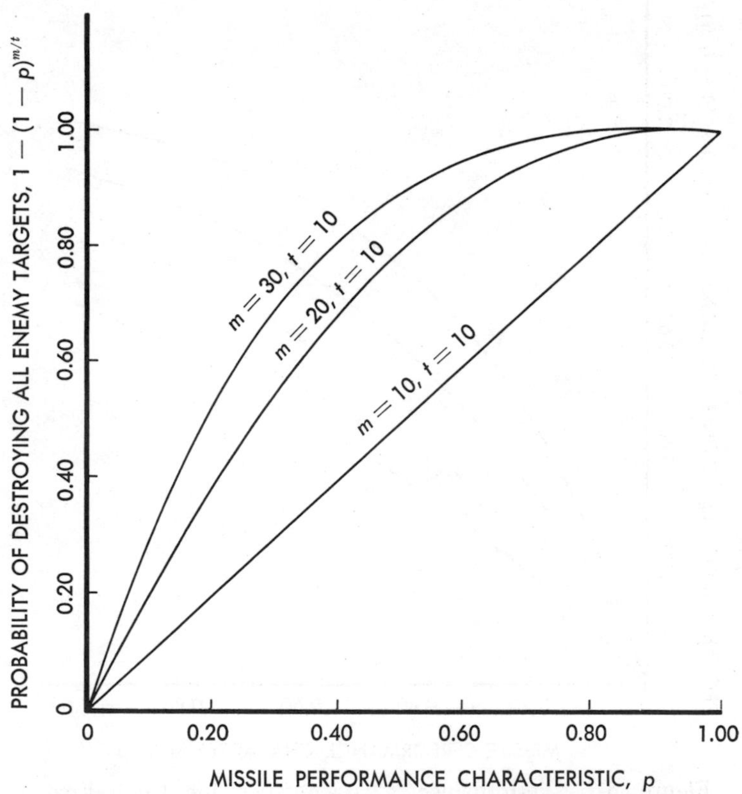

Figure 8-2. Performance Characteristics For Centralized Control.

system in the same manner as we did for the local control system. These are shown in Fig. 8-2.

It is easier to compare the relative performance for the two schemes of control, which is the item of concern to us, if the curves for each control system are plotted on the same graph. In order to keep the plots from becoming too cluttered, we shall select only two values for m and t: $m = 30$, $t = 10$, and $m = 10$, $t = 10$. These are presented in Figs. 8-3 and 8-4. We can now evaluate the gain achieved from centralized control, and we can extend our analysis and evaluation to include a cost versus benefit statement of the various alternatives. We will not extend our presentation to include these, but they can be visualized by reference to Figs. 8-3 and 8-4. For $m = 30$, $t = 10$, and a missile performance characteristic $p = 0.50$ (point a, Fig. 8-3), the system performance is

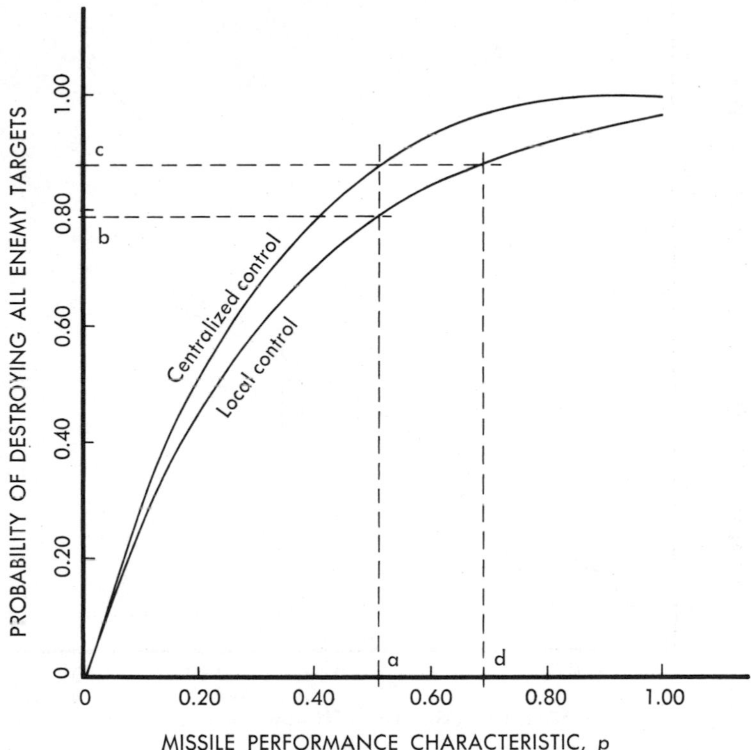

Figure 8-3. Comparison of Performance Characteristics of Local and Centralized Control for $m = 30$, $t = 10$.

indicated by point b (0.785) for local control. The system performance is improved (as measured by the probability of destroying the entire enemy fleet) to point c (0.875) by centralized control. We would be most interested in the alternative means of achieving this same increase, which can be done by:

1. Improving the performance characteristics of the missile from a (0.50) to a value d (approximately 0.69), or

2. Increasing the number of missiles, m, from 30 to some larger value which would cause the performance curve for local control to intersect point a, c. This will happen when m is increased to approximately 40.

The situation where both m and t are equal to 10 is illustrated in Fig. 8-4. Centralized control will improve the system performance from

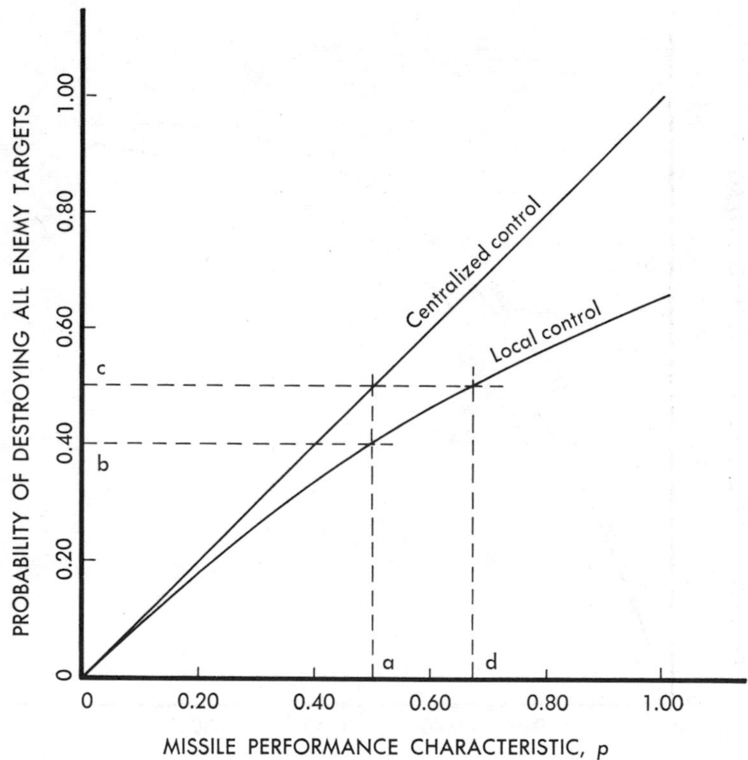

Figure 8-4. Comparison of Performance Characteristics of Local and Centralized Control for $m = 10, t = 10$.

0.401 to 0.50. This same amount of increase could be achieved by improving missile performance from 0.50 to about 0.67, or by increasing the number of missiles to 13 (or 14).

We are now in position to evaluate the economy and technological feasibility of the three approaches. Considering the range of situations of concern to us, of which Figs. 8-3 and 8-4 are only samples, we would determine the appropriate way to improve the system performance from the b value to the c level. This can be done by the centralized control approach, by improving the missile performance from *a* to *d*, or by increasing the allocation of missiles.

Evaluation of the alternatives would require the gathering of detailed information on costs, technological feasibility, time requirements, resource availability, etc. These considerations, when related to the system performance models, would be a grouping of factors (largely quantitative in nature) to be combined with consideration of the effect of simplifications and assumptions involved in the modeling process, and a host of additional factors relating this problem to the broader system of which it is but a part. The value of the analytical model is that it predicts the behavior of a portion of the problem situation and allows this portion to be treated in an objective manner, thus reducing the amount of the total problem which must be treated subjectively.

SUMMARY

The significance of using a model to portray a portion of the total real world situation should be obvious. We can, in effect, explore the consequences of a wide range of alternative decisions without actually making and implementing them. The model provides a tool for experimenting in a rather easy and economical way.

However, we should also recognize that manipulation of the model is not really experimenting with the real world situation. If our model is not a valid representation of reality, perhaps because of simplifications or assumptions that are not really justified, then our insights may lack reality and validity. The model does allow us to place one portion of the total problem on a factual basis. The factual knowledge is used in conjunction with other information in reaching a final decision. This combination should yield a result that is superior to decisions made without the insight and understanding derived from using the model.

A manager who uses an analysis of the sort described would likely have the analysis prepared for him by individuals skilled in analytical work. It is important that the manager thoroughly understand the general principles that have been utilized in modeling portions of a real world situation by means of abstractions, mathematical or otherwise, so that he can evaluate the total situation for which he is responsible. He need not necessarily be a mathematical expert himself, but he should know enough about the simplifications, abstractions, representations, and manipulations to be able to comfortably and realistically appraise their practical utility. He should not lose sight of the fact that even the best models are simplifications of reality, and are intended only as *aids* to the decision-making process—they are *not* a replacement for mature judgment.

REFERENCE

1. This example is an expansion of a problem in:
Harry Herbert Goode and R. E. Machol, *Systems Engineering*, McGraw-Hill, New York, 1957, p. 137.

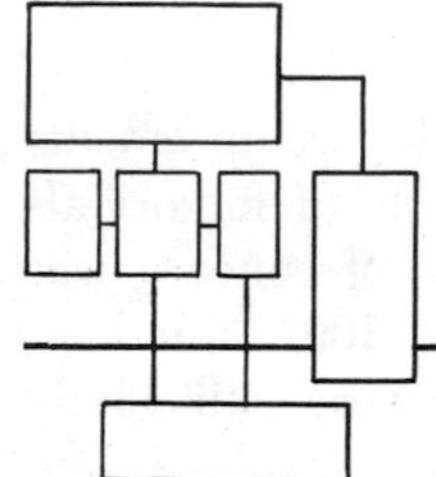

CHAPTER 9

THE TEAM APPROACH

THE TEAM APPROACH, as embodied in many operations research studies, is a manifestation of the old adage that two heads are better than one. Many of the problems for which a formal O.R. study seems appropriate are very complex and a full comprehension of the problem and its solution is beyond the capability of any one individual.

One of the rather startling aspects of O.R., noted from the early day of British operational research during World War II and on up to the present time, is the utility of concepts and techniques from widely diverse fields. There are many techniques that have been developed for more or less routine solution to specific types of problems. But, locating and solving significant operational problems still frequently requires the devising of new techniques and problem-solving tools. The interdisciplinary O.R. research team provides a variety of points of view in sizing-up a problem and frequently results in the devising of new ways to handle problems that could not have been achieved by an individual or by a group with the same backgrounds and inclinations.

The team approach is similar to the typical committee approach used in many organizations. A team allows a pooling of talent in terms of the needs for various skills in approaching a problem. It also is a means of providing representation and participation from various parts of the organization being researched, which can be a powerful vehicle for gaining understanding, cooperation, support, and information. This is particularly important where O.R. has not become an established and well-accepted activity within the organization, such as when an outside consultant is engaged to undertake the study. To illustrate these points, the following summary of a team O.R. study is presented.*

THE SETTING

A manufacturer of precision products with high quality requirements approached a local university to request a research study of factors affecting visual inspection performance. The specific item of concern was a critical component in their final product. It required 100% visual inspection for flaws and defects. Many of these flaws were sufficiently small that they were almost invisible. Large volumes were involved (approximately 2,000,000,000 per year) and inspection had to be done accurately but very rapidly. The company hoped that the research study would provide a better understanding of the factors affecting the accuracy and speed of inspection, and that this understanding would lead to better work methods which would result in improved operator performance and cost reduction.

APPROACH

The project was undertaken as a team endeavor in order to have available the necessary specialized skills for considering the important aspects of the problem. The company assigned their director of quality control as project administrator. It was his responsibility to coordinate and facilitate the company–university activity. The university assembled a team composed of an industrial engineer (who served as the project director), a psychologist, and a research optometrist. It was felt that each of these four individuals could make unique and essential contributions to the project and would provide the necessary skills to adequately consider the significant aspects of the problem.

The primary objective of the research project was to determine the factors which significantly influence inspector performance and to develop measures for evaluating the influence of these factors upon po-

* This project was executed by the operations research group of Ohio State University under the direction of L. G. Mitten. It has been published as an example of team research and is regarded somewhat as a classic example. The reader is referred to Chapter 3 of *Introduction to Operations Research*, edited by Churchman, Ackoff, and Arnoff, Wiley, New York, 1957 for further details. It is regrettable that permission to reproduce Mitten's original presentation was refused, for this brief presentation must of necessity be only a summary.

It is interesting to note as a sidelight that Mitten's informal reactions relative to the original publication of this material indicated considerable surprise. The material was presented as an example of team research, reflecting good engineering. He has often mentioned his amazement in learning that what he had been doing was O.R.

tential performance. Eye-movement patterns, vision characteristics of the inspectors, intensity and type of illumination, fatigue, job satisfaction, motivation, the influence of various types of design of inspection equipment, and similar factors were investigated. Each team member contributed in a unique manner, providing specialized knowledge and skill relative to those aspects of the problem related to his own area of specialization.

The preliminary investigation indicated that the inspection operation could theoretically be improved by a factor of 3 or 4 and that the most significant factors influencing performance were attitude and motivation. These results lead to further activity directed toward developing the preliminary research results into practical procedures for improving inspector performance. New inspection lenses and lighting fixtures were designed. Inspector attitude and motivational factors were carefully studied. Eye-movement patterns were streamlined. Operators were allowed to control the speed at which materials were presented for inspection. New training procedures were developed. An incentive payment scheme was tested and evaluated.

RESULTS

The various changes developed and tested by the research team resulted in considerable improvement in the quality and quantity performance of the inspection operators. The new lenses and lighting fixtures relieved eye strain and more effectively presented the surface being inspected. Operator control of the speed of the inspection operation allowed varying the speed in accord with the proportion of defective items in the batch being inspected and in accord with the inspector's own individual capabilities. Quantity and quality of inspection were both improved. The previous eye movement patterns resulted in less than 100% of the surface of each item being covered. The new pattern was more efficient and achieved complete coverage. The new training procedures reduced training time to half that previously required.

The wage incentive payment scheme, which was advocated by the company management rather than by the researchers, achieved considerable improvement but not nearly to the extent indicated as the achievable potential. The attitude studies and in-depth psychological interviews indicated that pay was not the most significant motivational factor of the inspector group. Many of the inspectors were either young girls living at home or married women working only to supplement their husband's income. A number of problems not previously recognized by management were discovered by this phase of the research study, and the basis for a new "incentive" payment plan was developed. It seemed reasonable to conclude from the attitudes and values held by the inspector group that a time-off incentive would provide a far stronger motivation than an extra-pay incentive. Such a scheme was devised and installed. Production increased dramatically, to a level of almost 300% of the usual performance. Many inspectors were able to complete the week's quota in 2 or 2½ days, and thus earned a full week's wages *and* time off to spend with their families and tend to personal affairs. The amount of time-off bonus was determined by quantity and quality of performance such that a maximum bonus was achieved when total costs to the company were minimized.

COMMENTS

This study clearly indicates the contributions of an interdisciplinary team in executing an O.R. study. Each team member made a unique contribution not only by virtue of his specific skill and knowledge, but also from the standpoint of integration of the study with the on-going activities of the organization. The project required considerable research, and specialized knowledge from the individual team members, and a unification of these efforts in terms of the nature of the problem encountered.

Another interesting aspect of the study has to do with the use of incentives to provide individual motivation. The use of financial incentives in conjunction with performance standards has been associated with industrial engineering ever since the pioneering work of Frederick W. Taylor. Very substantial increases in productivity are usually obtained with the installation of a financial incentive or payment-for-results scheme. It is typical in most organizations to experience a 20 to 30% increase in performance and productivity when a financial incentive scheme is first installed. There are many problems associated with wage incentive installations and their operation. Successful installation requires great care in devising an appropriate scheme and a means for insuring its continued smooth functioning. Wage incentives are not a cure all, even though they have often been sold as such. At best, they provide a complement to other basic management and leadership fundamentals. They are based upon the concept that extra money for extra production will motivate workers to produce at above normal levels. Frequently, however, a situation of conflict develops that obscures this assumed relationship. Sometimes, workers desire other things more than an increment of pay for above normal output. This study clearly indicates the uniqueness of key motivational factors that have value within a given group. The operators placed more premium on earning time-off for superior performance than they did on money as a reward. This takes on added meaning when one recognizes that several of the women involved in the study were married to men working a different shift than they were. The extra time off represented an opportunity for time to enjoy a more normal family life.

This brief discussion of incentives is not intended to be a complete treatment of the subject, nor is it intended to imply that time-off is the most appropriate approach to motivation of women workers. These points have been brought up to highlight the effectiveness of the research approach by an interdisciplinary team in solving production problems relative to the values implicit in a *specific* situation. Wage incentive installations have long been regarded by many managements as a sure way to improve productivity, decrease costs, and aid management effectiveness. These schemes are frequently applied without due consideration of the unique needs of individuals and groups involved. Sometimes these installations fail to produce the desired results. The present study is a specific case where the incentives were tailored to the needs of the situation, and where previous pat-solution approaches had failed to produce acceptable results.

IS A TEAM ESSENTIAL?

Although the team approach is a characteristic frequently associated with operations research, the necessity of using a team is open to debate. Operations research *can* be performed by individuals. The nature of the problem, the needs of the organization, and the available personnel will determine the need for a team. As previously mentioned, many operations research problems are so complex and extensive that one individual cannot possibly have the skill, knowledge, ability, and time to handle them. However, the popular notion that a team is a prerequisite to O.R. is frequently used as an excuse for lack of understanding and capability to handle an assignment. The team approach has validity. But it is not *essential,* and it is no substitute for competency on the part of those engaged in O.R. work. A team approach may be desirable solely to simplify the process of gaining acceptance and to facilitate implementation. It should also be recognized that the absence of trained personnel who possess the required knowledge and skill may make the team approach the only reasonable course of action.

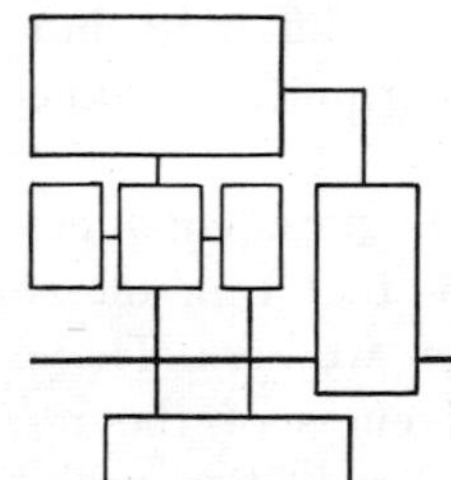

CHAPTER 10

CONSULTIVE TO TOP MANAGEMENT

ONE CHARACTERISTIC frequently stated to be essential to operations research, particularly when this service is provided by outside consultants, is that it must be consultive to top management. This, in the actual situation, may or may not be true, depending upon the nature of the problem and the specific situation. Just as a team is not prerequisite to good O.R. work, so it is with this characteristic. To claim otherwise is to perpetuate the wishful thinking of early O.R. practitioners.

Some operations research work is of a nature that top management problems are involved. The systematic approach, attention to the systems aspect of problems, use of powerful analytical techniques for considering a multitude of interrelated factors, and the glamor that has been attached to the name *operations research* have caused the generation of considerable interest on the part of top management in O.R. Also, the growing complexity of top management decisions, particularly those associated with long-range planning, has caused top management to become receptive to O.R. as a possible means of aiding them in their decision making activities.

When broad problems which cross organizational lines are involved, O.R. personnel do require high level backing if reasonable cooperation is to be expected. In situations where a long range project is involved or a new staff activity must be created and new technical personnel recruited, these activities naturally receive very close attention from top management. It is reasonable to expect that any expensive and likely-to-be-slow-in-paying-off activity will receive very close scrutiny by top management and will have a better chance of surviving and succeeding if it is supported actively by top management.

The nature of the problems to be researched and the peculiarities of the specific situation determine whether or not operations research should be consultive to top management. There are many top management problems for which O.R. is a likely aid, but there are many other activities within every organization which are not of direct interest to top management. In the latter situation, requiring O.R. to be consultive to top management may actually decrease the likelihood of obtaining successful results. The problem should be the boss in determining what is appropriate for its solution. O.R. can be of positive value when it is consultive to top management, but it can also be of positive value when put to use at lower organizational levels. It can be of most value when it represents *one* of a broad array of services to management at all levels, and when a systematic assessment of the needs for improvement reflect a realistic application of the engineering of operations as well as the science of O.R.

USE OF OPERATIONS RESEARCH

The American Management Association has long been active in promoting improvements in management activities. New approaches to management and new technical developments are continuously assessed and called to the attention of management. O.R. has been of interest to the A.M.A. for a number of years. This organization has called attention to the potential value of industrial operations research by publications, coverage in seminars, and by evaluating the impact of O.R. in industrial activities. In 1957, the A.M.A. studied 631 companies and their involvement with industrial O.R.[1] Of these, 324 or 57% were then using operations research; 144 of the 307 companies not using it were considering its adoption in the future. Chemical and allied companies seemed to be the biggest users of O.R., with electrical and electronics manufacturers a close second. Almost 25% of the O.R. personnel were employed by 19 firms in the aircraft industry, even though those firms represented only 5.5% of the 324 using O.R.

The background of individuals engaged in O.R. activities was predominantly engineering (42%); mathematics was the next most common (16%), and then statistics (11%). The average size of O.R. groups was 6.5. The aircraft industry had the largest group size, averaging 19.7 persons. The food industry had the smallest with an average of 3.1.

Of those companies indicating the areas of O.R. applications, 72% mentioned production problems, 64% sales and marketing, and 64% inventory problems. Of 288 companies indicating an evaluation of the results achieved by O.R., 55 (19%) indicated appreciable savings, 75 (26%) attributed considerable improvement in operations to O.R., and 167 (58%) felt it was too early to judge the results. Seventeen companies reported savings in excess of $100,000, five in excess of $1,000,000, and two in excess of $2,000,000.

The results of the A.M.A. survey indicate a lively interest in O.R. on the part of top management—both as an aid in solving problems within their immediate area of concern, and at lower organizational levels. A more recent evaluation of O.R. experience, based upon a much smaller but more closely studied group of companies, was subsequently made by McKinsey & Company, Inc., Management Consultants.* In viewing the results of this study the reader should keep in mind that the study was a limited one, confined to 25 corporations, and that it was not intended to be an exhaustive, all-industry evaluation. Even though the study was highly selective, it does result in some useful information on the use of O.R.—and on the organizational level of O.R. activity.

A Limited Survey of Industrial Progress in Operations Research

THIS memorandum summarizes the conclusions of a recently conducted survey of industrial progress in operations research. The material has been prepared specifically for those organizations participating in the survey. Our study was prompted by a major oil company's desire to place its accomplishments in operations research in perspective by obtaining a factual evaluation of current, realized O.R. contributions in other major industrial companies.

* Appreciation is expressed to McKinsey & Company, Inc. and to Socony Mobil Oil Company, Inc. for making this material available.

Because of its purpose, the survey was limited in both scope and coverage, both being biased strongly toward the oil industry. Further, interviews outside the oil industry were also biased to the extent that we sought companies which seemed good prospects for operations research success stories.

SOURCES

Our conclusions were drawn from the following sources:

Field interviews with 25 leading corporations
- Seven oil companies
- Eighteen companies in eleven other industries

Interviews with five government agencies and seven organizations doing O.R. work for government or industry.

Interviews were conducted with both operations researchers and operating managers.

SUMMARY OF SIGNIFICANT FINDINGS

The following salient findings emerged from our analysis:

Major oil companies have successfully and consistently applied O.R. approaches to industrial problem solving.

Much less progress has been made in the companies we interviewed outside the oil industry, although a few instances of outstanding accomplishment were observed.

Proven O.R. techniques are plentiful, but O.R. professionals, *particularly those effective in implementation,* are scarce. It is one thing to build a model; it is another thing to use it in running a business.

The specific horizontal location—finance, engineering, research, separate department, etc.—of the operations research group within the corporate structure is not a critical factor in the success of operations research. But a location of O.R. with some access to top management is desirable.

Among companies that have applied O.R. successfully, a clear pattern is usually discernible. O.R. has succeeded where:

(a) Management is:

Willing to direct, participate in, and take responsibility for O.R. studies. This is the most important ingredient in the successful application of operations research.

Sufficiently sophisticated to recognize the value and limitations of O.R.—and knowledgeable in the use of professional staff services.

(b) The O.R. group has capable, practical, "business-minded" leadership in addition to technical competence.

(c) Initial projects are selected on the basis of relatively short-term, provable profit contribution. Where O.R. practitioners have concentrated on problems of integration and on the whole business as a system, success has been severely limited. Emphasis on the application of well-developed techniques to areas of high potential payoff would greatly accelerate O.R. progress in most of the companies covered by this survey that are not now enjoying a high degree of success.

(d) O.R. effort is closely associated with line managers—the closer O.R. analysts work with affected decision makers, the greater the likelihood of success.

MAINTAINING PERSPECTIVE

In those companies that took part in this survey, progress in operations research has, so far, been somewhat limited, particularly outside the oil industry. This lack of progress does not in any way indicate that operations research lacks potential in industry; indeed, we believe that the converse is true. Success stories in the oil industry—and some in other industries—suggest that the potential for operations research is substantial. In many of the companies we visited, however, that potential has not yet been realized.

In conducting this survey, we found that the problems and difficulties in operations research programs more than offset the successes—at least thus far. "Success," as used in this memorandum, is defined as: (1) the satisfactory building of a mathematical model (a technical achievement); and (2) management use of the model. Unless management uses the model as an aid in the decision-making process, we do not judge the O.R. effort as successful from a management point of view.

Rather than limited opportunity, the disappointing progress reported in this memorandum means that many companies interviewed here have failed to bring their O.R. projects to the point of successful implementation. While there are a number of instances of technical success—an analytical model has been developed—in many cases, operations research has not yet had a real impact on how companies plan and make decisions.

The balance of this memorandum amplifies the findings summarized at the outset:

Oil industry a leader
Modest progress outside the oil industry
Implementation a key problem
Specific organization location of central O.R. group not critical
A pattern of success.

OIL INDUSTRY A LEADER

The oil companies we interviewed are well in front of most other corporations in applying an O.R. approach to industrial problem solving. Progress is most impressive in the refining function of the business, although advances have also been made in other areas.

In many ways the use of O.R. approaches in oil refining is a logical extension of analytical calculations that refinery engineers have made for many years. Oil companies often used computers first to mechanize calculations formerly made manually by engineers. It was a logical next step to go on and develop more rigorous models of refinery operations.

More importantly, O.R. found receptive audiences among refinery managers and planners who were able to follow and understand the mathematics involved and visualize how to use the available tools. Our findings indicate that this factor—sympathetic and understanding refinery management—more than any other reason probably accounts for oil industry leadership in operations research.

O.R. has been successfully integrated into the decision-making process in every oil company we interviewed, or learned of through other interviews. Oil industry leadership is evidenced by these findings:

Formally *organized* and *growing* O.R. groups are working in most oil companies.

A broad range of oil company decisions is now being influenced by O.R. approaches.

(*a*) *Formally Organized and Growing O.R. Groups.* With one exception, every oil company interviewed has an organized O.R. group and is actively seeking competent additions to its staff. Four major oil companies, recognizing the importance of operations research, have reorganized during the past year to facilitate O.R. work.

In the one oil company that does not have an organized O.R. group, an apparently successful O.R. program is spearheaded by staff groups with the aid of an internal O.R. consultant on the staff of the company president. This company has reported "striking success" with linear programming in manufacturing and distribution. After five years of experience, linear programming is now said to be used routinely at all management levels.

(*b*) *Broad Range of Decisions Affected.* Oil industry decisions influenced by O.R. can be grouped as follows:

1. Manufacturing
2. Distribution
3. Integrated planning
4. Miscellaneous decisions.

1. *Manufacturing:* Linear programming and/or process-flow simulations are used extensively by all of the major oil companies we interviewed. Most companies favor the linear-programming technique, but several companies combine these two approaches to refinery decision making.

In one company, linear programming is used to establish seasonal operating guidelines; then, within the limits of these guidelines, the company uses process-flow simulation to schedule refineries for short periods.

In both scheduling and longer range planning, most oil companies use L.P. and simulation to aid in making these kinds of decisions:

Select crudes and other input material to be used
Determine best product mix
Calculate incremental product cost
Identify settings for processing units that will minimize variable manufacturing costs
Evaluate planned additions to facilities
Schedule maintenance manpower and unit turnarounds
Blend gasolines and lube oils
Control refinery warehouse stock
Load crude stills.

2. *Distribution:* After introducing O.R. approaches to refinery decision making, many oil companies applied the linear-programming technique to distribution decisions. And many have developed or are developing models to help determine optimum plans for distributing products from refineries to terminals and bulk plants. The assigned task is to minimize product laid-down cost at specific intermediate or end points in the system. Further, several companies have completed distribution-facilities location studies. One company

is closing three out of every four warehouses in its distribution complex as a result of an operations research-based distribution study. Another major oil company has built a simulation of a major marine terminal in order to optimize facility-planning decisions.

3. *Integrated planning:* Several companies have combined models of crude allocation, manufacturing, and distribution to enable them to optimize an entire producing-refining-distribution complex. One major company links existing models manually by taking the results of refinery models and using these data as input to distribution models.

Other companies have constructed integrated models that are designed to examine a decision's effect throughout the business as a system. For example, one company's corporate profit-planning model includes two refineries, a tanker fleet, and marketing and production considerations.

Another company uses a series of detailed linear-programming models with an over-all simplified integrated model to do integrated planning on a regular basis. This is a "dynamic" system in that it considers a sequence of time periods. That is, the effect of simulated actions in a given time period becomes the input to an analysis of the subsequent period.

4. *Other decision areas:* In addition to manufacturing, distribution, and integrated planning decisions, various other aspects of oil company decision making are being influenced by O.R. approaches today. The variety of miscellaneous decision areas is great, but some of the problems being solved—or at least attacked—are:

(a) *Production.* One reservoir model is used today to determine optimum well spacing and to guide similar decisions in order to maximize reservoir yield. Reservoir models are also employed to maximize the profit contribution of producing wells. And linear programming is used to allocate owned or purchased crude oils between internal consumption and the outside sales, and then among owned refineries.

(b) *Marine operations.* Most major companies are using O.R. approaches to aid in making tanker procurement and scheduling decisions. Accurate determination of optimum size and scheduling of fleets and vessels, because of the dollar amounts involved, has significant impact on a company's over-all return on investment. One major company has built both tanker procurement and scheduling models, but neither—in the company's judgment—is very successful. The problems of the former when attempting to forecast tanker charter rates are said to resemble those of stock market prediction. And the scheduling model is reportedly more expensive and no more productive than manual scheduling. On the other hand, another corporation has a marine scheduling model, which was validated by comparisons to the manually developed schedules of previous years.

(c) *Finance.* In the finance-control area, models have been used to minimize cash balances and to analyze clerical procedures.

None of the oil companies interviewed discussed specific applications in the marketing function other than forecasting, inventory, and distribution models. Also, progress in the exploration function seems to be limited although some companies did not choose to discuss this function. However, on balance, decisions being affected in oil companies by O.R. approaches now cover a very broad range.

MODEST PROGRESS OUTSIDE OIL INDUSTRY

In contrast to the major oil companies, the great majority of other companies interviewed are moving slowly and cautiously in utilizing O.R. approaches to aid in decision making.

Although the profusion of writing on improved decision-making and the dollar-saving potential of industrial O.R. might indicate that it is being successfully applied very widely, only a few of the companies that we visited can demonstrate actual O.R. accomplishments in the sense of having successfully implemented new decision-making methods. These points stand out in our findings on companies outside of the oil industry:

Several major companies have cut back or eliminated O.R. activity
Some large companies are having difficulty getting O.R. work started
Some other companies have a significant amount of work underway, but much of it has not reached the all-important implementation phase
There are only a relatively few instances where O.R. successes have created management enthusiasm for an accelerated O.R. effort.

(*a*) *O.R. Work Cut Back.* Progress so far has generally been halting and erratic—examples of disillusionment are numerous. Of the companies we interviewed, three have cut back or eliminated moderately large, central O.R. staffs. The most common reason: elimination of staff groups not showing results in a period of continued pressure on profits.

Other examples illustrate the pitfalls that have caused many companies to abandon their O.R. efforts:

One company eliminated its central O.R. group after several unsatisfactory experiences in attacking distribution problems, mainly warehousing and inventory. Failure was attributed to:

"Ivory tower" O.R. thinking

Invalid assumptions in O.R. studies

Inability of technically competent O.R. staff to gain line management's acceptance

Another major corporation disbanded its corporate O.R. group when a central planning staff was eliminated. This company's view is that O.R. is better carried on at divisional levels—closer to operating management. So far, O.R. is not playing a significant role in this company's divisions, but work in the development stage by ten O.R. people in four divisions could yield significant results in the near future.

In 1958, a third company eliminated a 15-man corporate O.R. group that had been established in 1953. Several problems were cited, but lack of line-management acceptance and participation was the primary factor. One analyst of this original group, now an employee of the production control section, has achieved considerable success in solving machine-loading, inventory-control, and waiting-line problems. This company is not planning to expand its O.R. efforts or staff.

(*b*) *Major Companies Unable to Begin.* Although several companies can clearly see the potential of operations research and are eager to get work started, they have been unable to do so as yet. For example:

One company has extensive data-processing experience with computers and wants to apply O.R. to production scheduling, distribution, and market research problems. Reportedly, however, fear and jealousy, emanating from the functional departments and line managers potentially affected, have prevented initiation of work.

Another company sees O.R. as a useful tool but is having serious difficulty in gaining sufficiently widespread management understanding and acceptance.

In still other organizations work has been slow in starting because of an inability to recruit competent operations researchers.

(*c*) *Development but Not Implementation.* Several other companies, although able to get substantial O.R. work started, cannot yet demonstrate tangible results. Considerable O.R. development work is going on in several companies, but much of it has not yet reached the all-important implementation phase. For example:

One company can apparently point to more completed O.R. models in use than can most companies outside of the oil industry covered by our survey. But accomplishment to date is minor compared to the potential of a variety of models being developed. Several of these models are now approaching the crucial implementation phase; the company appears on the verge of making several dramatic breakthroughs in O.R. if operating managers can be completely convinced of the usefulness of these new models.

A major government agency has now nearly completed a competently directed study of one of its most involved systems. This study which started five years ago, initially involved the efforts of one analyst and now requires four full-time analysts, in addition to consultants. The work has yielded a series of models, and initial implementation is hoped for within the next 18 months.

The development of the models cited in the foregoing examples represents significant accomplishment, of course. Where some managers view at least a segment of company O.R. work worthwhile as a purely research activity, the development of these models would represent some measure of success. And, of course, to some operations researchers, solving the technical problems involved in developing difficult analytical models represents a full measure of success.

But the final test remains for those who have developed analytical models and have not yet achieved implementation: getting operating managers to use the new tools. If managers use the models in their decision-making processes, the O.R. effort will be truly successful. If not, there will be no genuine progress. And it is the absence of successfully implemented O.R. models to date in the companies surveyed which leads to our conclusion that progress outside the oil industry has been modest.

(d) A Few Examples of Outstanding Success. Outside the oil industry, we did not find many examples of current, realized, and continuing results from O.R. work in the form of management action evidenced by changes in decision-making processes. Aside from several major military contractors we found only a few companies where management enthusiasm can be readily seen.

One shipping company uses a model to simulate fleet operations. This model permits studies concerning scheduling change effects, vessel type and capacity, cargo handling methods and techniques, and tariff structure and commodity mix.

Another and successful but unique model is a simulation used to analyze the costs of contract "packages" offered to a union during wage negotiation sessions. The economic consequences of new operating and performance conditions can be assessed while negotiations are in progress.

A large freight hauling company uses a linear programming model to help determine the optimum time to replace diesel engines for its truck fleet.

These examples illustrate the benefits being realized by several of the companies interviewed which have overcome the critical problem of gaining implementation of O.R. models.

IMPLEMENTATION A KEY PROBLEM

Proven O.R. techniques are plentiful but O.R. professionals skilled in implementation of O.R. project results are scarce. By implementation we mean the actual use of an O.R. model or decision method in the regular management processes of a company. Although in some areas, O.R. is technique-limited (where a body of theory does not exist that can be applied to solve important problems) this lack is minor compared to that of finding professionals who can gain management understanding and acceptance of the O.R. approach to problem solving.

In our view, implementation is both the measure of O.R. effectiveness and the key to O.R. success. So far, as seen by the companies we surveyed the inability to gain implementation is a significant failure in industrial O.R. Lack of people skilled in gaining implementation was continually cited during our interviews. And companies that have O.R. professionals skilled in implementation can usually point to satisfactory O.R. results.

Our limited survey uncovered examples of *technically* successful O.R. effort in the form of completed models which *could* be used to help managers solve problems. This is not success from a management point of view. Success—in our judgment—exists where managers actually use an O.R. model or decision method in the regular decision-making processes of a company.

SPECIFIC O.R. LOCATION NOT CRITICAL

There does not appear to be any correlation between the location of an O.R. staff horizontally in a corporate organization structure and O.R. success. That is: it appears to make little difference whether O.R. is formally located in finance, research, engineering, corporate planning, as a separate department or in some other spot. There are cases of both success and failure for all these alternatives. None guarantees accomplishment; none ensures disappointment.

On the other hand organizational location vertically in a company's structure does seem to have a bearing on progress. Operations research tends to be more successful when it has direct access to top management. This is not uncommon with the introduction of new ideas or management concepts. At the same time, however, some O.R. staffs organized within operating divisions or as part of existing departmental staff units such as market research or production scheduling seem to have had marked success.

It is not surprising to find that O.R. has succeeded where top management has been attentive and accessible. But the important point with regard to organization is this: the specific location of the operations research function within the corporate structure is not crucial. Regardless of the organizational location of the O.R. function, success can usually be traced to close, effective working relationships between operating managers and O.R. personnel. Thus, success is attained through the operations researcher's use of sound working methods and his achieving effective communications. Gaining the understanding and willing cooperation of operating managers is vital; precision in fixing reporting relationships and organizational location is not.

A PATTERN OF SUCCESS

Among companies that have applied O.R. successfully, a fairly definite pattern is usually discernible. In addition to skillful implementation, the pattern has these additional elements:

Management plays an active role in O.R. projects
Capable practical O.R. leadership exists
Initial work on problems with demonstrable and short-term payout
Close association between O.R. effort and line management
Equitable allocation of expense charges where a central O.R. group is used.

This pattern can be seen in one form or another in all of the successful company cases encountered in our interviewing. And most of these factors were also cited by the staffs of the organizations we interviewed that do O.R. consulting work for government and industry.

(a) An Active Management Role. Active management interest is a fundamental requirement of successful O.R. The expression of active management interest ranges from direct involvement and

participation on the part of operating managers in spelling out assumptions and project timetables to active supervision of the O.R. function by a member of top management.

Several quotations illustrate this point well:

"O.R. people should not be expected to be supersalesmen. Management should establish that the O.R. staff has something to offer and then see to it that operating managers use these capabilities. The controller doesn't sell accounting procedures, and yet there is a little argument that they be used at the local level. . . . There is little likelihood, without firm top management backing, that an operating manager would increase long-range corporate profits at what he thinks is his own short-range expense."

MANAGER, RESEARCH DEPARTMENT
MAJOR OIL COMPANY

"In order for O.R. to be successful, the manager of the O.R. activity must have direct access to a progressive top management."

MANAGER, RESEARCH DEPARTMENT
MAJOR INDUSTRIAL CORPORATION

The first statement might indicate that a dictum from top management will ensure O.R. success, but emphasis seems better placed on the need for firm backing and stature for the company's O.R. program. It is frequently easier to secure a manager's interest and active participation if he is sure that his boss is vitally interested in the program.

(*b*) *Need Capable, Practical O.R. Leadership.* Lack of capable, practical leadership was cited as the cause for reorganizing a major operations research consulting firm. This appears to be the most prominent example of a serious lack of competent O.R. leadership, but it is by no means an isolated one.

A comment on the man who led a now defunct industrial O.R. group sheds additional light on the need for competent O.R. leadership:

"He was very well qualified technically but could not communicate with management either up or down the line."

The numerous complaints about ivory tower thinking, use of invalid assumptions, and failure of O.R. people to gain the acceptance of line management indicate that *practical* O.R. leadership is needed. Further, this leadership must be provided by O.R. men who understand business necessities and profit motivation and can cope with *operating* problems, as well as with technical and research matters.

Emphasizing practical leadership should not, of course, overshadow the need for technical excellence in O.R. leadership. Professionals in O.R. can cite a number of unsuccessful O.R. applications where failure was traced to the limitations of unqualified individuals who had the ear of appropriate company vice-presidents and operating personnel. But in the companies interviewed the lack of *practical* leadership was stressed; no one complained of the need for additional technical competence in O.R. leadership. But operations research in industry is of necessity required to furnish both if successful implementation is to be achieved.

(*c*) *Initial Short-Term Work Critical.* Where management has quickly realized the value of O.R., work has centered on projects of relatively short duration and with demonstrable payout. This obvious point needs emphasis because it appears in the pattern of successful O.R. and is lacking in many other cases. Several instances of grand-scale model development, which sometimes continue over long periods of time despite lack of success, are evident in our interviews. The following examples from our survey illustrate this point.

In one division of a large corporation, O.R. analysts spent a long time with a consultant developing a model for production scheduling and inventory control that turned out to be unsuccessful. Against this shaky background a project was undertaken about 13 months prior to the interview to develop a production scheduling, inventory control and distribution model for one of the company's major product lines. Since the results of this work are not yet implemented or felt in any way, management is understandably dubious about value being received for O.R. expenditures.

In describing a financial forecasting model under study for four years, an O.R. manager in another company stated, "The O.R. team has been successful in simulating the mechanical aspects of our accounting system but has found it very difficult to simulate the over-all business enterprise, particularly the interfaces between the business and the national economy." This apparent tendency to keep expanding the scope of models frequently yields impractical and unrealistic results. Or so much time is consumed in developing the model that management loses patience because of lack of tangible results.

(*d*) *Close Link to Line Management Required.* Close association between line management and the O.R. effort greatly facilitates implementation. At one major corporation, which is more successful than the typical, meticulous training programs are undertaken before implementation of any model. Conversely, when another company's O.R. group developed models and turned them over to operating managers without their project participation or indoctrination, the program was unsuccessful and was discontinued.

A key to effective implementation—which in turn is fundamental to successful industrial O.R.—is ensuring an adequate degree of line management understanding. This may be achieved through line management participation in carrying out the O.R. project and by training down-the-line personnel in implementing results. The O.R. team must also talk to management in management's—not O.R.—language.

(*e*) *Allocating Charges A Potential Inhibiter.* Direct charging for O.R. services would seem to have benefits in that the "customer" is more likely to direct attention to the quality of the service. Furthermore, a "budget" tends to instill greater discipline into an O.R. project. Nevertheless, our findings indicated that direct charging probably inhibits rather than encourages the use of operations research by operating managers. This is particularly critical in the early months of establishing an O.R. function.

It is surprising how important the method of allocating charges appears to be in the minds of many executives. In one major oil company, much O.R. is reportedly carried out in the operating units without liaison with the central O.R. group. Rather than pay direct charges, operating managers develop "in-house" capability. Consequently, progress is not what it might have been had the divisional O.R. programs had the advantage of consultation with the central group.

Another major company also appears to have stultified O.R. by directly charging operating managers for its services. The impression gained at headquarters is that little O.R. work is being done. Yet other evidence indicates that O.R. work is accomplished in parts of the company which do not request assistance of the central staff.

A third company tried direct charging at first, and quickly reversed this approach when slow progress ensued. In encouraging the O.R. approach to problem solving, a company executive stated that until O.R. is well ingrained in the managers' decision-making process, direct charging is out of the question.

A fourth company's O.R. group is termed by management a "service group" and is fully supported and budgeted through corporate services administration. The cost is spread as a burden cost throughout the company. At still another company, the executive committee of the board of directors funds the operations research department directly. Both of these latter companies can point to successful O.R. applications.

SUMMARY

Despite the impression one might gain from the business press that operations research is firmly integrated into the decision-making processes of a great many American business enterprises, the evidence uncovered in our limited survey will not support such a conclusion. A factual evaluation of current realized operations research contributions in a selected sample of well-managed companies indicates that progress in a large proportion of them has been slight so far. Actual accomplishments in terms of new decision-making practices is modest, and management acceptance and understanding of the O.R. approach to problem solving are growing at a slow rate in these companies.

Our survey did not in any way indicate, however, that lack of progress means lack of opportunity. The potential of operations research methods to contribute significantly to better, more profit-oriented decision making is unquestionably still there. The inability of companies to exploit this potential is not attributable to inadequate techniques or methodologies, but rather to the continuing lag in the number of professional people truly skillful in the application of these techniques in a way that gains the confidence and support of management.

REFERENCE

1. American Management Association, Management Report No. 10, Finance Division, *Operations Research Reconsidered,* 1958.

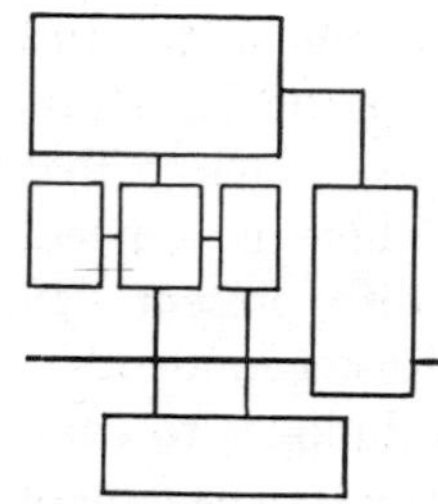

CHAPTER 11

SYSTEMS SIMPLIFICATION

The definition of *system* is an illusive and somewhat nebulous thing. The thoughts behind the systems approach have been presented. In the present chapter we will expand these thoughts, particularly those concerning the basic approach and mental frame of reference in dealing with problems in their broad, or systems, setting. In the next two chapters specific examples of systems work will be presented: one dealing with a producing system, the other with a managing system. These presentations are made in keeping with the main theme of the book—the management of improvement. Problems of significance to an organization must be approached and solved in such a manner that the *system* benefits as much as possible. Remember that the determination of what problems are important to improvement on the systems level requires broad vision, insight, and careful analysis. The potential payoff, and the likely costs of achieving the payoff, should guide the evaluation and selection of alternative improvement endeavors within an organization. Some of these alternatives will concentrate upon restricted problem areas, confined to much less than the concept of a system. Others will be broad, similar in nature to systems problems, but still confined to much less than the total system or entity represented by the organization. Other alternatives may approach the broad system, either in simplified terms or in all its extensiveness and complexity.

Regardless of which approach is pursued—and the determination of which one is appropriate is a highly individual matter relative to the specific situation and the specific time—it is sound procedure to relate the impact of change and improvement within the immediate problem area to the impact upon and the performance of the broader system.

In the following presentation[1] the author directs attention to the full range of management improvement possibilities, with particular stress upon systems simplification. His thesis, which is not stated as such, is that we frequently lose sight of the forest for the trees. There is a need, because of the bigness of the enterprises associated with present day living, to refocus our attention on the system. Taylor also recommends a combination of various improvement approaches and techniques to complement one another in order to achieve improvement at all management levels within an organization. It is a refreshing approach. His message has universal implications for all business and industry—large or small—even though it is directed to individuals concerned with paperwork problems within the government.

Full Spectrum Management Improvement

by **W. SIDNEY TAYLOR**

Headquarters, United States Air Force

ARE we attacking the wrong end of the paperwork dragon? In a sense, yes. More improvement effort is needed at top management or total system levels, if we are to achieve substantial reduction or streamlining in government paperwork requirements.

To a large extent, government paperwork originates in the operational and administrative concepts, laws, regulations and directives developed by government administrators, executives, engineers, and legislators. These are often developed with limited comprehension as to their administrative cost or paperwork impact. Congress enacts approximately 400 new Federal laws each year. The State of Virginia, for example, enacted 637 new State laws in the 1962 legislative session. Multiply this by 49 other States in the Union, and you begin to see one reason why "cost, change, and complexity" are becoming keynote words of the space age. The regulatory, procedural, or administrative impact of thousands of new Federal and State laws enacted each year can hardly be measured or imagined. In terms of paperwork requirements—I feel, that this is the head of the paperwork dragon.

There are at least 20 government systems now in the billion dollar investment (cradle to grave) category. The national highway program is estimated as a $27,000,000,000 operation. The Social Security System, as another example, involves funds totaling near $22,000,000,000. Agriculture, housing, health, and welfare and education are other programs or systems involving billion dollar commitments. In the "big league" category of space and missile systems some programs may run into the tens of billions of dollars. The paperwork or administrative systems supporting or guiding these massive programs may in themselves involve hundreds of millions of dollars. For this reason, it is becoming as important to simplify or modernize the paperwork components of a large-scale missile or space system as it is the hardware or engineering components.

A common problem in space and paperwork systems is the element of component reliability. Particularly in records management and paperwork processing, human linkages are a real problem. It is not just a matter of simple clerical error or mistakes. The problem revolves around honest human misinterpretation of the meaning or intent of published regulations, directives, instructions, or operations manuals. . . . This is one reason for emphasizing more effective writing courses and directives management programs. One good "directive" can eliminate or prevent thousands of paperwork errors or corrections later on.

We've got to attack the paperwork dragon at both ends, and in several dimensions at one time. This requires "full spectrum management improvement." This type of improvement involves the entire range of management effort from the ideas or concepts of a business or system to the records or data generated at work levels. It requires entirely new perspectives and approaches to the problem of comprehending, controlling, and improving large scale administrative or operational systems. This brings us to the subject of our talk, and also to what may become a new expression in the space age management field—system simplification.

SYSTEM SIMPLIFICATION

System simplification is a term describing the concept to document, simulate, and interrogate any large-scale "man-machine-

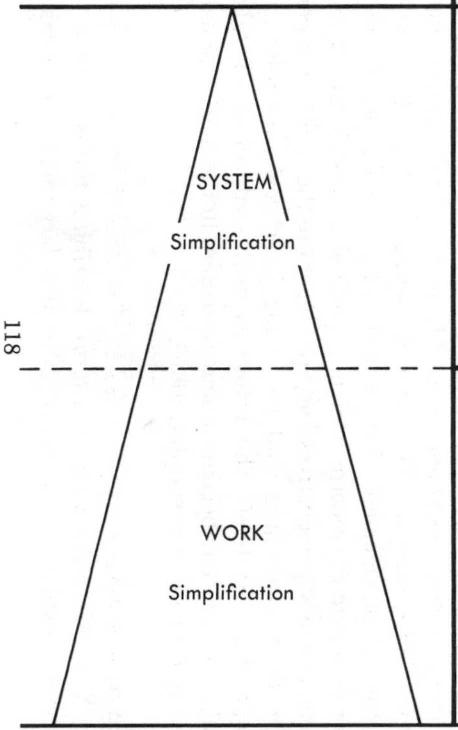

	Prime Mover (Who)	Decision Impact	Application Areas (Where)	Objective or Goal	Technique (How)
SYSTEM Simplification	Executives, Managers, or Engineers	Megabuck down to $10,000	Objectives Plans Policies Organization Functions Resources Directives Controls Linkages Data Feedback	Simplify, Modernize, or Reconceive an entire program or system	Document Simulate Interrogate
WORK Simplification	Foremen, First line supervisors and Employees	$10,000 down to $50	Shop or plant productivity Methods procedures Work processes Office/plant layout Work flow	Improve functions or components Increase productivity Labor, time, or motion economy	Flow process charts Work count Work distribution Man-machine charts Work study

Figure. 11-1

environment" system (objectives, functions, forces, etc.) in total system network perspective. Purpose: (1) Uncover opportunities at top management levels to simplify, modernize, or reconceive entire programs or major components; (2) Reduce total system costs and/or increase operational effectiveness.

The easiest way to introduce system simplification is to relate it to a technique with which most management people are familiar, namely, *work* simplification (Fig. 11-1). In a comparative sense, system simplification is a direct expansion upon principles long employed in industrial engineering and work simplification. However, system simplification applies at a different level of management, and it is a different kind of simplification. While work simplification is oriented toward methods, work processes, and office or factory production, system simplification is directed toward gross simplification of total business or system objectives, plans, policies, operations, etc.

System simplification is a space age management concept designed to offset the growing complexity, cost, and change overtaking many of our government, business, and industrial operations. As both a philosophy and a technique, it is designed to induce executives, managers, and engineers to explore the potential of simplicity at major program or system planning levels.

It is aimed at the major building blocks or black boxes, so to speak, of an entire system or program. As outlined in my previous articles,[2,3] system simplification begins where work simplification leaves off. It is preautomation technique designed to insure full spectrum management improvement.

WHY THE NEED FOR SYSTEM SIMPLIFICATION?

The needs listed in Fig. 11-2 begin with the fact that we now live in an age of *big* business, industry, and government. There are around 58 American corporations now in the billion dollar sales category. This is only one measure of a new trend toward bigness and complexity that extends even beyond the problems of paperwork or administration.

We now live in an era of exploding science and technology which in the electronics field has generated the truism, "If it works it is obsolescent." In our educational system, for example, one leading professor recently opinioned that many of the chemistry text books being used in schools today are 30 years behind the state of art.

This pace of progress creates deadly by-products. Obsolescence is not only affecting factory and office systems, but entire industries and areas of government. It places a new premium on our managerial ability to promptly respond and adapt to new challenges, changes, and complexities. Otherwise we may find ourselves as shown in Item 3 of Fig. 11-2 "polishing brass on sinking ships." Or

1. The New Complexity (government, business, and industry)
   More than paperwork—total operational

2. Inability to comprehend large scale "man-machine-environment" operations
   Age of massive engineering/administration

3. Tendency toward "piecemeal" analysis and improvement
   Polishing brass on sinking ships

4. Impact of space age technology on outdated management techniques
   Efficiency engineering versus effectiveness engineering

5. Dilemma of automation (office and factory)
   Problem of instant inefficiency

Figure 11-2. Why the Need for System Simplification?

we may be confronted by the dilemma of many modern automation programs (Item 5 of Fig. 11-2) namely the tendency to convert inefficiency or obsolescence into *instant* inefficiency.

TOOLS AND TECHNIQUES

The details of system simplification are summarized in Fig. 11-3.

1. *Documentation.* In order to comprehend a large-scale system, it is necessary to first have some idea of what the system looks like, its objectives, characteristics, and parameters, etc. Nobody would attempt to build a house without a master plan or blueprint. Unfortunately, some large scale systems are today being designed, modernized, or automated with little or no total system perspective.

I know of a million dollar automation project that had no master plan or blueprint. They just simply started automating the status quo—on a piecemeal basis. This can cost a lot of money. Fortunately, the growth of PERT techniques throughout industry and government is inducing greater total system documentation of large-scale system *networks.* In fact, I feel that one of the most valuable by-products of PERT is its tendency to promote more adequate system documentation and comprehension.

2. *Simulation.* Simulation is used in many areas today partly because of the growing number of computers. Mathematical models, equations, business or war games, wind tunnels, prototypes or pilot tests are but a few examples. The purpose or advantage of model building or simulation is to manipulate, test or try-out, on a small scale, without risking large investments or delaying current operations.

TECHNIQUES	TOOLS
1. Documentation: Document all significant elements of the total system, operation, or phenomenon under study.	Block diagrams—Flow networks System objectives; requirements Forces and functions Control room or Data center Performance; costs; deployment; milestones; program status; problems; improvement projects
2. Simulation: Where feasible, construct models or simulations of how the system or organization performs or operates in action.	Models (mathematical, physical, economic) Business games; prototypes; pilot tests; computerized operations; PERT/CPM Force Distribution Chart Economic interaction: system/function Payload analysis: mission versus support
3. Interrogation: Ask big questions. Approach old problems from new perspectives. Encourage imagineering, innovation, creative thinking, etc.	Systems Validation Study Periodic reappraisal of operations Checklist plus critiques Cost/effectiveness studies Value judgments Goals/alternatives

Figure 11-3. System Simplification.

3. *Interrogation.* This is the most promising area. The right ques-

tion at the right time can change the nature or direction of an entire business or operation. Secretary of Defense, Robert S. McNamara's task force approach (involving key questions) concerning Department of Defense operations, for example, has already resulted in complete reorganizations of the defense supply system and the defense intelligence system. In industry, Mr. Jackson Martindell, Chairman of the American Institute of Management in New York, has developed a 300 question check list which is used to analyze

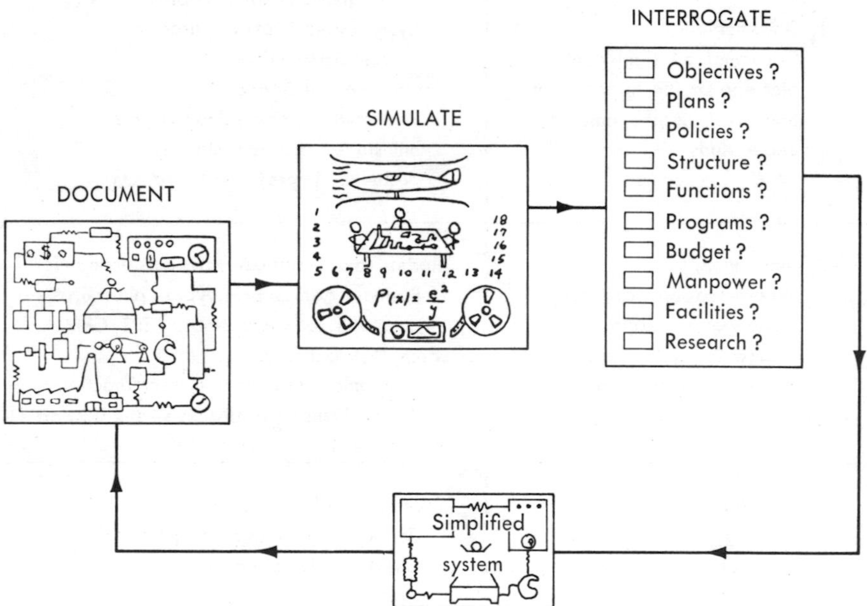

Figure 11-4. System Simplification—Technique.

large corporations or organizations. His rating process has been used on such wide ranging organizations as General Motors and the Catholic Church.

There are at least five or six ways to document a system. There may be 10 or 20 ways to simulate it. There are at least 300 questions that can be asked about it. A basic feature of system simplification, unlike PERT, is that it does not prescribe standardized format or charting process for evaluating a large scale system. It prescribes a three-step approach as shown in Fig. 11-4. The tools shown must be flexibly designed or modified to fit the specific system or operation under study. Many of the tools shown are now being used by various large corporations and some government agencies. The important objective is to achieve multi-dimensional perspectives as to how and why the total business or system operates.

At least 500 companies today have active work simplification programs. Around 100 corporations and defense contractors now use PERT techniques to reduce time, costs or increase reliability. In spite of this, some large organizations still tend to engage in "piecemeal" analysis or improvement. Care must be exercised to avoid im-

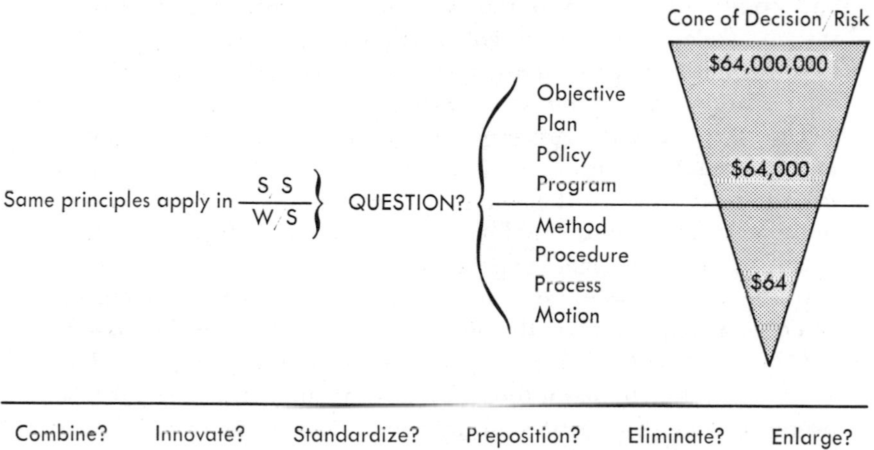

Figure 11-5. Work Simplification plus System Simplification Means "Full Spectrum" Management Improvement.

proving (or automating) the wrong things at the wrong time at the wrong levels.

In many cases, modern managements devote more time and energy to $64 questions than they to $64,000,000 questions (Fig. 11-5). As Mr. C. Northcote Parkinson pointed out in his famous book[4] Law of Triviality "the time spent on any item will be in inverse proportion to the sum involved." He gives the example of a financial committee that spent 2½ minutes discussing a $10,000,000 atomic reactor (as nobody understood it) and then came up with a unanimous approval. The same committee then spent 45 minutes deliberating on a $2,350 bicycle shed. They reduced this request by $300. Apparently everybody understood bicycles.

This problem is particularly acute in large scale system decision making. For this reason it is desirable to achieve a balance between both work simplification beginning at the $64 level, and system simplification at the $64,000,000 level in order to insure "full spectrum management improvement."

BACKGROUND DISCUSSION

Fig. 11-6 is designed for people over 40. If you were born before 1922 you can say that you have lived in *four* distinct ages. This chart not only reflects the progressive trend toward increasing costs and complexity, but also the new emphasis on management by system. Today's problem is not productivity, speed, or power. We have surpluses in many areas, speeds of 25,000 mph, and nuclear or solar energy sources promise unlimited power.

The new challenge concerns our managerial ability, or inability, to comprehend, control, and improve large scale man-machine-environment systems. It involves achieving order, balance, or logic in the vast forces and complex componentry of large-scale business, industrial, and government operations.

In the area of space travel, for example, it has been estimated that when we reach the moon the only visible man-made object on earth will be the Great Wall of China, which is about 2000 miles long. Historians estimate that it took 15 years and approximately 1,000,000 people to build this great wall. By comparison, some of our modern space or missile systems may soon involve as much effort and investment (and much more complexity) than was required to build the Great Wall of China.

Today's problems of total system comprehension and control are partly indicated by the fact that the Atlas missile involved 3000 business and industrial contractors located in 41 states. This should indicate why it may often take six months or more to intelligently document a large-scale, world-wide system. It also indicates why there is a growing inability in many areas of the management profession, to comprehend large-scale fast-moving space age operations.

Many of today's management techniques are being bypassed by technology. An electronic engineer told me about a project he had to install, a microwave network in a foreign country. While he was inspecting one of the microwave towers he looked down to see one of his customer/users who was standing at the bottom of the tower complete with loin cloth, spear, and shield. This customer had not yet learned to read or write, but here as a paradox of the space age

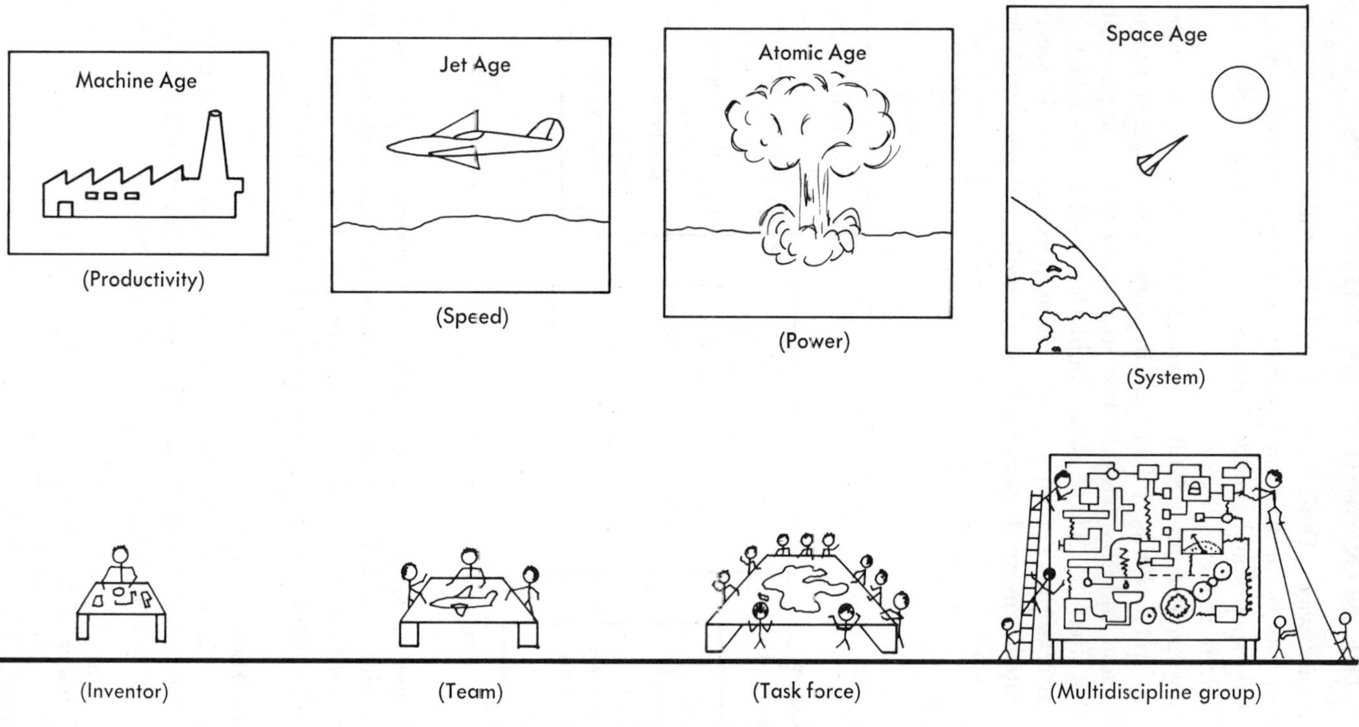

Figure 11-6. Trend Toward *Systems* Management.

he had microwave. Don't laugh. I feel that today's management profession may be in the same position. In many cases we may still be carrying spears and shields. However, I must admit I don't see any loin cloths in the audience.

We now have around 8000 electronic computers in the United States. In spite of this, I feel that in some areas of government, business, and industry we continue to put *radar* on stagecoaches (Fig. 11-2, Item 5). There is no doubt that "real time" data feedback networks plus computers are a giant step forward. However, sophisticated sensory devices must be carefully balanced with im-

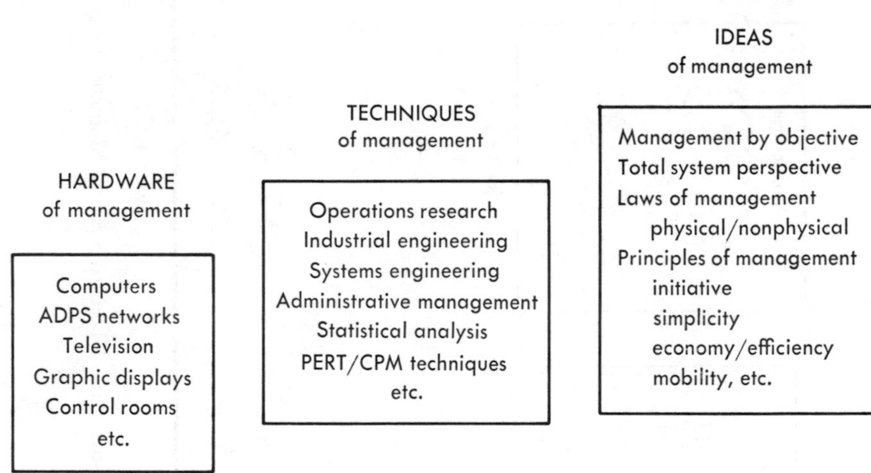

Figure 11-7. The Management of Improvement.

proved operational perspectives, better total system comprehension, and broader knowledge of the laws and principles of management as opposed to the hardware of management (Fig. 11-7). Information leads to control and control should lead to improvement.

LAWS OF MANAGEMENT

There are many undiscovered or unrecognized laws in the field of management. Fig. 11-8 reflects four amusing or interesting laws that have an indirect bearing upon *systems* management:

1. Parkinson's Law(s):
   "Work expands to fill the time available to do it."
   "Expenditure rises to meet income."
2. Murphy's law is an old Navy expression:

"If it's possible to assemble or operate anything wrong, Murphy will find it." This is a basic assumption in aircraft design, maintenance, and repair. Unfortunately, the law doesn't stop here. It also applies in paperwork where if it's possible to interpret or read something wrong, Clerk Murphy will find it.

3. Newton's Law of action/reaction has a direct bearing when we evaluate system costs. When money is added to one system or function, it generally must be taken from another system or function. This often has painful economic or operational repercussions.

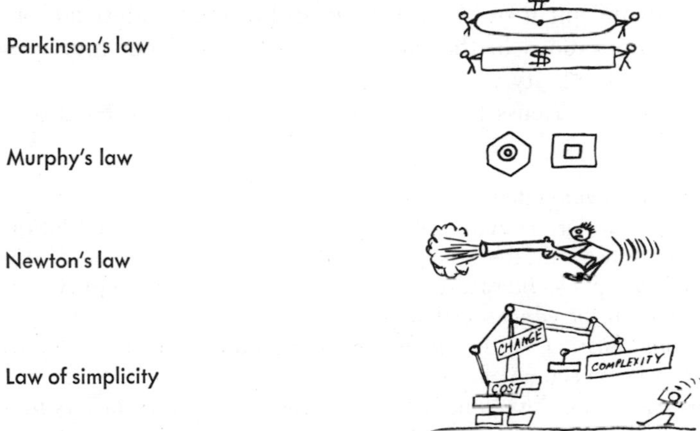

Figure 11-8. Laws of Management.

4. The fourth law on this chart is one I would like to propose for recognition. It may well be the most important for our discussion. Similar to "necessity is the mother of invention," the law of simplicity comes, or explodes into action when an organization, system, or product reaches that point where cost, change, and complexity overtake the purpose for which the system was originally designed. In many cases the means have become or outweigh the end. The organization, system, or product begins to collapse of its own weight. This can be due to excessive complexity, costs (operating or maintenance), changes or simply falling victim to more flexible or imaginative competition. This law applies to people, systems, businesses, entire industries, or nations.

EXAMPLES OF SYSTEM SIMPLIFICATION

Listed below are seven examples of the so-called law of simplicity in action:

AREA OR FIELD	EXAMPLE
Paperwork	Electric computer
Missiles	Solid propellants
Electronics	Transistors
Autos	Compact car
Railroads	Piggy-back freight
Television	Magnetic tape
Communications	TV satellites

In almost every case simplicity was either the cause or the by-product of the resulting breakthrough. I don't know of a single major advancement or breakthrough in business, industrial, or government operations in the last 15 years that did not involve some element of simplicity.

Even as we discuss this list new developments are coming down the road.

1. *Sonic cleaning* devices may replace detergents.
2. New cars are coming out with built-in *grease jobs.* Self-lubricating metals are indicated as a possible next step.
3. *Teaching machines* are in one sense the law of simplicity, taking effect in the educational fields.
4. Simplification in the home involves cordless electrical appliances: *Cordless* vacuum cleaners, mixers, TVs, etc.

However, one development near to most taxpayers' hearts involves State *income tax*. Alaska and West Virginia, for example, have simplified their tax systems by using the Federal income tax as a basis for computing State taxes. This is real *paperwork* simplification. It will eliminate thousands of forms, records, reports, and paperwork investigations. However, I must hasten to add that the ultimate paperwork simplicity in this area is the State of Texas, which has no State *income* taxes.

PROGRESS THROUGH SIMPLICITY

Fig. 11-9 shows the steps by which transition was made in airplanes through jets to aerospace vehicles and missiles. Each advancement or quantum-jump shown on this chart involved simplification (through elimination) of a major component or requirement. When the biplane became a monoplane, one wing was eliminated. Engine-in-wing configuration was the next improvement. Then retractable landing gear resulted in less frontal drag. Jet engines next eliminated the need for propellers. Rocket propulsion bypassed the need for air breathing jet engines. And finally, today we have the wingless, solid propellant, ICBM. However, even this is no "ultimate" weapon. Some imaginative inventor or engineer is probably now working on a gross simplification which will revolutionize operations even in this area.

While this chart portrays aerospace systems it could just as well have been paperwork or records management systems. We could make a similar chart starting with the quill pen and working through the old style typewriters to the new electrics, which when

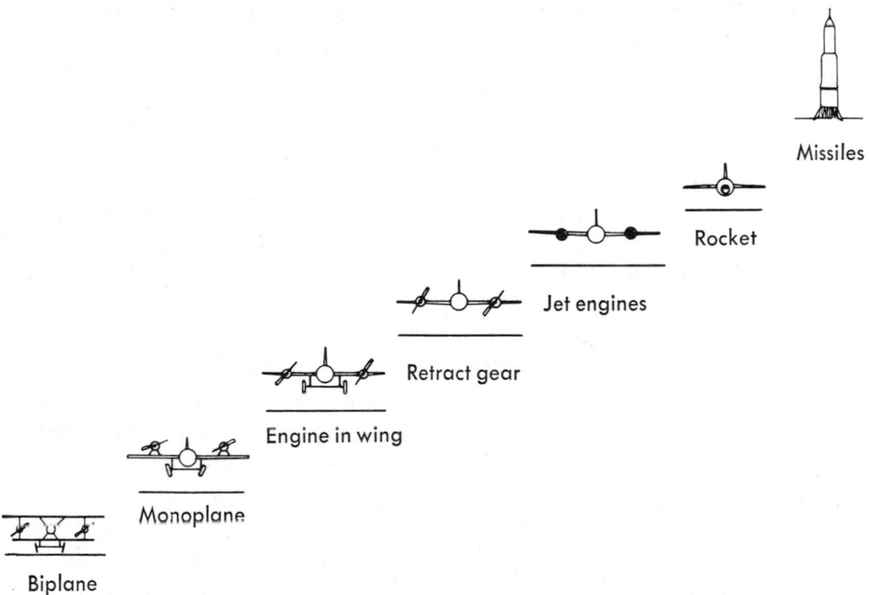

Figure 11-9. Progress Through Simplicity, in Total "Cost/Effectiveness" Perspective.

tied into an electronic computer system provide source data automation for an entire record-keeping system. Simplicity is a fundamental element of invention and progress.

However, there is a unique paradox in progress through simplicity. Wilbur Wright's original airplane (like a sort of aeronautical quill pen) only cost around $10,000. Today's missiles (similar to a high cost electronic computer system) may cost around $2,000,000 each. A comparison of these figures might indicate that we received more for our money in the good old days. This is not the case. In total "cost/effectiveness" perspective, the biplane could only do 41 mph. Today's missiles can travel at 25,000 mph. And whoever heard of a biplane going to the moon? In this sense, today's missiles and aerospace systems are a bargain.

The paradox of this situation is that as missiles (and office machines) become technologically more complicated, at the same time, in cost/effectiveness perspective, they also achieve new levels of total operational simplicity and capability. In the Alice in Wonderland world of space age systemry, technological complication is often the most direct route to over-all operational simplicity. A similar point was highlighted by Mr. Thomas V. Jones, President of the Northrop Corporation (*Time* magazine, 27 Oct. 61), when he said:

> "We must make our new technology the liberator of our resources rather than a ravenous consumer. We must recognize the power and value of technical simplicity as distinguished from the complexity that we too often regard as sophistication. We have tended to ignore something that the best Paris dress designers, and Sir Isaac Newton, never forgot: the ultimate of sophistication is simplicity itself."

SPACE AGE DRAGONS

Few Americans would believe that here in the space age dragons still exist. Unfortunately these new dragons not only exist but they are so massive, complicated, costly, and far ranging that most of us do not see, comprehend, or understand their deadly work.

These new dragons are called "systems." Not only are we surrounded by them, but they can devour, destroy, or enslave us in a hundred subtle ways. They exist in the form of obsolete, malfunctioning, or ill-conceived administrative or operational systems or programs. These dragons reduce productivity, increase taxes, raise costs, consume profits, and exact a toll in human lives, discomfort and misery. They are barricaded behind mountains of obsolete laws, customs, regulations, and procedures. Once "legalized" they are seldom repealed, modernized, or reconceived. Once born these dragons (particularly the administrative type) are hard to slay. Few have ever been mortally wounded.

Their power exists in their lack of personality. Nobody can be responsible or blamed for what the "system" does. If a real, live, visible old time fire-breathing dragon roamed the land, eating up 800 American men, women, and children per week, I am sure that the Army, the Navy, and the Air Force (and the Marines) would be galvanized into instant action. Unfortunately, the auto traffic dragon (system) is doing just this. However, as he is about 2800 miles long and 1500 miles wide and is composed of thousands of interacting "man-machine-environment" components, plus conflicting state laws and regulations, nobody knows where to begin. He's too big to comprehend. So, the slaughter goes on.

This is only one dragon. We also have the air transportation dragon which as a "system" can consume 130 lives in a single gulp. The inflation dragon has been busily eating up savings accounts, insurance policy values, and the American dollar for years. There are many others.

Today's management profession is not threatened by the old time lions and tigers of simple inefficiency. Rather, today we are confronted with massive mismanagement at the total system or top planning level. In dragon or dinosaur terms, it is now possible to misspend or lose a billion dollars as the result of a single system decision.

New magnitudes of risk, change, and complexity require entirely new approaches, concepts, and techniques. Today's manager must first be able to see these dragons. He must comprehend how, why, and where they operate. With this perspective, he can then begin to ask *big* questions. These are one of the most potent weapons against space age dragons.

This is what "full spectrum management improvement" and "system simplification" are all about. They are terms and techniques that can kill the dragons I talk about. To you in the space age records management and paperwork improvement business, I can only conclude by saying . . . Good hunting in the land of administrative dragons.

QUESTION AND ANSWER SESSION

1. Do ADPS networks, PERT, "real time" data processing, control rooms or closed circuit television networks *insure* "full spectrum" management improvement?

No. They are a giant step toward improving management communication, responsiveness, and control. But, they do not insure "full spectrum" management improvement. Advancements in the so-called hardware of management tend to prevent more effective comprehension and awareness of the basic principles and laws of management. In some cases, sophisticated management techniques or systems induce top management to "rest on their oars." Throne room decision-makers often feel that nothing can go wrong competitively if they have a million dollar computer or control system. There are few more deadly misconceptions. Computers or control systems are powerful tools. However, unless management knows how to use computerized information—as a beginning point and not as an end in itself—they may actually be "under-managing."

2. With 8000 electronic computers or thinking machines in the USA today, why do we have so many unsolved problems?

A primary reason is piecemeal perspectives, analysis, and improvement efforts. We tend to analyze or improve by individual function or component when, in many cases, we should step back and reconceive the entire system or program.

A second factor is underestimation of the impact of "value" judgments. I feel that the great unexplored frontier of management today exists in the area of value judgments concerning large scale "man-machine-environment" systems. In the past ten years, leapfrog advances in computers, ADPS and automation hardware has produced better "digital" judgments at all levels of management. However, these have obscured the fact that the most significant area of management decision-making exists in value or analog-type judgments made at top or middle management levels. This brings us to our next question.

3. Which category of decision-making has the greatest impact in large scale, high cost/risk systems—(1) *value* judgments, or (2) *data* judgments?

In space age operations, management is being conducted on a grand scale. Unfortunately, so is mismanagement. It is now easy to make billion dollar mistakes.

As we move up the ladder of decision-making in large scale systems (administrative or operational) we find fewer "yes or no" decisions which can be computer-programmed, based upon neatly quantified or well-structured data or information. Even at middle management levels, many decisions become multiple choice. There is no doubt that the digital computer is a powerful aid. However, in many cases, the manager or executive must ultimately rely on his own experience, knowledge, skill, or ability. He may face five or six alternatives or choices involving factors of time, risk, cost, competitive situation, resource availability, etc. Only he can assign appropriate "values" to the elements involved. Only he can decide.

Value judgments often determine the objectives, operational requirements, policies and plans of the *entire* business or system. Often there is nothing to count, measure, or compare. There may be no precedent and few standards or sign posts. The direction or even existence of a billion dollar system or program may hinge on a single value judgment. At this level, a sort of managerial weightlessness begins to set in. Entirely new forces and influences come into play which are often nondigital. It is here that the principles and laws of management often assume more significance—particularly in competitive situations—than the mere possession of empirical data, information, or knowledge. This may also be one reason why Einstein once said "Imagination is more important than knowledge." At total system levels, today's manager must have the imagination to know what to do, not only with the facts, but also with the forces, functions, and opportunities at his disposal.

4. The Hoover Commission found that revising one line on a government form saved $22,000,000—what would happen if an entire paperwork program, or system was simplified?

It would incure vast savings to say the least. Imaginative reconception or innovation in any large-scale Federal program or system, like income tax or Social Security, might conceivably save hundreds of millions of dollars. Simplification of administrative, procedural or human effort—could benefit both the taxpayer and the government. This is a real challenge to government administrators.

5. Did Khrushchev say "We will bury you . . ."? Can we bury ourselves under tons of paperwork, procedural complexity and ill-conceived systemry?

Yes, Mr. Khrushchev did say this. But, I feel that he underestimates American imagination and ingenuity. However, by the same token we must not underestimate the deadly impact of paperwork complexity. The path to the moon, I am sure, will be paved with millions of records, forms, and reports. In fact, when we get there, we will probably find a records management man waiting with a form for astronauts to fill out. In the meantime, we could unwittingly bury ourselves under excessive paperwork, procedural complexity, and ill-conceived or obsolete administrative systemry. Today's massive engineering and massive administration requires better knowledge, perception, and insight into the interaction between people, forces, functions, and environments. This is a priority challenge to all management people throughout government.

6. Is "extra-sensory" perception becoming a standard feature in many modern management control systems? Are human sensory

abilities inadequate in view of space age time-compressions, complexity, and change?

Space age complexity, change, and time-compressions are making human sensory abilities grossly inadequate. It is not enough to merely see, feel, taste, hear, or smell—modern problems or opportunities. Electronic computers, television, telemetry, oscillographs, geiger counters, radar, microwave, bionics, etc., are but a few recent developments that, in effect, are expanding human abilities into the "extra-sensory" perception range.

7. Is it true that the only thing "ultimate" about modern weapons, products, processes, or systems—is that they are ultimately *obsolete*?

There is no such thing as an "ultimate" weapon, product, or system. The Great Wall of China, Greek Fire, the bow and arrow, the Merrimac and the Maginot Line were probably considered ultimate weapons in their day. However, the only thing ultimate about modern weapons, products, processes, or systems is that they are ultimately *obsolete*. This is illustrated by an excerpt from Jack Anderson's column in the *Washington Post* (27 May 62):

> "Others describe the intercontinental missile as the "ultimate weapon" and cannot conceive of its becoming obsolete. Yet weapons are already on the drawing boards that could vaporize missiles and make Nikita Khrushchev's many-megaton bombs seem like BB shot.
>
> "One is called the laser, a ray of concentrated light, which could strike its target with heat, greater than that of the actual surface of the sun. Already, small lasers have been built which can drill holes through a diamond. Traveling at the speed of light, this ray woud overtake a 19,000 mile-an-hour missile in a split second."

A similar situation is developing in the management field where space age technology is upsetting long established management concepts and techniques. These too were once considered "ultimate."

8. Is the organization man being overtaken by the system man? Do space age events sometimes give "unity of purpose" a higher priority than "unity of command?"

Today's system managers, in some cases, direct and control greater resources and investments than are managed by many large-scale corporations. Some of our major systems (particularly in space and defense) now cut across the entire business, industrial, and government spectrum. The *Apollo* space system, for example, is a truly national effort. The *Minuteman* and the *Polaris* missile systems are billion dollar operations. Social Security, health, and education are only several of many important government programs or systems that affect almost everybody.

The organization man is rapidly being overtaken by the system man. A unique managerial phenomenon is taking place wherein "unity of command" is being accorded less priority than "unity of purpose." Mission-oriented products or systems of the organization, in many cases, are becoming more significant than the basic functions of the organization. Technological change, growing system investments and program complexities have combined to create this new priority or emphasis.

The Department of Defense, for example, now has around 200 major systems. These systems are becoming the dominant element in defense planning, budgeting, and organization. Establishment of the Air Force Systems Command, and the Bureau of Naval Weapons are two indications of this new trend.

In a sense, space age management is rapidly becoming two-dimensional. It is necessary to integrate both management by *function* (organization) and management by *system* (product). This requires the teamwork and imaginations of both the organization man and the system man.

CLOSING REMARKS

COMPARATIVE MANAGEMENT TECHNIQUES

System simplification approaches a system or organization from an entirely different perspective than PERT or *value engineering* (Fig. 11-10). It concentrates on questioning the *why* and *how* of total operations or total administration as compared with the PERT emphasis on program scheduling, events, milestones, time, cost, etc., or the *value engineering* emphasis on component or hardware improvement.

System simplification is a gross approach aimed at the major building block level of operations. It begins by questioning the objectives, goals, or concepts of an entire business or operation. It looks at a system as an interacting, interdependent, assemblage of forces, functions, linkages, activators and controls.

At this level of management perspective, a single improvement, innovation, or simplification can mean million dollar savings.

However, system simplification does not replace any of the techniques shown in Fig. 11-10. Rather, it complements them. In fact, the appropriate use and combination of all four techniques can

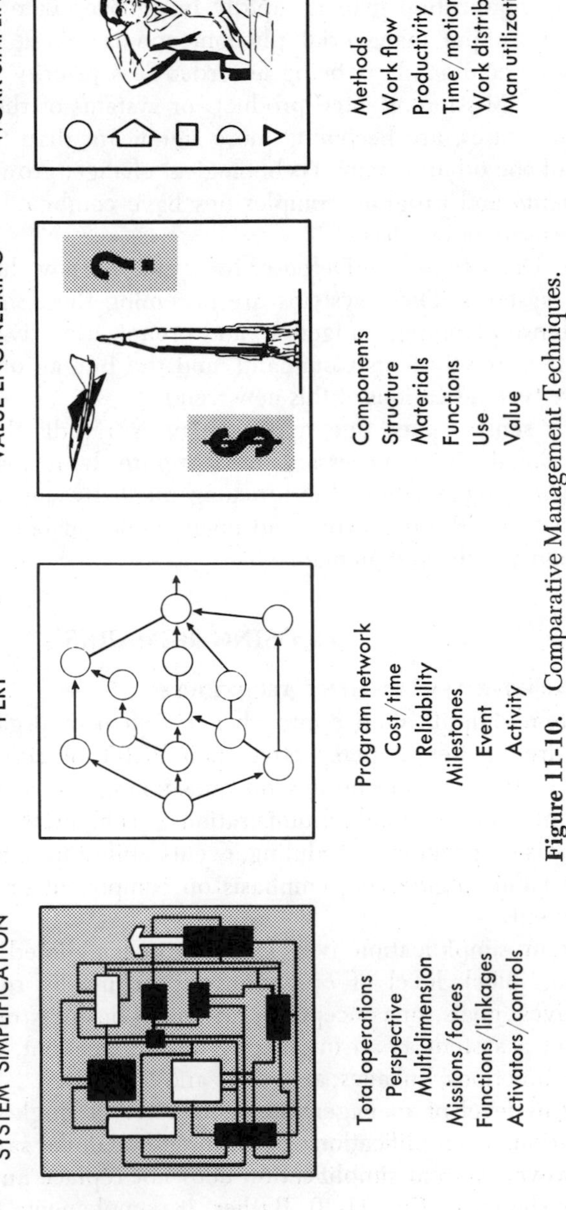

Figure 11-10. Comparative Management Techniques.

mean substantial savings or impovements in almost any large scale hardware or paperwork type of system.

STRUCTURE OF SYSTEMS

Taylor's approach indicates a need, particularly in reference to the many very large systems that have emerged in present day government, defense installations and activities, business, and industry, to reorient our conventional thinking away from preoccupation with bits and pieces of total problems and toward consideration of the total system.

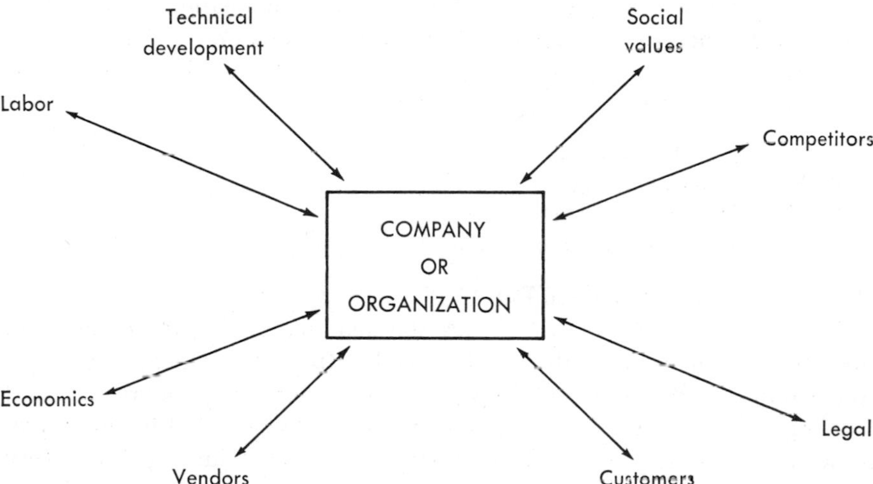

Figure 11-11. The Concept of Isolating an Entire Organization as a System Interconnected with its Environment.

When studying a system it is helpful to keep in mind the particular system involved, how it relates to the larger systems of which it is but a part, and also its subsystems and components. The system is an entity by itself, self-contained and internally compatible, but it operates as an entity with interconnections to its environment. Internally it is composed of a variety of components that are not so easily isolated in terms of their independent behavior as entities by themselves.[5]

The system of most concern in business and industry is the company, or as we have been referring to it—the organization. This may be viewed, as in Fig. 11-11, as a "free body," isolated from its environment but connected to it by links of action and interaction. Theoretically, this view of an organization isolated from its environment does not influence its behavior. It can be treated as a system by itself, and it can be interconnected adequately with the broader system by the links. For example, we might visualize a business enterprise as a system by itself, isolated from its environment for analytical purposes, but related to it by the various links, representing its influence upon—and the influence of—the economic system, labor, customers, competitors, the legal system, vendors, etc.

This degree of system isolation is seldom achieved. From an analytical point of view it almost defies formal representation with the techniques available. From a conceptual point of view, it is a very useful approach.

Most systems of the scope implied are more amenable to analysis if they are further subdivided into functional systems, or in terms of the main subsystems. The partitioning into subsystems may be visualized as follows:

1. The physical subsystem
2. The human subsystem
3. The information subsystem, and
4. The management and organizational subsystem.

This concept is illustrated in Fig. 11-12.

The *physical* subsystem includes the inanimate objects—equipment, facilities, and materials—that are involved in the organization. In general, these objects obey physical laws that are rather well understood, and analysis of this subsystem is a rather straightforward, although sometimes very complex, engineering undertaking. New technology has a very substantial and direct effect upon this subsystem.

The *human* subsystem brings life to the physical subsystem and allows the organization to be productive. Human behavior is a very complex thing, and we are only currently beginning to understand some of the fundamentals involved in it. Developments in the behaviorial sciences allow better insight into problems associated with this subsystem, but formal or analytical treatment of most human problems is far from a reality. Even so, this area cannot be ignored, for the human subsystem in any organization is a critical, creative, and sustaining element.

The *information* subsystem is in effect the life blood of any organization. It provides the flow and interchange of information that gives an organization direction, authorizes activity, guides efforts, and evaluates performance. Developments in the technology of computers, data or information processing, and decision theory have had a substantial influence upon the information subsystem. Many problems can be handled in a formalized or semiformalized manner, even though the overlapping of this subsystem with others is pervasive and complicating.

The *organizational and management* subsystem involves the establishment of goals and objectives for the organization and its functional parts, the allocation of authority and responsibility, and the general guidance of activities for the total organization and its parts. One of its main objectives is to obtain an integration of the bits and pieces of the total organization into a system—with all parts performing so that the total system

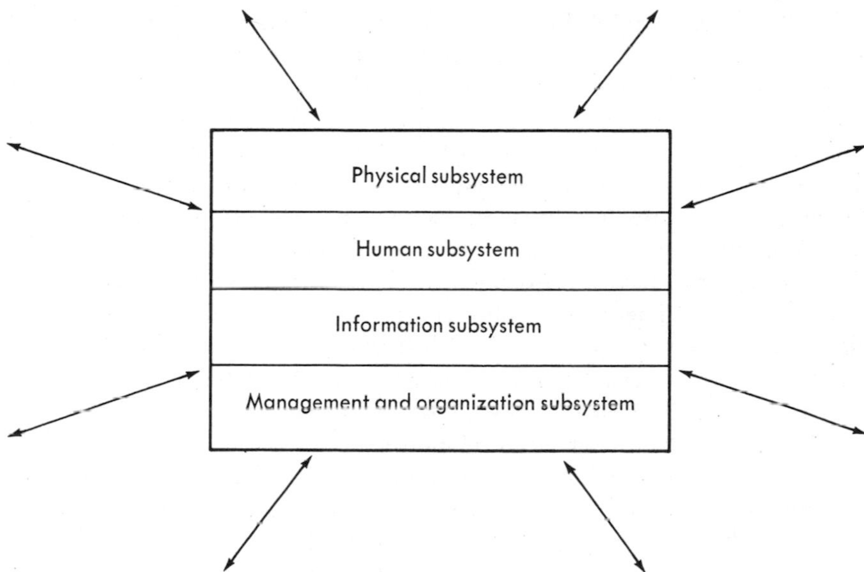

Figure 11-12. The Division of the Organization as a System Into Four Main Subsystems

performs in an acceptable and successful manner. Many of the developments in the art of management have great utility in solving problems in this subsystem, as have developments in decision theory, operations research, and management science. But, this subsystem still is in the semiscientific stage of analysis, at best.

Functional subsystems are usually much more restricted in scope than the four just discussed. They may be structured in terms of cost control, production control, production scheduling, quality control, etc. (to follow one particular line of subdivision). In general, they are primarily concerned with one function and can be isolated, treated as entities, and related to the broader systems of which they are a part. Some of these subsystems can be treated formally, others cannot. Subdivision of problem areas according to functional subsystems can be of great value in analyzing problems of improvement.

SYSTEM VALIDATION

An extension of Taylor's concept of systems simplification is currently being developed (by Taylor) in the form of system validation study (SVS). The motivation for concentrating attention toward system revalidation is very straightforward: some systems may be achieving a high level of internal efficiency and productivity, but are not contributing effectively to the larger system of which they are a part. This situation can and frequently does arise within almost all types of organizations because when a problem arises—for example, with customer service, quality control, or excessive absenteeism—it seems to be human nature to develop an expedient way to handle the current problem without regarding its source. The result is a proliferation of stopgap measures that continue on, past the existence of the situations which caused them to be originated. The system validation study is an approach to correcting this, both on a small scale and with large-scale programs. Rather than checking on the internal efficiency or productivity of the system activity, the study directs attention toward the effectiveness of the system and its objective relative to external relationships.

The SVS approach has been developed within the environment of governmental activity. The opportunity for systems, and very expensive ones at that, to be perpetuated beyond their period of useful contribution is somewhat obvious in governmental activities. The same general situation, however, exists within many other organizations, even though not so generally recognized.

The SVS approach is potentially a very useful one. It involves a systematic re-evaluation of system objectives, need, worth, policies, plans, assumptions, and of how well the system is actually satisfying needs. The intent is to evaluate the external *effectiveness* of the system rather than the internal *efficiency*. Major decisions, programs, planning, policies, assumptions, and requirements should be re-examined periodically, and their real worth determined, for it is possible that misdirection of resources can go undetected for years unless systematic analysis and evaluation is undertaken. It is also possible that while the system is becoming less effective relative to external criteria, it is becoming more efficient in its internal operation. The usual management audit or organizational survey is likely to evaluate the internal efficiency but to miss any evaluation of external effectiveness of activities. What may have been valid objectives, plans, policies, etc. last year may no longer be appropriate. SVS is an approach to correcting this situation.

All organizations can profit from Taylor's approach to reevaluation of policies, programs, and systems. SVS also is a useful precaution as a prerequisite to the redesign and improvement of existing systems, and as a general evaluation procedure preceding the development or automation of new systems.

SUMMARY

One of the characteristics usually associated with operations research is the systems approach, which is not confined just to O.R., but has wide applicability in a variety of endeavors—both in the sciences and in every day life. Relative to the problems of the management of improvement and the improvement function, the systems approach has particular significance. Broad problems must be continually kept in view, and in proper perspective relative to the more confined and easier to recognize daily problems. Both are important, but in proper relation to each other. Alternative approaches to improvement should be evaluated in terms of the potential benefits and costs associated with these alternatives—relative to the "system." In some cases, the appropriate approaches to improvement will be broad—within the systems setting. This point has been made by Taylor in his advocacy of system simplification and system validation study. In other cases the proper approach will be more confined, or perhaps be a combination of systems simplification and more restricted improvement endeavors. This is also advocated by Taylor.*

A word of caution is in order. Many operations researchers have been preoccupied with the "grand-scale" approach—an analytical model of the system—to the extent that they have entirely lost sight of the practicality associated with achieving improvement within their organization. While the author personally thinks that these approaches are very worthwhile, he also feels quite strongly that a balanced approach to the improvement

* Taylor implies that systems simplification extends the sphere of influence of work simplification (see Figs. 11-1 and 11-5). This is undoubtedly true in terms of the common usage of the term work simplification, but it need not be, and it does not reflect my thinking concerning what work simplification should be. Further information is contained in my book *Work Simplification: Creative Thinking About Work Problems*, Prentice-Hall, Englewood Cliffs, New Jersey, 1957.

I should also mention my support of Taylor's approach. I have no objection to the coining of words to focus attention upon neglected areas. The concept of systems simplification is a much needed one.

function is essential. The needs of the organization—and these should *not* be determined in an arbitrary manner but by systematic and thorough analysis—should determine what approaches should be used and what problems should be studied.

Some of the failures of industrial use of operations research have been caused by lack of proper perspective in selecting significant problems relative to the needs of the system or organization. This was mentioned in the previous chapter, but merits repeating for emphasis.[6]

Where management has quickly realized the value of O.R., work has centered on projects of relatively short duration and with demonstrable payout. This obvious point needs emphasis because it appears in the pattern of successful O.R. and is lacking in many other cases. Several instances of grand-scale model development, which sometimes continue over long periods of time despite lack of success, are evident in our interviews. The following examples from our survey illustrate this point.

In one division of a large corporation, O.R. analysts spent a long time with a consultant developing a model for production scheduling and inventory control that turned out to be unsuccessful. Against this shaky background a project was undertaken about 13 months prior to the interview to develop a production scheduling, inventory control, and distribution model for one of the company's major product lines. Since the results of this work are not yet implemented or felt in any way, management is understandably dubious about value being received for O.R. expenditures.

In describing a financial forecasting model under study for four years, an O.R. manager in another company stated, "The O.R. team has been successful in simulating the mechanical aspects of our accounting system but has found it very difficult to simulate the over-all business enterprise, particularly the interfaces between the business and the national economy." This apparent tendency to keep expanding the scope of models frequently yields impractical and unrealistic results. Or, so much time is consumed in developing the model that management loses patience because of lack of tangible results.

REFERENCES

1. W. Sidney Taylor, "Full Spectrum Management Improvement," *Proceedings of the Interagency Records Administration Conference,* Philadelphia, June 4, 1962, National Archives and Records Service, General Services Administration, Washington, D.C., 1962, p. 23.
2. W. Sidney Taylor, "System Simplification," *The Journal of Industrial Engineering,* January–February 1961.
3. W. Sidney Taylor, "Full Spectrum Management Improvement," *Advanced Management,* November 1961.

4. C. Northcote Parkinson, *Parkinson's Law and Other Studies in Administration,* Houghton, Boston, 1957.
5. Additional comments about the structure of systems can be found in R. N. Lehrer, *Work Simplification: Creative Thinking About Work Problems,* Prentice-Hall, Englewood Cliffs, N.J., 1957.
6. "A Limited Survey of Industrial Progress in Operations Research," McKinsey & Company, Inc., 1962, p. 15. (See Chapter 10.)

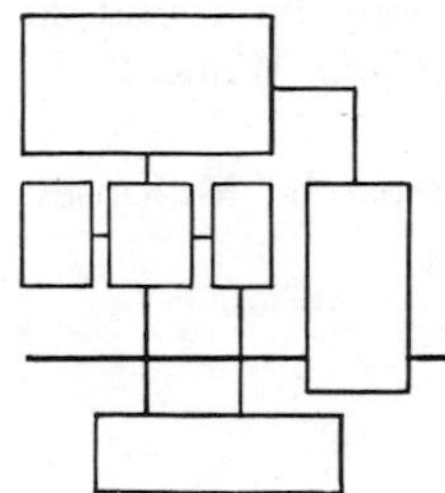

CHAPTER 12

DESIGN OF SYSTEMS FOR PRODUCING

THE IMPROVEMENT FUNCTION has been described as being principally concerned with pursuing systematic and continuing improvement within an organization. These improvement endeavors may be directed toward restricted problems involving portions of the organization or they may take the form of systems considerations. Ideally, both approaches should be used, with primary attention directed toward systems problems, and subsequent consideration focused on less expansive problems. It is very difficult to consider an entire organization as a system for detailed analysis, evaluation, and improvement. In some cases this can be done. In most cases, however, it is more profitable to consider a portion of the entire system, such as a subsystem or a confined functional system.

It has been pointed out that industrial engineering improvement endeavors are mainly concerned with problems of systems for producing and systems for managing. In this chapter some of the problems of designing producing systems will be considered. The following example illustrates the complete redesign of a producing system and the related management system for programming and controlling its operation. It is an excellent example of creative systems engineering involving considerable research, development, and engineering relative to the systems design, the systems components, and the manufacturing technology involved.*

* Appreciation is expressed to the Western Electric Company for furnishing information upon which this example is based, and for furnishing illustrations. Further information can be found in the references listed at the end of the chapter.

THE PROBLEM

In modern communication and defense systems extremely large numbers of electronic components are required, the reliability of which, by and large, determines the reliability of the operation of the system. For acceptable systems performance a fantastically high reliability is required of these components. A look to the future indicates that the problem will become significantly more complex and that the quality levels acceptable today will be totally unacceptable in not very many years. For these reasons the engineers at the Winston Salem Plant of Western Electric Company have for several years directed substantial effort toward a systematic improvement of component reliability by redesign of the components and the processes whereby they are produced.

One of these components is the precision deposited-carbon resistor. It is composed of a ceramic core coated with carbon (which is usually grooved), end connections, and a protective covering (see Fig. 12-1).

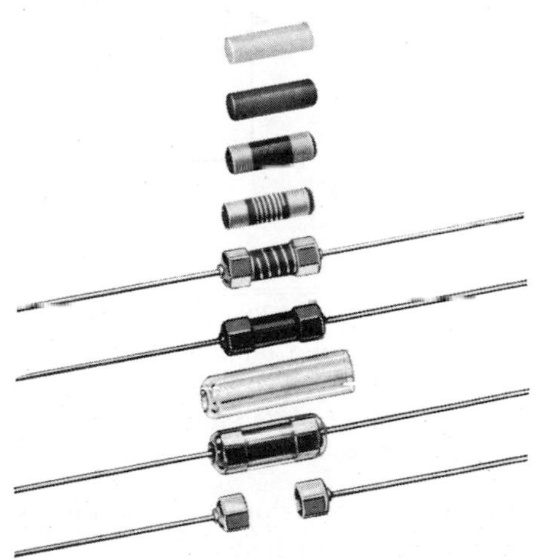

Figure 12-1. Manufacturing Sequence for the Conventional Deposited-Carbon Resistor. From top to bottom: ceramic core, carbon-coated core; metallic paint terminations; helixed resistor; capped resistor; lacquered resistor; plastic sleeve; resistor in plastic sleeve; cap-lead assemblies.

The importance of the reliability of this item is graphically illustrated in Figs. 12-2 and 12-3. It is not uncommon to have up to a million of these components in a large scale electronic system. The typical high quality level for a precision resistor was, at the time this study was started, one failure in 20,000,000 operating hours. The goal was to improve this level of reliability by a factor of ten, to a performance level of one failure in 200,000,000 operating hours (five failures per 1,000,000,000 component-hours). Although the main objective of the study was to achieve improvement in product quality, costs were an important, but secondary, consideration. The final results more than achieved the desired quality-reliability improvement, and production costs were substantially reduced. Many man-years of engineering and research were

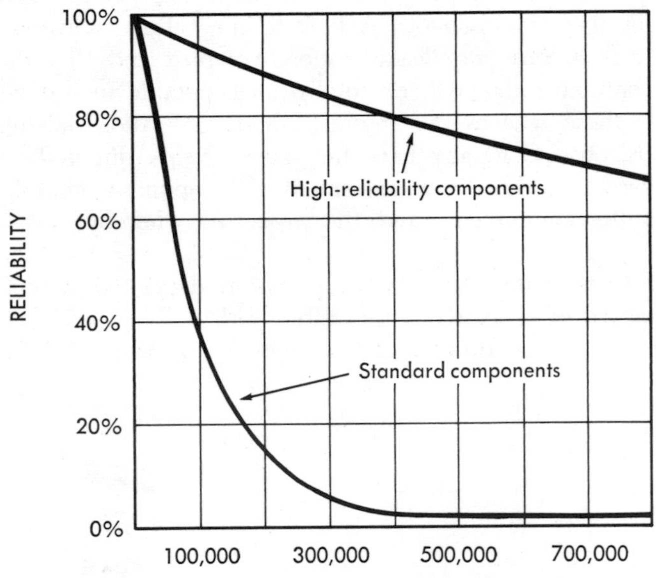

Figure 12-2. Relationship between Reliability and Number of Components for Two Levels of Component Reliability. (Highest = 5 failures per billion component-hours; low = 100 failures per billion component-hours.)

required to develop a workable system, and a substantial investment was required to install it.

THE PROCESS

Deposited-carbon resistors are conventionally manufactured by coating a ceramic cylinder (or core) with crystalline carbon by thermal decomposition of hydrocarbon gases. The coating is done by placing a batch of ceramic cores in a quartz bottle, which is then heated and flushed with methane gas. The cores are stirred during coating, and the temperature and gas flow are carefully controlled in an attempt to achieve uniformity of carbon deposition.

After the cores have cooled, each of the ends is coated with a metallic paint, which is subsequently baked for many hours, to provide a low resistance termination (conductive film covering the carbon at the core

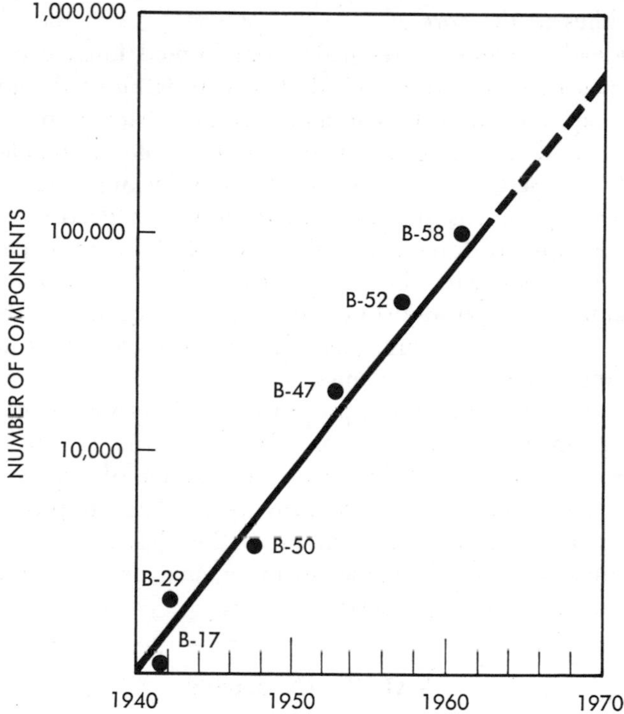

Figure 12-3. Logarithmic Plot of Number of Components per System, Based on Various Airborne Systems —Illustrating a High Rate of Increase in Complexity With Time.

ends) to which the cap-lead assemblies can later be attached. The resistance value of each core is measured, and they are sorted in order to reduce variability and to facilitate subsequent processing. The wide range of resistance values, approximately 40%, is caused by variability in the film of deposited carbon, which is characteristic of this process of manufacture.

The next operation is to cut a helix groove in the surface of the coated cylinder. This is done by a wet grinding operation in which the core is rotated while a narrow abrasive wheel is passed across its surface. The relative speed of core rotation and traverse feed of the grinding wheel determine the pitch of the helix and thus the increase in core resistance. Core resistance is increased to a value just slightly below the final required value. Final resistance values are achieved by a rubbing operation, which follows drying and attaching of the terminal cap-lead assemblies to the cores.

The cap-lead assemblies are made from formed brass caps to which the terminal lead wires are attached. The wire is inserted into a square hole in the cap, and both the cap and wire are distorted by a combination swaging and upsetting action so that the hole is completely filled and the lead is increased in diameter, thereby locking it in place. Usually, the lead-cap joint is also soldered to provide a good electrical connection. The caps are forced over the ends of the core, making a low-resistance connection with the carbon coating by close contact with the metallic paint. The final adjustment of resistance values by the rubbing operation follows the capping operation, because capping causes a significant change in resistance values.

The final operations provide a protective covering for the carbon coating and markings for identification. Typically, the carbon coating is covered by lacquer to provide a moisture barrier, the assembly is enclosed in a loose plastic cover to provide mechanical protection, and identifying markings are offset printed on the plastic cover. The manufacturing process is largely made up of manual or semimanual operations, performed on a batch basis.

VALUE ANALYSIS

The primary motivation for the study was the recognized need for substantial improvement in product quality. The general approach was one frequently associated with systems design in the communication, large-scale electronics, and military fields, but seldom applied to production systems. Some aspects of the over-all procedure were similar to value analysis which attempts to evaluate product function, design, materials and parts purchasing, manufacturing, and product use as a closed system.

The quality characteristics and problems of reliability of the resistors were carefully analyzed, and causes of failure determined. These then served as the basis for establishing the specifications for redesign of the resistor, and performance requirements for the system which would produce them. From these determinations the systems parameters were defined, as were the requirements for research and development to obtain the components required for the producing systems.

The pre-established reliability goal indicated that approximately 96% of all failures must be eliminated. A systematic investigation of the problem revealed that the most prevalent failures were:

a. Complete failure of the resistor, involving cracks or burnouts in the carbon coating, cracks in ceramic cores, and loose cap-lead connections;
b. Major shifts in resistance values, either permanent or intermittent, involving cracks in the coating, and poor connections at the terminations and cap-lead joint.

Causes of these failures were determined to be:

a. Burnouts: directly associated with localized excessive current density, resulting from chips in the helixed film, thin spots due to uneven removal of carbon in the rubbing operation, and to migration of carbon resulting from chemical reactions to ionic contaminants.
b. Cracking of carbon coating: due to unequal expansion under temperature change, the presence of moisture, or lacquer and plastic in contact with the carbon coating.
c. Poor connection between the cap and terminal wire: due in part to improper assembly, but also inherent in the swaging and upsetting process used in manufacture.

PRODUCT REDESIGN

When the sources of failure and their causes were determined, it was then possible to establish the basis for an improved product design and a better production process. The new design is illustrated in Fig. 12-4. The main design criteria were:

a. Uniform carbon film on the ceramic core.
b. No lacquer or other foreign substance in contact with the carbon film.
c. An air space between the carbon coating and the protective covering.
d. Termination to be provided by a pure metallic film.
e. Connection of the caps and terminal wires by welding.

These specifications were related to the manufacturing process and feasible processing technology. Further parameters for the producing system were specified as follows:

a. Continuous rather than intermittent processing.
b. Short cycle time for producing one unit.
c. Elimination of contamination by (a) and (b) and by elimination of manual handling.

d. Improved consistency in all operations.
e. Elimination of the rubbing operation by helixing to the final resistance value.
f. Detection of chips and thin spots in the carbon film during the manufacturing operations and automatic elimination of units possessing these defects.

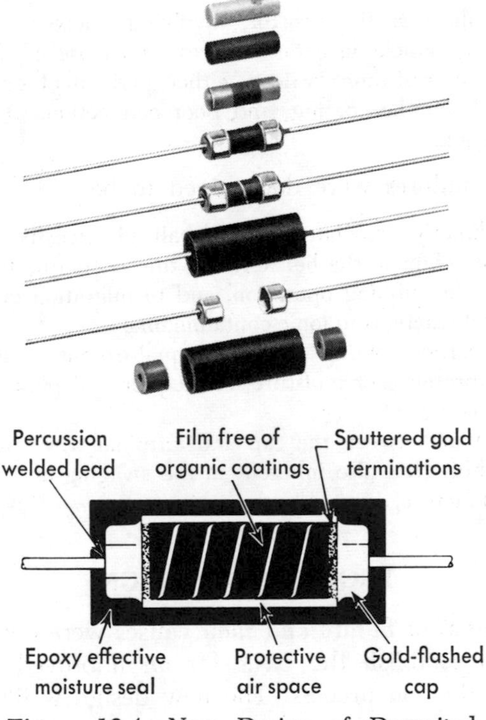

Figure 12-4. New Design of Deposited-Carbon Resistor Developed for High Reliability and Automation (Photographs of Sequential Assembly Top, Diagram Below). In the photograph, top to bottom: ceramic core; carbon-coated core; sputtered-gold termination; capped resistor; helixed resistor; encapsulated resistor; cap-lead assemblies; epoxy shell and pellets.

g. Feedback control at critical points in the process, with a minimum lag time between performance of critical operations, evaluation of performance, and corrective adjustment of the operation.

These sets of specifications logically lead to further specifications:

a. An integrated but flexible production line.
b. Completely automated or mechanized operations and handling of materials.
c. Completely automatic setup of each operation (or machine).
d. Automatic feedback control at critical operations.
e. Automatic monitoring of quality and inspection.
f. Automatic inventory control and programing of production.

A large number of factors were of necessity considered and interrelated in reaching the decisions implicit in the above listings. Some of these are presented in Fig. 12-5. A synthesis of interrelated factors allowed further specification of the system characteristics: It should:

a. Produce at the rate of 1200 units per hour.
b. Be flexible—produce four different power sizes (¼, ½, 1 and 2 watt capacity) and a wide range of resistance values.
c. Provide for completely automatic adjustment of individual operations when the production program is shifted.
d. Utilize a continuous-process carbon-coating furnace with all subsequent operations performing on a demand basis.
e. Provide for parts inventory between operations to obtain further flexibility and to decrease sensitivity of the integrated line to short interruptions in output of individual operations.
f. Utilize a digital computer for process control and program management.

Alternative processing technology was considered, preliminary selections made, and research and development undertaken to determine practicability of the processing methods desired. As the system was further designed, so were the detailed components for the individual operations.

SYSTEM REDESIGN

The carbon-coating operation was changed from batch to continuous processing, with feedback control used to hold temperature at a constant predetermined level and to control gas composition as a gross control variable and feed rate as a fine control variable. Variability in carbon film deposition was to be held to less than $\pm 5\%$. The measuring point for the feedback control was established close to the point of exit of the coated cores from the furnace, and a computer program was to be used to perform nonparametric statistical quality control analysis, plot control charts, calculate corrections for furnace operation, and to generate orders to adjust feed control and/or gas composition.

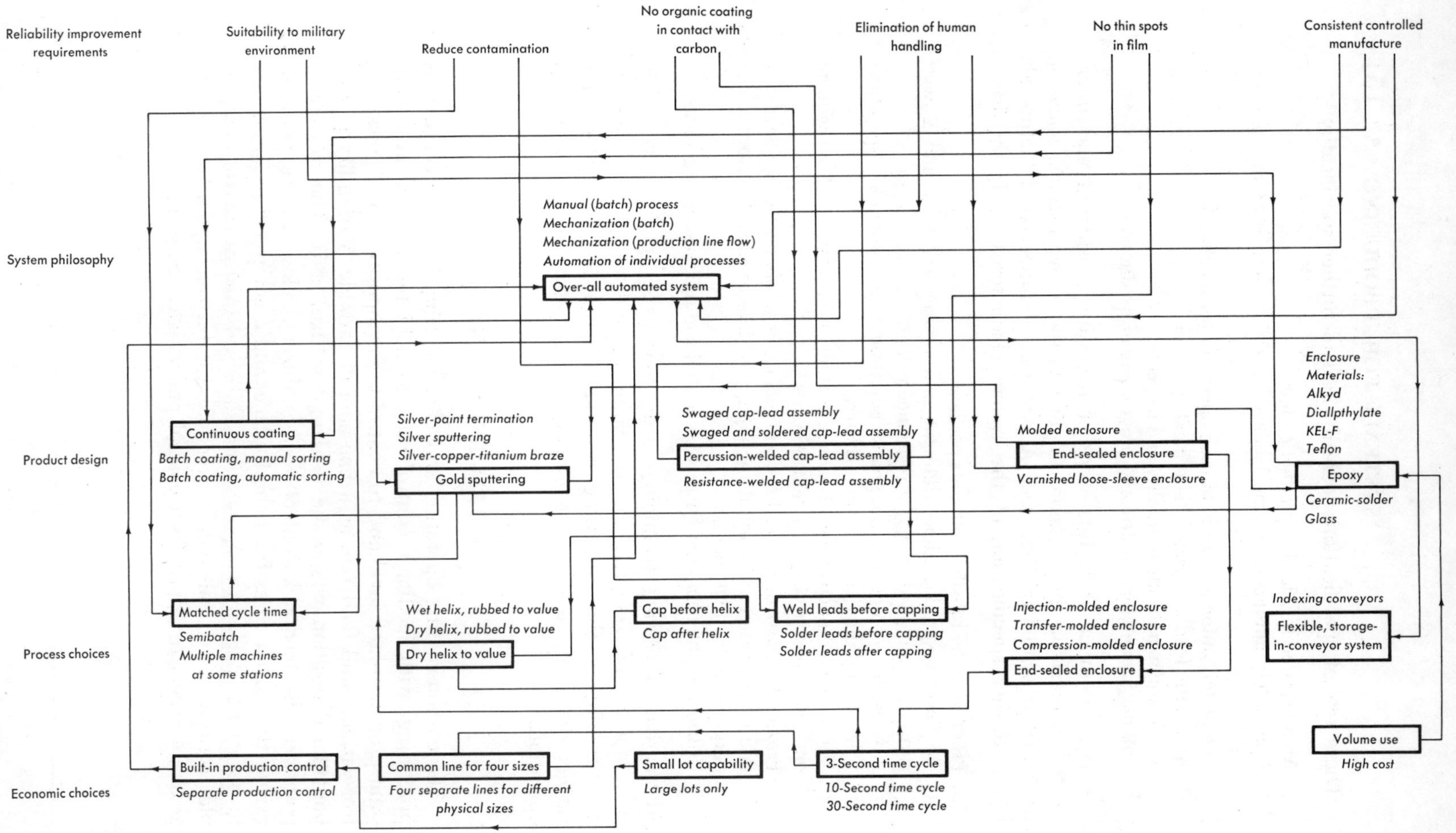
Reliability improvement requirements
Suitability to military environment
Reduce contamination
No organic coating in contact with carbon
Elimination of human handling
No thin spots in film
Consistent controlled manufacture
System philosophy
Manual (batch) process
Mechanization (batch)
Mechanization (production line flow)
Automation of individual processes
Over-all automated system
Product design
Continuous coating
Batch coating, manual sorting
Batch coating, automatic sorting
Silver-paint termination
Silver sputtering
Silver-copper-titanium braze
Gold sputtering
Swaged cap-lead assembly
Swaged and soldered cap-lead assembly
Percussion-welded cap-lead assembly
Resistance-welded cap-lead assembly
Molded enclosure
End-sealed enclosure
Varnished loose-sleeve enclosure
Enclosure
Materials:
Alkyd
Diallpthylate
KEL-F
Teflon
Epoxy
Ceramic-solder
Glass
Process choices
Matched cycle time
Semibatch
Multiple machines
at some stations
Wet helix, rubbed to value
Dry helix, rubbed to value
Dry helix to value
Cap before helix
Cap after helix
Weld leads before capping
Solder leads before capping
Solder leads after capping
Injection-molded enclosure
Transfer-molded enclosure
Compression-molded enclosure
End-sealed enclosure
Indexing conveyors
Flexible, storage-in-conveyor system
Economic choices
Built-in production control
Separate production control
Common line for four sizes
Four separate lines for different physical sizes
Small lot capability
Large lots only
3-Second time cycle
10-Second time cycle
30-Second time cycle
Volume use
High cost

Various alternatives for the termination were considered and evaluated. Metallic paint had the principal disadvantage of a long curing

---

Figure 12-5. (Opposite) Diagram of the Interrelationships Involved in the Chief Decisions on the Deposited-Carbon Resistor Project: Reliability requirements across top; unaccepted choices in italic; four horizontal rows of decisions by type (left). The basic reliability requirement demanding reduction of contamination led directly to two different decisions connected with the process choice: matched cycle times for individual machines so as to reduce inventory between stations and therefore avoid exposure to airborne sources of contamination; welding cap-lead assemblies before capping to avoid contamination by flux splashes or weld splashes. The decision to eliminate human handling (for reliability) favored percussion welded cap-lead assemblies instead of solder-type assemblies which might have necessitated manual operations. The elimination of human handling also favored an end-seal type of enclosure as contrasted to the conventional molding techniques normally requiring manual loading or unloading from molds. The desire for elimination of organic coatings from the carbon film assisted in the decision for an end-seal enclosure. The desire for consistent, controlled manufacture, together with the elimination of human handling, dictated an over-all automatically controlled system. This consistency requirement also forced the decision for continuous coating and for percussion welded cap-lead assemblies as contrasted to resistance welded assemblies. The requirement for no thin spots in the film dictated both the continuous coating and dry helixing to value.

Each of these decisions stimulated by basic reliability requirements, however, in turn limited other choices. For example, having chosen to helix the resistor to value, it became necessary to cap before helixing since the application of the resistor cap to the terminated resistor would change the resistance value appreciably. This, in turn, further limited the choice of methods for applying leads in the cap-lead assembly. Similarly, the choice of an end-seal type enclosure immediately limited the choices of materials to the epoxy, ceramic and solder, or glass and together with other factors, assisted in the choice of epoxy.

Economic factors entered also. The necessity for small lot capability, inherent in the North Carolina Works operation, required the built-in production control eventually utilized in this production line; and this in turn assisted in the decision to provide an over-all automated system as contrasted to batch or semi-automated techniques. A production-capacity analysis of the resistors indicated that a single production line with 3-second cycle time would probably be adequate. However, the requirements were split between four physical sizes of resistors so that the economic choice had to be made between a single line with 3-second cycle time and automatic changeover between sizes, as compared to four separate lines of longer cycle time. The choice of the single line in turn favored the over-all automated system. The 3-second cycle time, thus chosen, favored the choice of gold sputtering, as contrasted to paint-type terminations which require considerably longer process intervals.

time, originally 16 hours but finally reduced to 1½ hours, which was incompatible with the basic requirements for continuous and automatic production. Gold sputtering was finally selected—not only because of the technology allowing easy integration of the operation into the production system, but also because of improved adherence of the gold to the carbon film and superior resistance and noise characteristics.

Percussion welding was used to join the caps and terminal wires. The caps were gold plated to provide a superior contact between the caps and the gold-sputtered terminations on the carbon-coated cores. The cap-terminal units were attached to the cores before the helixing

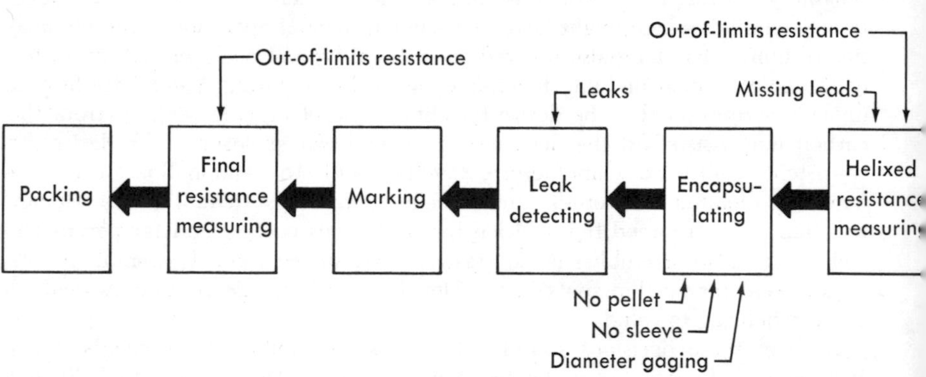

Figure 12-6. A Block Diagram of the Line Showing Its Inspection Functions. The actual characteristics used for rejection are indicated, but they often include several different defects. The less-than-75% length rejection includes high resistance of the cap-to-body junction, gross damage to the core, wrong core resistance value. An abrupt change in the rate of resistance change at helixing

operation to allow for shifts in resistance due to capping and to facilitate helixing to final resistance value.

The helixing operation was to cut a helix into the carbon film of the necessary pitch and length so that the resistance value of the units would be controlled to within 1%. This operation was to be performed without the use of coolants. The feedback control was to be provided in two parts: (1) during the helixing operation where the final resistance was controlled and where the rate of change in resistance during helixing was used to detect and reject cores with defective carbon coating, and (2) after the helixing operation, where measurement of resistance immediately following the encapsulation operation provided correction for small changes in resistance that might arise from the elevated temperatures of the operations.

Encapsulation was achieved by placing a loose fitting plastic sleeve over the resistor, into which were heat sealed plastic plugs at each end. The final assembly would be tested for airtightness by emersion in heated water, containing a wetting agent, and by the detection of air bubbles by photoelectric bubble monitors. As the water heats the assembly and the air enclosed between the core and the plastic capsule, leaks will be indicated by bubbles caused by air forced out of the heated capsule.

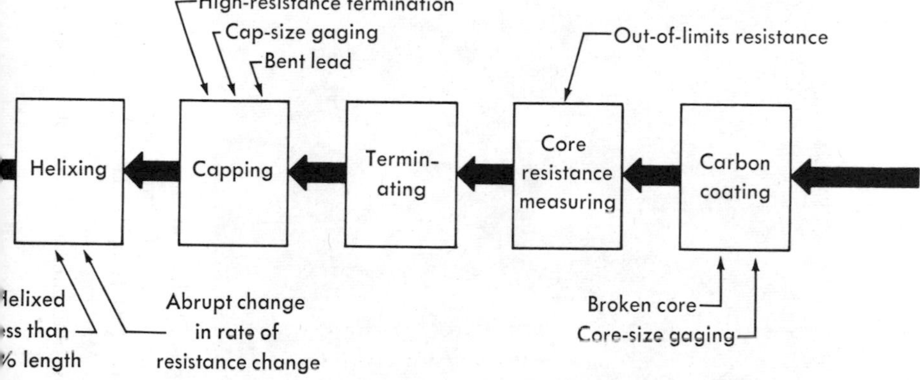

could be the result of thin spots, metallic spots, chipping, sooty spots. A leak could mean a pin hole, caps not seated, no pellet or defective pellets. A failure at the final resistance measuring station could be no sleeve, epoxy on the resistive film or instability.

After the encapsulated units are checked for airtightness and dried, the manufacturing and size identification data are automatically printed on the outer surface, and they are packaged for shipment. A schematic diagram of the new process is shown in Fig. 12-6, and an artist's rendition in Fig. 12-7.

SYSTEM CONTROL

In addition to the use of systems design concepts and methodology to redesign a product and the manufacturing system for automatic production of piece parts, the present example illustrates a unique application of a small scale, general purpose digital computer for controlling

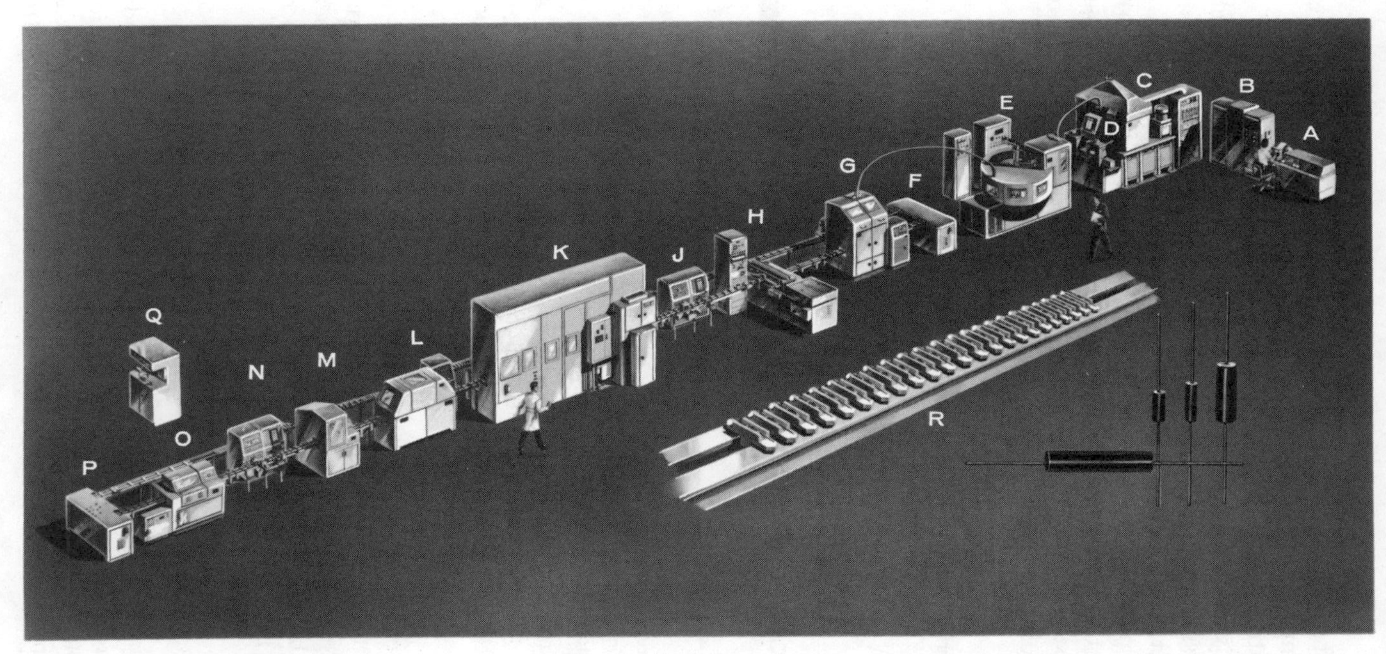

Figure 12-7. Machine Stations in the Automated Production Line for Manufacturing Deposited-Carbon Resistors. Legend: A. Computer, B. Output-input control station, C. Coating station, D. First inspection station, E. Terminating station, F. Conveyor control equipment, G. Capping station, H. Helixing station, J. Second inspection station, K. Encapsulating station, L. Leak detector station, M. Marking station, N. Third inspection station, O. Packing station, P. Conveyor control equipment, Q. Cap-lead welding machine, R. Detail of conveyor line.

the entire system. This control includes the individual feedback controls previously mentioned, and the following; the statistical quality control of critical operations; the control of inventory and adjustment of operations to accommodate changes within the process as production lots and product characteristics are changed; and the determination of what products are to be produced, in what quantities and when—based upon order requirements fed randomly to the computer. This degree of control requires a carefully designed information system as an integral part of the automated producing system. The information system requires the

TABLE 12-1

Types of Signals of the Control System

Operation	Function	Linking Equipment	Types of Signal
	PRINCIPAL SIGNALS		
Carbon Coating (Furnace)	Temperature readings	Input	Analog, 10 volts or less
	Heat control	Output	8-bit binary
	Core speed control	Output	6-bit binary
	Gas flow control	Output	11-bit binary
Core Resistance Measuring	Resistance readings	Input	Analog, 10 volts or less
	Measurement set value	Output	2-bit binary
Helixing	Resistance set value	Output	8-digit binary-coded decimal
	Helix pitch setting	Output	8-bit binary
Helixed Resistance Measuring	Resistance readings	Input	Analog, +1 to −1 volt
	Resistance set value	Output	4-digit binary-coded decimal
Marking	Code information	Output	6-digit binary-coded decimal
Final Resistance Measuring	Resistance readings	Input	Analog, +1 to −1 volt
	Resistance set value	Output	4-digit binary-coded decimal
	MINOR SIGNALS		
	Size	Output	2-bit binary
	End of lot, time to measure temperature,[a] resistor is present	Input	1-bit binary
	Accept-reject with order for next resistor[b]	Output	2-bit binary

[a] This signal which causes the computer to read-in the binary signal representing the furnace temperature is generated by a simple timer, manually set, usually for intervals of about 10 minutes.

[b] The computer's analysis of a resistance reading results in a signal to the measuring station to bring up the next resistor and to accept or reject the measured resistor. Absence of a pulse in accept-reject bit causes rejection (a fail-safe provision).

sensing of critical processing characteristics, their translation to the language of the computer, the communication and timing of this information to the computer, the evaluation of the information relative to pre-established criteria, the making of decisions concerning what should or should not be done to adjust the system and the generation, transmission, and execution of adjustment orders. The information obtained by

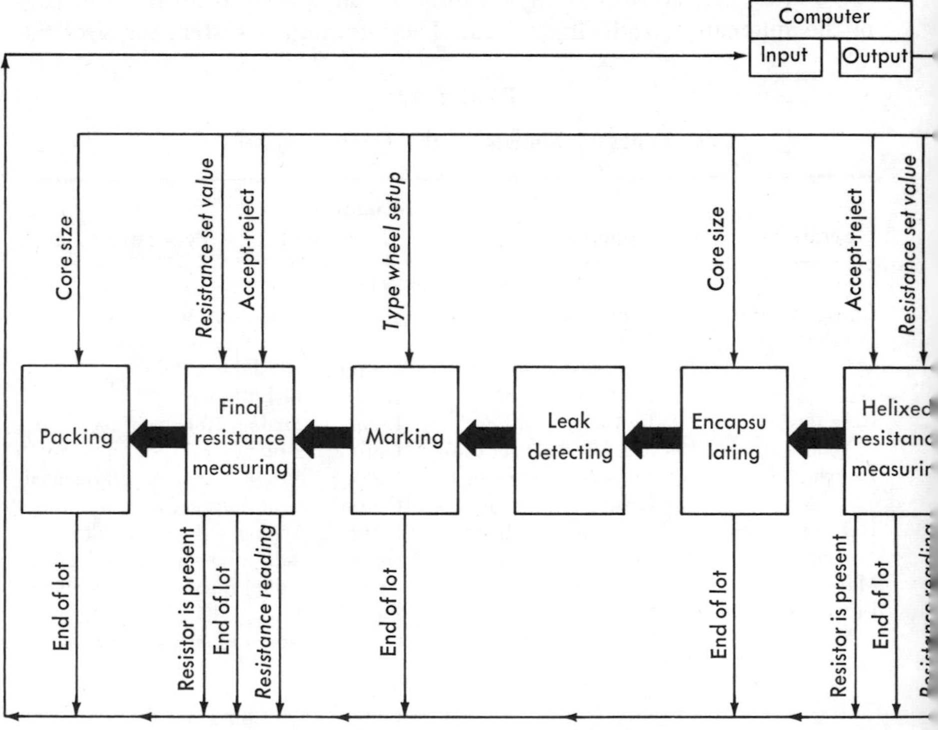

Figure 12-8. Signals of the Control System and Stations Which They Serve (principal signals in italic).

monitoring the process and the signals sent to the process for achieving control are indicated in Table 12-1 and Fig. 12-8. Interposed between the computer and the production system is specially designed input-output equipment to control the acquisition of data, to accumulate it, and to translate signals into the necessary form. In addition to the above information being fed into, processed, and fed out of the computer, data concerning production orders, manual intervention, and internally stored programs are involved in the control systems.

SUMMARY

The *systems* approach to the design (or redesign) of systems for producing is an extremely important aspect of over-all improvement function endeavors. There are many examples of automation, as applied to

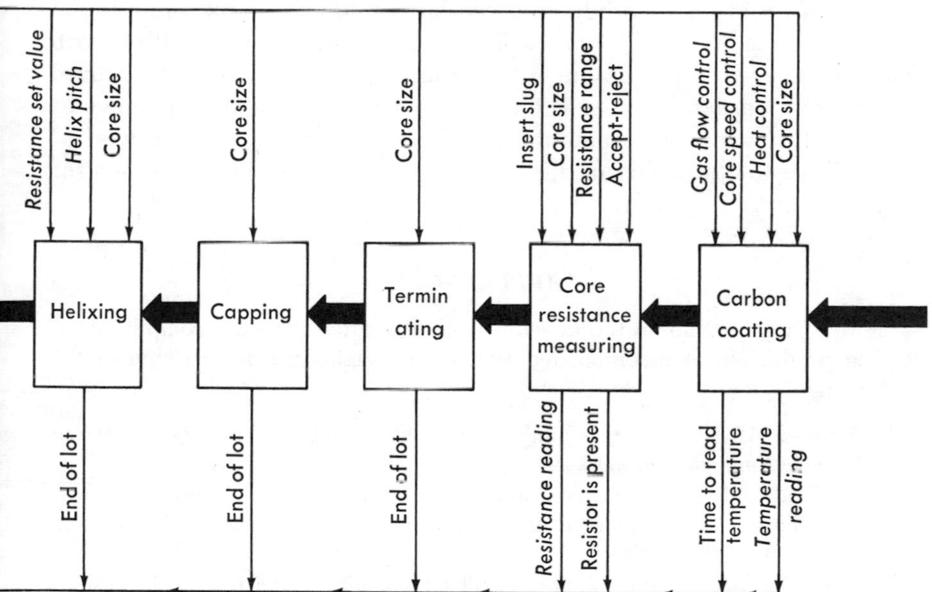

both automatic operations and automatic processes, in present day industry. Few of these applications, however, have had the benefit of true systems design as implicit in the example we have discussed. This area of technology, systems design, has had wider application in communications, electronic and defense systems design. Its application to problems of manufacturing, other than in some processing or flow-type industries, has been very limited. It is of growing importance and should become more commonplace in the near future.

The objective of presenting the foregoing example, which was presented in only summary form, obviously was *not* to illustrate how precision deposited-carbon resistors should be made. The objective *was* to illustrate the essence of systems design by means of an interesting real-world example. The reader should recognize the basic procedure used, and he should also visualize the great amount of creative engineering work required to execute the project. The original objectives of improving quality by a factor of ten was more than achieved. The unit manufacturing costs were also substantially reduced, as indicated by the fact that the entire investment will be liquidated by savings in production cost in a period of two to three years.

Not all problems of production can be considered in the same broad manner as our example. Some will be much more confined. Others will encompass even larger producing systems. The proper approach will be geared to a consideration of the entire system (as presented in previous chapters), and the determination of which problems should be worked on relative to the needs of the organization and the opportunities for improvement.

REFERENCES

Further information on the developments associated with the computer-controlled production of precision deposited-carbon resistors can be found in the following:

1. Howard H. Arnold, "Reliability: A Benefit of Automation," *The Western Electric Engineer,* January 1962, p. 4.
2. H. H. Arnold, "A Computer-Controlled Production Line," *Control Through Information,* Management Bulletin 24, American Management Association, New York, 1963, p. 14.
3. James H. Boatwright, "Computer-Plotted Control Charts," *The Western Electric Engineer,* January 1962, p. 20.
4. Marion D. Clark, Harold K. Jordan, and Robert C. Ward, "Precision Carbon Coating by Computer Control," *The Western Electric Engineer,* April 1962, p. 21.
5. "A Computer-Controlled Production Line," *The Western Electric Engineer,* January 1962, p. 2.
6. Albert R. Fairchild and Marion D. Clark, "Termination by Sputtering," *The Western Electric Engineer,* July 1962, p. 2.
7. John C. Huffman and Henry D. Mitchell, Jr., "Automatic Leak Detection," *The Western Electric Engineer,* April 1962, p. 28.
8. Donald E. Johnson and Robert C. Ward, "Systems Engineering," *The Western Electric Engineer,* January 1962, p. 11.

9. Harold K. Jordan and Carey W. McCachern, Jr., "Automatic Printer for Cylindrical Components," *The Western Electric Engineer,* April 1962, p. 16.
10. "Making Deposited-Carbon Resistors," *Automation,* September 1961, p. 61.
11. R. N. Marshall, H. H. Arnold, and J. D. Schiller, "A Totally Integrated Computer-Controlled Production Line at Western Electric Company," Eighth Annual E.D.P. Conference, American Management Association, New York, February 26, 1962. (Not published.)
12. Henry D. Mitchell, Jr., "Capping Deposited-Carbon Resistors," *The Western Electric Engineer,* January 1963, p. 31.
13. James L. Owens, Donald E. Johnson, and Robert C. Ward, "Computer-Controlled Helixing," *The Western Electric Engineer,* July 1962, p. 40.
14. J. D. Schiller and H. H. Arnold, "Developing a Multimachine Complex," *Automation,* September 1961, p. 52.
15. "The Tyranny of Large Numbers," a 16 mm. sound, color movie illustrating the development of the automated production facility for manufacture of precision deposited-carbon resistors. Running time 16 minutes. Available from Western Electric Company.

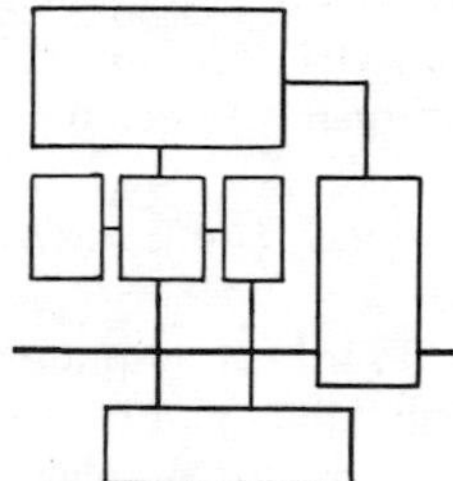

CHAPTER 13

DESIGN OF SYSTEMS FOR MANAGING

FROM THE EARLIEST DAYS of scientific management the problems of developing systems for managing have received considerable attention. F. W. Taylor's original concern with relating engineering and management stemmed from his recognition that management did not really manage—they did not have the necessary information to preplan what should be done, and to develop a definite and detailed plan of action to be followed in the execution of the work required to produce the desired production. Taylor's subsequent investigation led to the development of a rational plan of action—a *system* of shop management. The keynote of this *system* was to plan the work and then work the plan. The implication was:

1. A complete plan of action could be pre-established.
2. This plan would represent an efficient way of accomplishing the end results and the necessary parts of the total activity.
3. The plan would be used as the guide for taking action.
4. Action and results would continually be compared with the plan and evaluated.
5. Corrective action would be taken to obtain efficient operation (that is, deviations from the plan would signal the need for management attention to either change the activities to adhere to the plan or to modify the plan).
6. Final results would be evaluated so that future planning could be done more effectively.

The same basic procedure is fundamental to management efficiency in all activities. Key features are recognized in the management cycle:

1. Planning
2. Organizing
3. Execution
4. Evaluation and corrective action

The *planning* step involves determining basic requirements for accomplishment and developing detailed plans. This step results in the design of a plan which defines all of the necessary subplans and measures these in appropriate terms. The *organizing* step involves marshaling necessary resources and fitting new plans into other plans and commitments. It results in a modification of both new and old plans in order to integrate all plans into a grand plan of action. The *execution* step involves releasing authority for carrying out the plan, according to time requirements and restrictions of other commitments. It provides the specific authority for performing work, purchasing materials, assigning manpower, using equipment, etc. The *evaluation and corrective action* step involves continual comparison of actual versus planned performance, and taking appropriate corrective action—an evaluation of what is happening compared with what should be happening. If all goes according to the plan (and if the plan is a good one), no corrective action is necessary—operation becomes routine. However, if things do not proceed according to plan, an exception occurs. Management is alerted to determine why this has happened and what needs to be done to return operations to a condition of stability relative to the plan. This allows *management by exception.*

Business and industry literally are kept alive and functioning by systems. Only very small organizations can operate by informal personal direction, and even in these cases the rudiments of systems for managing are essential. As these organizations grow, the systems must become more formalized in order for the organization and its management to operate effectively. The life blood of these systems is information—and until recently, paperwork.

Management systems have developed since the early days of scientific management to include all of the basic functional areas. In the production area are systems of production planning and control, labor cost control, materials management and inventory control, quality control, etc. In personnel are systems for hiring, training, promotion, payment, payroll deductions, etc. In marketing are systems for promoting sales, distribution, advertising, sales evaluation, etc. In finance are systems for accounting, cost control, budgeting, profit planning, investment analysis, etc.

All of these systems represent plans for achieving the desired results of the organization's activities. They are plans representing the formalization of policy so that the involved activities can be executed in a routine manner and decisions can be made according to rules implicit in the individual systems. Situations not programed into the system are handled on an exception basis.

The development of various systems formalizing the managing and operating policies of functional activities has resulted in substantial increases in paperwork and clerical operations. Clerical employees in American industry have increased approximately twice as fast as production employees during the period from 1950 to 1960. Not all of this increase has been caused by further formalization of functional systems. Some of it has resulted from increasing demands for information and reports by various government agencies. Some has been caused by increased size and complexity of business. The combined effect, however, has been the development of a paperwork jungle and a tangle of overformalized procedures which have sprung up without due consideration of the organization's *total* needs.

Fortunately, the second and third industrial revolutions have come forth with developments in information systems design and a variety of equipment for information processing that represent potential solutions to the problem. Programs of paperwork simplification, forms control, procedures analysis, clerical work measurement, forms design—and computers—have gone a long way toward solving the problems of an organization becoming bogged down in paperwork and systems. Several breakthroughs in the design of effective information systems, which fully utilize the concepts of systems design, computers, and related information systems technology, have occurred in the past few years. These developments allow mechanization of existing systems, and more importantly, they allow the designing of entirely new systems from a total organizational point of view, which was impossible or uneconomical previously.

The greatest benefit derived from computers and information systems technology, as far as management efficiency is concerned, is the design of new, broader, and integrated systems for managing. Early applications of computers for business data processing were associated with mechanization of clerical procedures. More recent developments are directed toward management needs and the design of unified information-control systems.

IMPACT OF COMPUTERS

The impact of computer-based systems design relative to management control is clearly indicated by the following quotation appearing in *Time* magazine.[1] The rising U.S. economy is being discussed, and reference is made to the impact of computerized management control systems as a means of achieving improved management.

> Companies are better managed and better prepared, wisely make many decisions not for the short but for the long term. The computer population has grown from 300 to 11,000 in eight years, and is forecasting demand faster and more accurately, making sharp swings in inventory unnecessary. As a result, recessions are becoming less frequent, and periods of prosperity are lengthening.

The way in which better inventory management is made possible by the development of improved control systems is illustrated by Westinghouse Electric Company's approach to the problem.[2] This company has a teletype network serving 265 company operations in 188 cities in the United States and Canada. All of these facilities can be placed in almost immediate contact, through a switching center, with the order-processing and inventory-control center located in Pittsburgh. This center is devoted entirely to the automatic processing of teletyped orders and the managing of inventory on a company-wide basis, using an IBM 1401–1405 computer and data processing installation. At the heart of this installation is a random access file of inventory records for all standard industrial products in warehouses or factories. The file also contains the billing and shipping addresses of thousands of regular customers.

Orders originate by teletype from any of nearly 100 sales offices. These orders are received in the order-processing and inventory-control center, via the switching center, and are converted from the teletype tape directly to punched cards. These cards are then fed into the computer system where the desired items are located in the random access disc-file inventory records. If an item is out of stock at the warehouse nearest the customer, it is searched for at other warehouses and the factory, and shipment is ordered from the closest location to minimize transportation costs.

Once the required items have been located, the computer issues the order instructions on punched cards which are converted to punched tape for teletype transmission to the appropriate warehouse. The processed order tape, when received by the warehouse, authorizes shipment of the items and is used to automatically generate the labels, bills of lading, packing lists, and completely extended invoices ready for mailing. Within the computer, the processing of each order involves updating of inventory records and automatic checking of inventory levels in comparison with reorder points to determine if reordering is necessary. If a reorder point has been reached, appropriate economic lot size formulas are brought into play to calculate the proper replenishment quantity, and a card authorizing manufacture of the necessary items is produced. Sales statistic cards are also produced by the computer for each order processed.

The speed achieved by the Westinghouse system is almost unbelievable—a maximum elapsed time of 15 minutes from the dispatching of a teletype order from a sales office to the receipt of complete shipping instructions at the selected warehouse.

Prior to the establishment of the order processing and inventory-control center each sales office transmitted orders to the nearest warehouse, usually in writing. These orders would be processed by the warehouse clerical staff. Orders would be compared with local inventory records, shipping documents would be prepared, and billing information would be forwarded to the appropriate accounting office. Out-of-stock items would be located and shipped from other warehouses, which required extensive telephone and teletype communications among the various warehouses. Stock control was effected by stock-control groups at individual warehouses with coordination provided by the manufacturing plant.

The results of centralized order processing and inventory control have been substantial. Rapid processing of orders and better control of national inventories has allowed sizable reductions in inventory and has made unnecessary the number of warehouses previously required. Overnight delivery from factory stock has also reduced the need for area warehousing. Seven of the original 26 field warehouses have been closed and three others have been reduced to one half of their previous size. An example of the extent of stock reduction is provided by integral-horsepower a-c motors, which is a major product line. The inventory of these items has been reduced to 35% of the former levels (a 65% reduction). Customer service has at the same time been greatly improved.

Significant direct cost savings have been realized from elimination of stock control, order handling, and accounting in the many field locations previously performing these functions independently. However, the real payoff in the view of Westinghouse management has been in the areas of indirect savings—improved cash flow (a savings of five days in the time from order receipt to billing), reduced but more adequate inventory levels, and better customer service.

SYSTEMS FOR OPERATING CONTROL

For many organizations the most important single aspect of their operation is manufacturing. It is logical, therefore, that many management systems have been developed within this area of activity and that the power of computers and information systems technology has been applied to these problems. Many companies have become interested in achieving real-time control of their operations in order to effect better management of their organizations. Extensive interest is indicated in the following comment appearing in the business section of *Time* magazine.[3]

Management by Computer

In the midst of a corporate board meeting, the chief executive officer flips a switch, and instantly a screen overhead lights up with the company's profit-and-loss statement, tallied up to the minute. Another flip of the switch, and the screen glows with a graph disclosing just what progress the company has made up to the moment on Contract X.

This Brave New World technology is now a possibility in a score of major U.S. corporations, which are deep in a new phase of computer technology known as management information systems. The goal of these systems: to give a manager instant reports on the latest developments in every phase of his business.

Before computers, the dozens of departments within a major corporation kept independent records, the essentials of which might filter up to top management with agonizing slowness. When computers first came along, all they did was to speed up the flow of information within departments. Sometimes, by generating too many new reports, they actually gummed up the works. Management information systems seek to feed current information from every department of a company into a central computer network which, after correlating progress in all areas, will feed back fresh instructions.

So far, no company has developed a system to do all its basic thinking for it, but this may come. Some new approaches:

► General Precision has a new system called LOCS (Librascope Operations Control System), which it claims cuts its costs $1,000,000 a year by tightening up controls throughout the company.

► Sperry Rand, with its new PACC (Product Administration and Contract

Control) system, now has nine people handling data-processing assignments that previously occupied 201 employees.

► Standard Oil of New Jersey is in the middle of a four-year installation of its URS (Uniform Reporting System). URS will keep worldwide tabs on all Standard's "dollars, barrels and people," and for management's benefit will separate out the statistics vital to top-level decision making.

► Lockheed Corp., in collaboration with RCA, is building a system called ADA (Automatic Data Acquisition). Under ADA, an employee on the production line tells the central computer when he has finished a given job, promptly gets back orders on what to tackle next.

All of these systems share a basic structure, which is similar to the conventional noncomputerized management control systems, but also allows for minimum time lag in the monitoring and evaluation of performance, and in taking corrective action when necessary. Real-time control implies that activities are monitored and evaluated while they are taking place and that corrective action can be effected without delay. Real-time control is usually attempted by supervisory and management monitoring of activities and redirection of efforts where difficulties seem to be developing. In these situations the human is the processor for comparing what is observed with some pre-established plan, and the human is the corrective device for deciding and issuing appropriate orders and instructions to achieve proper performance. Real-time control can only be achieved by continual on-the-spot observation. With small businesses it is often possible for the owner or manager to be completely informed of what is and should be happening and to control operations very effectively—thus approaching real-time control. With larger operations the need for formalizing procedures and for automatic monitoring of performance is essential if real-time control is desired.

Computer-based control systems attempt to duplicate the essence of human control, but in a more rapid and reliable manner. This is done by:

1. Using pre-established plans for guiding activities
2. Storing these within the computer memory
3. Providing for input of information relating the performance being achieved
4. Comparing actual performance with the stored plan
5. Evaluating performance relative to pre-established decision rules stored within the computer memory
6. Issuing instructions for further activity based upon the stored plan and the application of decision rules
7. Accumulating performance measures to relate how the production system

is operating, and to allow management to be informed of performance and difficulties.

This general scheme was involved in the computer-controlled automated production system for manufacture of precision deposited-carbon resistors which was described in Chapter 12. Operating control systems for multiple product manufacturing systems become considerably more complex.

When a product is ordered, if it is a new product, it must first be designed. If the product has previously been produced, the records are already available. From the desired quantity of the product the necessary subassemblies, components, and parts can be determined. The materials required, which components and parts are to be purchased, which are to be manufactured, and the exact operation-by-operation manufacturing procedure can be determined. Allowances for shrinkage in quantities due to spoilage at each operation, rejection of parts at inspections, and other losses will be included in the quantity requirements. Each step in manufacture, including issuance of materials and tooling, each manufacturing operation, inspection, assembly, and testing operation, the moving of parts and materials, and all the other necessary activities must be planned. The time requirements for all of these activities must also be determined, both relative to the requirements for performing each activity to produce the necessary quantities, and for the time-phasing of the activities in order to complete the final product prior to a given date.

Once the above planning has been completed, and necessary parts, materials, and tooling have been ordered, the plan must be integrated into the activities already underway or scheduled for production. The previous schedules must be adjusted to allow for production of the new order while still providing for execution of the work for previous commitments. Deviations from the planned performance will also require modification of the schedule. This is a highly dynamic situation, characterized by continual adjustments in an attempt to make efficient use of resources while still meeting commitments for completion of production for all orders underway.

The actual initiation of work activities is geared to the schedule by a dispatching activity, which is greatly influenced by current knowledge of all shop activities as they are progressing in comparison with all scheduled activities. The schedule is the master plan. Dispatching allows execution of work according to the plan.

Computerized operating control systems provide for developing the basic plan, storing this along with other plans in the computer memory, and withdrawing the plan, as needed, in a form that will specify all requirements for producing a given product in any desired quantity. This output is then used as the basis for input into the memory containing the current schedule and inventory. The two are compared, and by the application of built-in decision rules a new schedule is developed which incorporates both the previous and the new requirements. Materials, parts, supplies, and tooling can be reserved from inventory or ordered, and the scheduling of all work can be performed automatically.

The complexity of scheduling by computer can be appreciated by considering only a few of the decision alternatives that are continually involved in the scheduling and rescheduling activities.[4]

"Decision rules are needed in order to determine when to:

1. Combine several orders to make larger lots in order to save set-up time.
2. Run similar jobs in sequence to reduce the amount of set-up time.
3. Run jobs with the same material to avoid cleaning up the chips at the machine.
4. Overlap operations—that is, run the same job simultaneously on two or more machines.
5. Change the sequence or the routing of parts through the machines.
6. Change the type of machine used for the particular operation.
7. Substitute different material for parts being run.
8. Run a different product which can substitute for the one desired.
9. Work overtime, subcontract, or use the tool room or facilities in another section of the plant.
10. Switch men from one machine to another or to a second-shift operation.
11. Borrow men from a different section of the plant for overloads.
12. Move material from one operation to the next as soon as each is completed.
13. Partially fabricate components ahead of critical operations.
14. Process partial orders or split lots."

The consequences of rescheduling and the application of formal decision rules considering factors such as those listed above can be evaluated by simulation, allowing for expected variability in performance and testing alternative schedules.

The effectiveness of a computerized operating control system will be greatly influenced by the speed with which information concerning happenings in the actual situation can be communicated to the computer, evaluated and made ready for guiding performance of the actual situation. A large-scale computer with random access memory is required, as is a system of data input which truly reflects the status of the situation being controlled. In some cases the input data may be automatically recorded by monitoring devices attached to production equipment. In other cases the input may be provided for by data-logging devices actuated by workers using precoded input cards at periodic intervals. The correct approach will depend upon the needs of the total system.

Operating control systems can be extended beyond just the manufacturing area. Some of the significant extensions would be related to cost reporting and control, manpower management, marketing, and forecasting. The objective of the extensions would be to approach the design of a total information and management control system for an entire organization. The operating control systems referred to in the *Time* quote approach this ideal in varying degrees. A completely integrated real-time management control system blanketing all facets of an organization is still in the future, but many constructive approaches are being made.

SUMMARY

One of the very fundamental concepts basic to the design of management control systems is to avoid a hardware orientation. The needs of the situation should determine the basic characteristics of the system, and then hardware should be selected or designed to meet the pre-established requirements. This approach is frequently not used, and the resulting systems usually fall far short of meeting the real needs of the organization. One example of a sound approach to management control systems design was outlined in Chapter 3 in the development of a computer-controlled reservation system by United Air Lines. The functional specifications for the system were developed in terms of the real needs for information and control. These were then translated to technical specifications which were used as the basis for determining hardware needs. No computer manufacturer could meet the performance requirements thus specified with equipment currently available or being developed. The equipment and the system had to be developed, and was developed by intercompany cooperation. The resulting control system is far superior to any that could have resulted from designing the system around existing equipment.

The economic justification for developing computer-based control systems is an important consideration and one that is intimately associated with the individual situation. It is extremely difficult to translate better management control into appropriate dollar values. It is much easier to calculate direct savings in clerical activities resulting from the installation of data-processing equipment. The final justification must compare direct cost savings and intangible benefits with the costs for designing, installing, and using the new system. Careful economic evaluation will frequently indicate that a partly manual system is preferable to a completely automatic system. In either case substantial benefits will result from the designing of the information-control system according to the real needs of the situation.

Continuing technological developments are affecting management control systems design efforts. New equipment and new techniques for achieving control are continually being developed. The application of control theory, which is a well-developed discipline in physical systems, is coming to have direct application in the design of management control systems. These concepts can and are being used to determine ways to achieve stability in the performance of the system being managed. The areas of activity which are incorporated in unified management control systems are continually being expanded, and complete organization-wide systems are in the offing.

REFERENCES

1. *Time,* May 31, 1963, p. 77.
2. R. C. Cheek, "A System for General Management Control," *Control Through Information,* Management Bulletin 24, American Management Association, New York, 1963, p. 5.
3. *Time,* December 21, 1962, pp. 67–68.
4. Alan J. Rowe, "Real-Time Control in Manufacturing," *Control Through Information,* Management Bulletin 24, American Management Association, New York, 1963, p. 36.

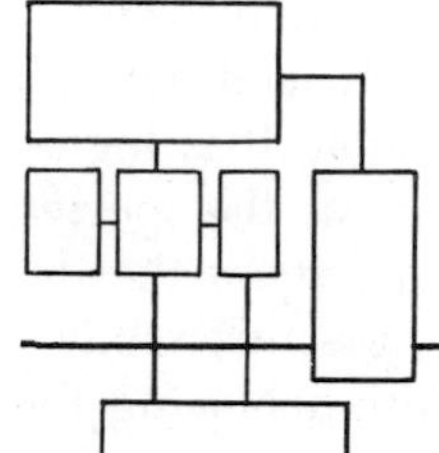

CHAPTER 14

INTRODUCING A NEW FUNCTION

So far we have been concerned with various approaches to an improvement function and with general background information concerning its use. We have seen several examples of extensive use of modern industrial engineering illustrative of improvement function activities. At this point we will shift our approach to a consideration of how improvement activities can be integrated into an operating organization. This will be done first by presenting an analysis of the problem of integrating operations research into the firm.[1] Although the presentation is directed toward the problems associated with O.R., the basic considerations are relevant in respect to the introduction of any new functional responsibility and activity. Basically, there are two options: the new activities and responsibilities might be assigned in whole or in part to existing segments of the organization or new organizational positions might be created for them. Obviously, there are many variations of these two basic approaches and many ways in which the final pattern might be developed. The correct approach will depend not only upon basic considerations of organization and human behavior but also upon the specific situation confronting the organization. The "personality" of the organization, the social and work mores, and the present organizational pattern (both formal and informal), will have a profound influence upon what is a correct or profitable course of action. We must also recognize the dynamic nature of organizational interaction. Things change with time, and correct timing is extremely important to the achievement of effective changes in organizational behavior.

Following this chapter we will briefly consider some of the characteristics of human behavior, particularly as they influence change—for change is always a part of improvement activities. Change is desired not for its own sake, but as a means of achieving continual improvement within the organization. Human nature is intimately intertwined with all organizational patterns and the behavior of the organization. It is highly important that the basic nature of human nature, as well as the specific conditions of a current situation, have a primary influence upon the development of patterns for bringing about *desirable* changes in organizational and individual behavior which are compatible with achieving the desired changes for improvement.

In several subsequent chapters we will present a series of case examples of the development of improvement activities. These have been selected to illustrate different facets of the quest for systematic and continuing improvement. They illustrate a variety of ways in which the improvement function has been brought to life. They are not intended to be patterns for the development of an improvement function within other organizations, for they are all evolutions relative to the needs of specific organizations at specific times. However, the general approaches to improvement should provide insight into the problems of developing profitable and individual approaches to the general problem of achieving continual and systematic improvement within any organization. A correct approach is a highly individual matter relative to the characteristics, personality, and needs of a given concern at a specific time.

Integration of Operations Research into the Firm

by **ALBERT H. RUBENSTEIN**

Professor of Industrial Engineering, the Technological Institute, Northwestern University

THREE phases are observable in the initiation and integration of a new staff function such as operations research into the firm.

First there is the introductory phase in which one or a few tentative overtures are made toward forming a group to carry on this new function or toward trying it on an experimental basis without commitment to a new department or group.

If the new function survives this phase—one in which sponsorship and the general auspices of the trial run are critical—a group may gradually be formed to carry it on as a full-time activity. This is the *second* or transitional phase.

A *third* phase—if it is ever reached by the new function—is its establishment as a continuing, routine company activity with no special consideration from top management that is not afforded to other important activities in the firm.

Many modern staff activities in the firm have passed through all three stages in the past few decades and are no longer considered new or unusual enough to occupy more than routine management attention. Industrial engineering, cost accounting, and production control are examples of such staff activities that have reached maturity in most progressive companies and which have been successfully integrated into the firm.

Other relatively new activities are still going through stages one or two in most firms although some of them appear to be well established. These might include quality control, controllership, market research, research and development, and integrated data processing, for example.

We must recognize, of course, that a particular function does not reach maturity simultaneously in all firms at once. For example, quality control in many firms may have been in stage three for years, but may not have completed stage one in many other firms in the same industries.

In each of these three phases, management has certain design decisions to make affecting the new activity which can strongly influence its success in that phase and its survival into the next.

Some of these decisions are minor tactical ones. They will have some influence on the success of particular projects and their results, but they may not be critical with respect to the ultimate success of the function. Some of these will be mentioned in passing, since they do have a cumulative importance. But this article will concentrate on a set of strategic decisions whose effect on the success of the new function can be direct and decisive.

Three sets of strategic design decisions make up the inputs to the new activity. They establish the conditions under which it will operate and the resources at its command.

They will be discussed in the following order, in connection with the operations research activity:

1. The *objectives and tasks* assigned to and undertaken by the operations research activity.
2. The *operating conditions* under which the operations research function is performed.
3. The *resources* assigned to the operations research activity.

OBJECTIVES AND TASKS

Under objectives and tasks, one may discern a hierarchy of decisions related to the motivation for initiating an operations research activity, the over-all objectives set for it, and the criteria for selecting and emphasizing specific projects.

When entering the first phase—which essentially amounts to flirting with the ultimate possibility of having a permanent operations research activity in the company—the motivations of the sponsors and their supporters are critical.

Is the sponsorship of an operations research activity motivated by the feeling that current methods of problem analysis in the firm are inadequate? Or is it less a question of adequacy than it is of convenience? For example, are the skills and procedures commonly employed by operations researchers available in the firm but not sufficiently accessible?

These motivations as well as the advertised objectives of the new activity should at least be clear in the minds of the sponsors of the group so that they can be logically and systematically translated into a basis for other strategic decisions such as project selection, organizational responsibility, effectiveness measurement, and so on.

Some of the confusion which has resulted from introduction of operations research and other new activities into the firm can be traced to a lack of a clear concept of the objectives of this activity *in* the firm.

In some instances the new activity was, incorrectly, viewed as a fire-fighting or emergency measure which would begin to pay off the day after it was initiated into the company. Disappointment with a failure to achieve this immediate goal has led to the quick death of the activity and, perhaps, a blocking of another attempt for some time to come.

If operations research is introduced primarily as a weapon in an organizational power struggle, its sponsors must recognize that it can not only fail to fire but can also backfire. A number of recent cases in the integrated data processing field illustrate this. The new activity was introduced as a move in a power struggle and backfired seriously—in two cases resulting in the termination of its proponents.

In the more general case—the one where power is not the issue—the necessity for careful consideration of objectives is also crucial. What is it that you want operations research to accomplish that is not now being accomplished in the firm? If this question can be answered in fairly specific terms, then the next step is to attempt to translate this statement of objectives into more precise terms—to develop criteria of effectiveness for the proposed activity.

In phase one—the flirtation or trial period—the criterion can be fairly simple and binary. For example: after the expenditure of so much time and effort (to be designated as a fair trial), does it look as though this activity has sufficient promise to carry it further?

One of the reasons for ultimate failure or unrealized potential of many such new activities is the unwillingness of its sponsors to establish and *use* clear criteria of their usefulness. No one is willing, for example, to say that this activity is or is not a good bet for further investment. Instead, in many cases, the activity either dies by default—through lack of budgetary provision for its continuance or continues by default—through lack of a decisive cut-off order.

In the latter phases, when operations research is evolving into a permanent, routine operation, the need for criteria of effectiveness continues. It is difficult, of course, to measure the gains from operations research or from similar activities such as quality control or research and development. This sometimes results in precipitous action in times when money is scarce or when sales and profits drop. For example, a company which spends a large amount of its cost dollar on engineering recently suffered a reduction in sales. One of the first activities cut out was the operations research group, despite the fact that it had been conducting a study attempting to reduce engineering costs.

The lack of ability to measure results completely in dollars and cents does not mean that evaluating the operations research function is a hopeless task. A number of operations research groups have recently reported dollar savings figures from specific projects. But the effectiveness of such an activity may not lie only in the direct annual dollar savings. Certainly in the third stage—the period of maturity

—there are many functions the progressive firm supports without asking for continual profit and loss figures. Research and development is one and quality control is another.

The point here is that if objectives are reasonable and clearly stated, it is possible to establish general criteria—some in dollars, some in other terms—that will provide control limits for the usefulness of the operations research activity. Such a strategy will provide the basis for changing objectives, if it appears that the criteria are unreasonable; or it may permit occasional redesign of the way that the operations research activity is organized and the conditions under which it operates.

If the objectives and effectiveness criteria for the operations research activity are properly stated, it should be possible to derive from them the general *project portfolio* for the activity and the specific projects to be undertaken.

If, for example, the objectives include only "cost savings in manufacturing" and the activity is to be evaluated on the basis of how much it saves each quarter or each year, then the project portfolio —the projects it works on at any given time—will be directed at short term cost savings in the factory.

If the objectives are broader and include general responsibility for "improvement of operations in the company"—then management must consider encouraging and supporting a much broader and longer-perspective program.

The important thing is that the people involved in operations research and others in the firm whose functions might be affected by operations research should be aware of the relative breadth and depth of mission assigned to the group. And there should be the opportunity to modify this mission and the project portfolio as the abilities of the operations research group change and its usefulness to the company is demonstrated.

One behavior of some operations research people in firms which are trying their wings in this field, is the absence of a clear strategy for gaining acceptance and achieving results in phases one or two. This, I believe, is one of the primary responsibilities of the sponsors of the new activity. Even in phase one, the person or people actually attempting to perform operations research may be new to the firm or at least new to the lofty corporate heights at which operations research is sometimes temporarily attached.

In these circumstances, the operations research technicians will probably not have a firm grasp of company-wide operations, corporate politics, and the personalities of the people in the firm who can boost it or knock it. It is here that sponsors who presumably have this knowledge can combine it with the analytical ability of the operations research people to evolve a project portfolio strategy that will assure survival into at least phase two.

Strangely, the analytical ability of the operations research man is seldom brought to bear on this problem, although it is no more complex than some of the others he tackles. In essence, it is a decision problem under risk, if his sponsor really knows the company, and under uncertainty if this knowledge is not very good.

The variables are those of a straightforward decision problem: there is a (usually) finite number or class of projects that might be undertaken, a probability distribution for the consequences associated with each alternative, and a way of evaluating these consequences either in units like dollars saved or prestige gained or some other such measure.

The analytic decision problem—given the set of alternatives, the probability of outcome, and the value of the outcomes—is simple. The difficult and critical part, of course, is getting to these "givens." It is here that the sponsor, the organizationally sophisticated management man, is vitally necessary. And here is where he frequently lets his operations research boys down. His attitude may be, "They're bright boys; let them sink or swim. I got them into the company, didn't I; what else do they want?"

What I am advocating here is a much different attitude—one in which the sponsor enters actively into this first model-building problem taken up by the operations research people.

The actual decision-making model for this strategic decision-making problem need not be very complex. A very simple graphical one—with analytic handles on it may be quite adequate. Consider, for example, all possible projects placed in a matrix or table constructed as in Fig. 14-1.

This is a very rough and ready approach, but can rapidly be refined analytically. The point here is the need for a strategy of project selection and of the project portfolio and a means for establishing time priority for projects.

Certainly, it may appear attractive for the operations research people in phase one to make a play for high gain, low cost projects, and to avoid low gain, high-cost projects. And this might be the proper thing to do strategically. But it might also be a bad thing to do strategically.

Suppose, for example, that there are a lot of high-gain, low-cost projects, lying around the company in various areas of the factory, the offices, the research laboratory, etc. These might conceivably be a sort of stockpile that various other staff groups—e.g., industrial engineering, office systems, the research lab—have not yet gotten to, or perhaps, are even hoarding against a rainy day. The momentary triumph of dusting them off quickly may doom the operations research activity from the start in the view of these other functional groups.

Probable gains from successful resolution of the problem				
		HIGH	MODERATE	LOW
Probable cost of performing this project (dollar cost, probability of prestige penalty, etc.)	LOW			
	MODERATE			
	HIGH			

Figure 14-1

Selection of only the easy projects with the quick, high payoff may serve as an initial impetus for the operations research activity, but continuance of this strategy into phase two may be suicidal. First of all, with the other staff groups better established and with more resources—both economic and organizational—this mine of problems will probably be worked out very soon.

Secondly, if all that the operations research activity serves to do is to point out that the other activities have been missing such problems, the result may be that the other activities are chastised or strengthened and the operations research activity receives a great big vote of thanks and a termination notice.

If there is a distinct legitimate function for the skills and approach of operations research in the firm, then it has to be demonstrated. The project portfolio must reflect not just a lucky strike of quick-fix problems, but an area of problem resolution and problem recognition that other staff groups or other bright individuals in the firm could not or would not deal with.

Some of these very important "exclusive" or "untouchable" problems—(untouched by other groups, that is), may be in the moderate and high cost area and they may lead to only moderate or, hopefully, high gains. The precise calculation of marginal return from certain classes of problems is a matter for the analytical refinement of the decision-making model mentioned above.

It is these moderate and high cost projects, often involving long time periods and high risk of failure that should distinguish the operations research group in phase two, and certainly in phase three from the many other routine problem-solving staff groups.

In the early phases, consideration should also be given, subject to the marginal considerations of the model, to knocking off in addition a number of the low-cost, low-gain projects as a prestige building or warming up exercise. Positive gains, no matter how small, may be important in the early phases when people may be counting problems solved as well as dollars saved. This class of problems, serving many warming up and orientation functions for the operations research group itself, may avoid the danger of robbing someone else's stockpile of problems; the other groups may not be interested or even aware of some of them.

The strategy I am proposing is a balanced portfolio of projects which is developed from the important strategic objectives in each phase. In the early stages, the project portfolio should, perhaps, be directed at building prestige and good will, achieving acceptance of the activity in the firm. Later, it may be necessary to include some projects with long term implications for the company and for the development of the operations research personnel.

Whatever the background and skills of the operations research people, attention must be paid to their professional and practical abilities. Problems of a routine nature with no theoretical implications can soon discourage operations research people who are interested in advancing their professional stature and tackling more advanced problems continually. Giving all members of the activity opportunity to learn about the company operations may also be an important, continuing strategic objective in project selection.

It may also be necessary for certain members of the operations research activity to specialize in a given class of problems over a long period in order to reach a high level of understanding of the phenomena involved so that the desires for breadth and depth of knowledge of company activities have to be reconciled in the project portfolio continually, not just in phase one.

One special class of problems has caused difficulty in a number of firms where operations research was still in phase one. In one or two of them I expect that they will never reach phase two and certainly not phase three. These are the class of organizational problems that involve issues like: division of responsibilities between executives, long range planning of the company's sales policies, effectiveness studies of particular functions, and the like.

Some of the problems fall into the class that might be called "politically difficult." They just may not be the kind of problems that a brand new group should undertake in its first few months or years in the company. I have seen several cases where this kind of study was not acceptable, coming from this kind of group because of its age, the age of its members, and its ambiguous position in the company—that is, sponsorship.

A second, and even more compelling reason to avoid this class of problem in the early stages, perhaps forever, is this: With the present state of knowledge about organizational behavior, or organizational theory, the operations research man may be in no better position to resolve organizational problems than anyone else in the firm and he may be in a lot worse position due to his lack of knowledge of the personalities involved and the organization's history. His mathematical models and abstractions from reality may get him into real trouble in problems where measurement is not feasible and abstraction is self-defeating.

The penalty for failure in a problem of organization—relations between groups, definitions of responsibilities, setting company objectives and policies, etc.—may be the guillotine, not just a black mark in the book.

As the operations research activity matures, of course, and as organizational problems are recognized which have analytical implications, then, the operations research activity may make an important contribution as part of a task force or in cooperation with the increasingly evident organizational research or planning groups.

OPERATING CONDITIONS

Under this heading, three aspects are discussed:

1. Organizational location of the operations research activity.
2. Relation to other groups in the company.
3. Organization of work within the operations research activity.

Organizational Location. The initial and ultimate organizational location of the operations research activity may be critical.

Certainly, in the early stages, a new activity of this type needs high level sponsorship and can use all of the derived status it can get. It needs this prestige and status in all phases of its work—getting information that people may be reluctant to supply, gaining cooperation in experiments, achieving implementation of its results, uncovering new problem areas, and so forth.

Two questions arise in this connection; one is whether the authority and power to elicit desired action should accompany this prestige and general status. That is, if the operations research activity is attached to the executive vice president on the organization chart, should it be implied that people in this group speak with his voice.

The difference here is between the prestige afforded by being attached at a high level, indicating that company management thinks this is an important activity, and the effective power imputed to the group by its organizational location or sponsorship.

The second question is: how long should this new activity be maintained in a usually ambiguous location of this type.

In the absence of clear policy on this issue of organizational location, it is easy for a temporary location, primarily for the purpose of providing an initial prestige impetus, or a bird's eye view of the company, to become a permanent attachment and an extension of the activities of the sponsoring executive.

In some cases, this may not be a bad idea. Perhaps the operations research activity should, logically, become a part of the controller's office or the staff of the vice president of something. This may not be a bad idea if the logic can be established independently of the historical accident that placed it there temporarily.

The easiest course of action is to say: "Well, the group has been working nicely in Bob's or Sam's department even though the original decision was somewhat accidental. Let's leave it there a while longer."

This issue of organizational location can be a two-edged sword. In addition to the prestige, etc., that a particular location can provide, there is also the possibility of a functional connotation being imputed to it. For example, if it is located in manufacturing, it may be natural to assume that it will confine itself, or at least concentrate on, manufacturing problems.

All of the historical company relationships between departments provide a set of expectations about how members of these departments will behave. Suppose the controller's office has historically been concerned with only budgetary and cost matters, in a technical accounting sense. If the new operations research activity is located there and begins to look into sales policies, personnel allocation problems without an immediately obvious accounting connection and other "apparently peripheral" matters, people's expectations will be violated and trouble will ensue.

In addition, the new activity will probably inherit all of the personal antagonisms and rivalries that exist between its sponsor and others in the company. This is the negative aspect of the derived prestige; it may derive some low status as well.

The question of how high level the location should be is relevant here. If operations research is to be introduced as a sort of cooperative problem solving venture for the various activities of the firm, then one should avoid giving the impression that this is a top management tool for checking upon or showing up the deficiencies of existing activities.

Location at too high a level, therefore, can ultimately doom operations research as well as give it initial impetus.

If the purpose of the initial location is merely impetus or the bird's eye view, then it should be relocated as soon as possible after these objectives have been accomplished. That is, as soon as the criteria of effectiveness for phase one indicate success in this phase, move it into phase two. And furthermore, if the disadvantages of high level initial location are to be reduced, it should be known in the company that phase one is merely temporary.

In addition to organization level, the other important location parameter is functional area. This is discussed next.

Relation to Other Groups in the Company. Relations with other activities in the company will always be an issue for an activity like operations research. By its nature, the operations research activity is concerned with areas of the firm's operations in which groups are already established—operating groups such as production, marketing, and finance—and the staff groups supporting them.

Questions of overlap, division of responsibility, conflict of interest and so on must eventually be resolved to the point at which they do not interfere significantly with the effectiveness of the operations research activity or that of the other groups. I do not believe that these questions can be resolved permanently or completely any more than similar issues involving research and development and other functions have been.

Where there is intimate contact, particularly in a flow-of-work relationship—one group feeding information to another—there is always the potential for conflict. The trick is to keep it below the critical level.

One way of helping this situation is to pay a good deal of attention to specialization and division of labor. This is important in both the initial phases where objectives are being evolved and in the continuing situation. In the latter case, the list of projects is examined continually to see who is to do a particular job and how it is to be shared by different groups.

The question of a legitimate role for operations research arises again here. Does operations research have a role defined primarily in terms of functional areas of the company? This was examined by surveying the articles in the *Journal of Operations Research* over a two-year period which had involved industrial operations. Here are the subjects they covered:

Value of an Engineering Design.
Economic-Lot-Size in Manufacture.
Manufacturing Specifications.
Production Scheduling.
Research in Marketing.
Sales Response to Advertising.
Distribution of Seasonal Inventory.
Allocation of Sales Effort.
Company Planning.
Spare Parts Programs.
Inventory Markdown.
Warehousing Problems.
Reorder Points.
Machine Repair.
Sales Operations.
Staff Organization.
Selection of Capital Equipment.
Management Planning and Control.

Additional data on this point are presented in a recent survey of operations research in the United States.[4]

There are few, if any, of these problem areas in which the modern manufacturing corporation does not already have a staff group primarily or secondarily concerned with the subject matter.

So it seems that subject matter, or functional area, is not an adequate basis for differentiation of the operations research activity from that of other staff activities.

This is in sharp contrast with the function of, say, quality control or physical research where the area of activity is clearly defined relative to other functional areas and the groups in those areas are undisputed (or relatively undisputed) entrepreneurs over them.

I believe that there *is* a clear and legitimate rationale for the operations research activity in the firm. It is based, not on *functional* specialization, but on the concept of depth or perspective in many areas of the firm's operations.

Consider the typical project portfolio, the allocation of effort, of the existing staff groups. At the risk of too broad a generalization, I will describe them this way: they are generally involved with immediate problems affecting current operations of the functions to which they are attached.

Thus, a typical production control staff group will be concerned with current production schedules, perhaps with schedules for products coming into production soon, and possibly for products that may be coming at a later date. They, or another group, may also spend some time on refining the production scheduling and control techniques they are currently using and examining newer techniques that have been suggested by suppliers or in the literature.

Very rarely will you find a traditional production control group considering issues like the following:

What is the concept of control of quantity of output?

What are the fundamental relations between quantity, quality, and method of manufacture?

What are the over-all capabilities of the firm with respect to delivery lead time and what does it cost, over-all, to produce much sooner or much later than promised?

What are the inherent capacity characteristics of a machine or a unit operation? How do these relate to economic lot size, minimum inventory levels, purchase terms, repair and maintenance policy and so on?

The rationale appears to me to include the necessity for a capable group to raise this kind of question and to undertake studies which other groups are not interested in or capable of undertaking.

The operations research activity is widely needed as a *research* activity and not an *operational* staff group. It can raise fundamental questions about operations, developing new methods of data collection and analysis and evolving new control and decision-making tools for use by operating people and their staff groups. They can be concerned with problems that cut across traditional functional lines, problems that may at present be in a functional no-man's land between staff groups or that may be inundated by too much uncoordinated effort from too many different points of view.

The lack of interest or ability of existing groups to undertake such problems may stem from a number of causes. For example, the training of the functional specialists in these groups may have excluded or been incompatible with the kind of analytical approach in which the operations research group is trained. In much traditional industrial engineering training, for example, the starting point is the existing operation or phenomenon. The questions raised are how can it be improved or changed, etc. In general, the question of the basic nature of an operation is not a part of the formal training. Further, the viewpoint is generally focused on isolated operations or parts of operations and the analysis is directed at optimizing that fragment of the company's activity.

The traditional training and behavior of many cost accounting groups do not generally involve questions of the source and the basic nature of cost information. In a very proper sense, organizationally proper, that is, they avoid raising questions which impinge on the prerogatives of other functional groups—those which supply their cost data or use it to control costs.

Research and development people may be uninterested in examining their own behavior from an efficiency or an effectiveness point of view. They may also be more interested in problem-solving than in how their problem solutions may affect the company's over-all business in years to come.

These comments are not intended as a flat statement that such staff groups do not ever undertake such studies and raise such questions. Quite to the contrary, some of the best of what we are currently calling industrial operations research is in fact being performed in a number of companies by industrial engineering, cost accounting and research and development groups.

The point is that where there is a basic lack of such activity in the firm, where these other staff groups do not undertake to raise such questions and conduct such studies, there is a need for the contribution that operations research can make.

I would like to draw a distinction here between the need for this kind of activity, where it is lacking, and the need for a specific group of people with separate organizational identity such as the "Operations Research Department" or "Operations Research Group." If the need for this broader-gage, longer-range analytical thinking can be met by existing groups in the firm, then this may be a better organizational policy.

My observations, however, suggest that in many companies the separate group would be a better solution. This viewpoint is related to the earlier discussion about the project portfolio. It is very unlikely that all of the research on methods and concepts of the firm's operations could compete successfully with the day-to-day routine and trouble shooting requirements in most of these staff groups.

Many staff groups, such as quality control, have pet projects of a long range nature that they would like to work on if given the facilities, the time, and, in some cases, specialized talents. But the pace of operations and the current requirements mitigate against such longer-range and broader-scope projects.

They fare well only when they are the major responsibility of a special group like operations research.

If a separate operations research activity is to be established in the firm, then the foregoing comments strongly imply the necessity for an integration of the operations research activity with these other staff groups.

In this connection, I visualize a flow of work between operations research and these other staff groups similar to that indicated in Fig. 14-2.

I visualize two major paths of information flow:

1. Problems arising in operations which the operating staff groups are not equipped to handle are referred to the operations research activity for longer range or broader or deeper examination. Solutions are transmitted back to the staff groups which in turn refine and translate them into operating tools.
2. New ideas, new methods, general concepts, which originate with the operations research group or which stem from problem solving in other functional areas, are transmitted in general form to the staff groups and again translated into operating rules and tools.

In other words, I visualize this process, at maturity, in terms analogous to the activity of the various research and development groups which are concerned primarily with the physical aspects of operations, contrasted with operations research's primary interest in the economic and other nonphysical aspects.

This process requires very strong links between operations research and other staff groups and a condition of mutual support rather than competition. Each is both a supplier of information to and a user of information coming from the other group.

There will, due to the differences in the nature of the people involved and the necessity for contact, be a high potential for conflict between these groups and this is where an alert management can make sure that the level of conflict does not interfere seriously with the flow of work.

The operations research group should avoid posing threats to the

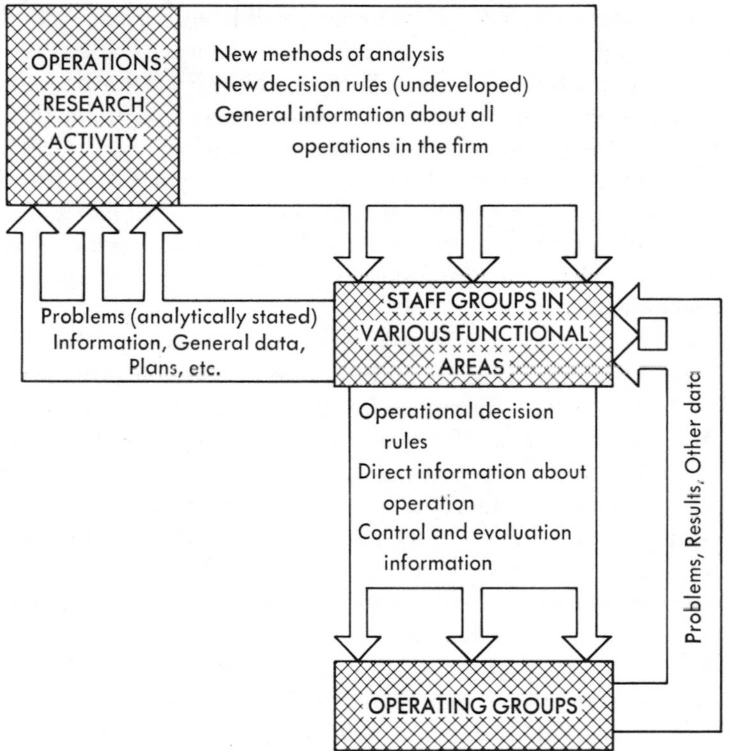

Figure 14-2

intellectual or job security of people in these other staff groups. To some extent this depends on the personal qualities of the people involved. But a lot can be done through organizational devices such as project task forces, exchange of personnel, and doing everything possible to indicate that this is a cooperative venture rather than a competitive one.

Organization of Work. In this connection, the internal organization of work of the operations research activity is important. The question is whether work should be organized on a functional basis —all specialists of one kind in a group, lending out their services as needed for particular problems—or on a project basis, in which all the skills necessary to solve a particular problem are grouped together for the duration of the project.

Combinations of these two "pure" forms are possible and more usual than the pure forms themselves. The actual pattern of operation in these terms, functional or project, will have a strong influence on the integration achieved with other staff groups. The pattern of internal organization will also affect the ability of the operations research activity to maintain a reasonable project portfolio including short and long term, broad and narrow problems.

In the recent literature of research management this particular issue is becoming a popular one and there are a number of good articles dealing with it in the research, development, and engineering functions that are also relevant for designing the operations research group.[3]

Resources. In this final section I would also like to refer to the voluminous and rapidly growing literature of research management. Under the heading of Resources for the Operations Research activity, are subjects such as the size of the group—on the assumption that an independent group is indicated in phase three; the mixture of skills necessary, the facilities and equipment required, budgetary procedures, accounting for costs, etc. There are also several pertinent bibliographies in the research management field.[2,5,6]

Finally, here are a few comments about several of these resources for the operations research activity.

First, on the size and make-up of the group, there is a notion in research management about what is called a "minimum effective" research group. This is a group with the minimum necessary skills and abilities to do useful research. This concept is usually discussed in connection with research creativity. The minimum requirement is for at least one highly imaginative and creative person as the nucleus for a research group in order to provide stimulation and leads for the group. Without such a person, the research group may be ordinary—capable of routine problem solving but not of imaginative new leaps into the unknown. The research department should then be made up of a number of these minimum effective groups, subject to the limitation of stretching the nucleus too far; that is, of exceeding a "maximum effective" group size.

An additional comment on make-up relates to the kind of specific skills. Because of the nature of operations research work, I believe that an operations research group should have, in addition to the analytical abilities usually supplied to it, an element of experience and sophistication about operations themselves and the business the company is in. Some operations research activities have been composed principally of industrially naive groups of physical scientists on what I believe to be a false assumption. This assumption appears to be that since many naive groups were so successful in wartime military operations research, that it is the very quality of naiveté about the specific operations they are studying that was responsible for their success. I reject this assumption for the industrial operations research group and advocate a high level of sophistication about company operations. This sophistication is not to be confused with mere years of experience which may simply be a repetition of a very low level of sophistication.

In summary, I have suggested that there are three phases in the integration of operations research into the firm. Three sets of strategic design decisions should be made in this connection. The first involves objectives and tasks of the operations research activity:

1. Here the motivations and sponsorship for the operations research activity are important.
2. If objectives are properly stated, the project portfolio can be derived.
3. A decision-making model was suggested for building the project portfolio.
4. Some specific classes of problems should be avoided in the early stages.

The second set of decisions involves operating conditions.

1. Organizational location was discussed, as well as the potential dangers of improper location.
2. Relations with other activities emphasized the flow of work between operations research and other staff groups, and proposed that operations research be a supporting group for these other activities, in a real research role.
3. The internal organization of work will affect this relationship.

The third set of decisions relates to resources assigned to the operations research activity in phase three, on the assumption that it becomes a permanent group.

1. The decision problems here are analogous to those in research and development which has a new and specialized literature that may be of great help.

2. The notion of the research nucleus was described, and I would like to close by saying that the quality of the operations research work done in the firm cannot be divorced from the quality of the people assigned to carry it out.

REFERENCES

1. Albert H. Rubenstein, "Integration of Operations Research Into the Firm," *The Journal of Industrial Engineering,* September–October 1960, pp. 421–428.
2. George P. Bush, *Bibliography on Research Administration,* Annotated, University Press of Washington, D. C., 1954.
3. Harry H. Goode, "Intra-Company Systems Management," *IRE Transactions on Engineering Management,* March 1960, Vol. EM 7, No. 1, pp. 14–19.
4. David Bendel Hertz, "Progress of Industrial Operations Research in the United States," *Proceedings of the First International Conference on Operations Research,* Operations Research Society of America, December 1957, pp. 455–467.
5. Albert H. Rubenstein, "Looking Around, Guides to R. and D," *Harvard Business Review,* May–June 1957, Vol. 35, No. 3, p. 133.
6. Albert H. Rubenstein, "The Technical Man, Prologue to Technological Productivity," *Industrial and Engineering Chemistry,* January 1959, Vol. 51, p. 10.

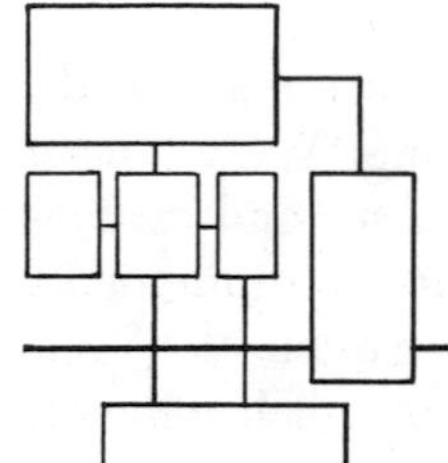

CHAPTER 15

THE KEY— THE HUMAN FACTOR

PROGRESS toward improvement within an organization is almost entirely a reflection of human nature and the mentality or point of view of the people within the organization. Human nature can be used constructively in the pursuit of improvement. This requires careful consideration of the nature of human nature and a meshing of it with the pursuits of improvement.

In this chapter we will consider the nature of human nature, several examples of how human nature can be used to bring about more effective approaches to improvement—at the working level and at the management level—and attempt to point out that the key to improvement is indeed the human factor.

THE NATURE OF HUMAN NATURE [1]

Man is unique. We believe man to be created in the image of God and to possess characteristics that distinguish him from the animal. All of the great religions of the world are based upon brotherly love and the dignity of the individual. These two concepts are fundamental, and they can provide a suitable foundation for developing satisfying and productive work relationships. Most all of our work systems provide a base for reinforcing the dignity of the individual through purposeful and creative activity.

It is extremely difficult to summarize the basic human characteristics in a complete but brief fashion. Rather than strive for completeness, we shall examine some of the more general concepts that have emerged from research in human behavior. You can add to these from your own experience.

Self-confidence, self-reliance, and self-respect are all basic human needs. Without them, it is impossible to live as a human being. We all have need to maintain our inner self in terms of our own values and evaluation. Our own values are tempered by what we feel are the judgments of others concerning us. The ability to predict the consequences of our actions is fundamental to maintaining our self-confidence, self-reliance, and self-respect. When our predictions of the future do not prove to be adequate, we become frustrated and doubt our basic values. Our inner security is threatened.

Curiosity is another basic human trait. When our living experiences become too routine, and our predictions of the consequences of our behavior become routinely accurate, we are challenged to enlarge our sphere of control and prediction. When we do not encounter new experiences in the ordinary course of events, we are inclined to seek them out. We avoid new experiences when our security is threatened because of our inability to predict the consequences, or when the new experience seems to hold undesirable consequences for us or our associates.

So far we have considered only the needs of the inner man. We have not mentioned the creature needs that must be satisfied in order for man to survive—food, clothing, shelter, and so on. There is no point in belaboring the importance of caring for these needs. In almost all jobs, these things are more than provided for in the basic wage rates, unemployment insurance, and other benefits. *It is the inner man's needs that have not been satisfied on the job.* This is the area of challenge.

Now for some examples of how the needs of the inner man—the need for security, understanding, and novelty—can be satisfied in the process of work. An important point to remember is that improvement is achieved when attempting to do so helps to achieve satisfaction of the basic needs of the inner man.

THE HAWTHORNE STUDIES

One of the classic studies of human behavior in a working environment is the research conducted at the Hawthorne Works of Western Electric Company during the twelve years from 1927 to 1939.[2] These studies were originally undertaken to evaluate the effect of intensity of illumination on the efficiency of output of workers. The original objectives of the study proved to be very inadequate, and the results of the study were negligible. However, the failure to obtain results concerning the original objectives was the very reason the project continued for many years and finally yielded very significant results relative to the human factor in industry.

The Hawthorne Works of the Western Electric Company was regarded as a very progressive organization from a technical and a human relations standpoint. It had always shown concern for the well-being of its employees and had maintained a high standard in the matter of wages, working conditions, vocational guidance, and employee benefits. The company enjoyed good industrial relations and had every reason to believe that the worker morale was high and that the employees had confidence in the abilities and motives of the company management.

ILLUMINATION STUDIES

The initial investigation failed to show any simple relationship between illumination and employee behavior. Even though the research was not aimed at increasing the production of the employees, rate of production was used as one of the criteria for evaluation of the experimental results. The rate of production seemed to be greatly influenced by the employee's interpretation of what the observers and management expected of them. Simple changes or rearrangement of the illumination, even though the intensity remained the same, caused changes in output. The researchers concluded that these results were obtained due to the influence of additional factors of a psychological nature that they were unable to control. This led directly to the second phase of the extended investigations.

TEST ROOM STUDIES

In an attempt to control the effect of psychological factors, the experimenters decided to continue their observations with a small group of workers who were isolated in a separate test room. They anticipated that the psychological factors would in time disappear if the group were asked to cooperate and if they were free from the distractions of their normal working environment. (Please note: a change is being made in the nonphysical working environment—we will be most interested in its impact.)

The experimentation in the test room was broadened to include consideration of other physical influences in addition to illumination, such as rest pauses, free snacks during rest pauses, changes in the length of rest pauses, change in the wage payment scheme, shorter hours, and a change in the number of days worked per week. The test room included bench and assembly equipment identical with that used in the regular department, and instrumentation for measuring output rate, weather conditions, temperature, humidity, and so forth. Six average girl operators were selected for observation. Five of them were to do the work, while the sixth supplied parts and materials as needed. An observer was assigned to the test room to maintain records, arrange the work, and develop a cooperative spirit on the part of the girls. Eventually, as his task became more complex, several assistants were assigned to help him.

PARTICIPATION

Prior to the experimentation, the girls were called to the superintendent's office for an explanation of the project. They were informed that the objectives were to evaluate the influence of changes in working conditions, and they were cautioned to work normally and not to make a race out of the test. There were many subsequent conferences as experimental changes were made. The girls were always asked for their comments, and certain changes that did not meet with their approval were abandoned.

RESULTS OF TEST ROOM STUDIES

The results obtained from the test room experiments indicated that rate of production in each experimental period was higher than in the preceding period, even though some periods duplicated the physical conditions of earlier periods. The obvious conclusions were that changes in physical factors were more than offset by other, more potent forces. These other, more potent forces were related to the psychological and social environment that had developed in the test room. Contrary to the expectation of the researchers, the psychological factors (that is, those things that were suspected of having caused confused results in the original illumination experiment) did not in time disappear.

Each girl was producing more in the test room than she ever had in the regular department. This was done without any conscious effort. The girls liked to work in the test room. They enjoyed their association. They were important. There was an absence of the regular supervisory "control." They could work without anxiety. They could talk to one another. They were a vital part of an important venture. The results they produced could lead to important improvements in the working conditions for their fellow employees.

INTERVIEWS

An extensive interviewing program was initiated at the completion of the test room experiments. These interviews were aimed directly at investigating human relations and were nondirective in nature. The employees were encouraged to talk about anything that was bothering them and to express themselves freely. The interviews eventually extended to more than 21,000 in number. The results strongly indicated that the employees were banding together informally in order to protect themselves against practices that they *thought* were a menace to their own welfare. Remember, these were results from an organization that was highly interested in the welfare of their employees—an organization with good employee morale.

The interview results also indicated that employee behavior was a highly complex matter, influenced by the individual's previous experiences and mental health and by the social factors sensed by the individual both on and off the job. There was strong indication that human behavior in this situation was not guided by logic alone. The wage incentive plan, designed logically to encourage the working force to increase productivity, was interpreted as a challenge to "beat the system" by straight-line output (the group adopted standards that they felt were proper, and no one exceeded them by very much) and by informal practices to enforce the group-established standards.

WORK SITUATION STUDIES

The interview program was followed by intensive observation and interview of selected groups working in their normal environment. These investigations revealed further evidence of informal social codes adopted by the work group. Some jobs were made to appear very difficult and involved, when in reality they were very simple. Production was established at levels regarded by the group as being correct to protect their interests. Technical changes were opposed, even when in the interests of making the jobs easier and better and the product more economical and salable. There was a conflict of interests, which caused dissatisfaction and unrest.

ANOTHER TEST ROOM

Finally, the series of experiments concluded with another test room investigation. The influences of the psychological factors found to be so potent in the previous test room investigation were recognized and guarded against. As a consequence of these precautions, the results were much different. Many things were found to be going on in the test room that should not have been happening—particularly not in an organization that was progressive and alert to the employee's needs. Production was held to the "socially acceptable" level established informally by the employees. Pressure was brought to bear on the fast workers. Technical changes were unofficially but effectively resisted.

The entire subject of the extensive Hawthorne Studies makes fascinating reading for the student of human nature. Now we will conclude our discussion of the researches with two generalizations:

1. No change in the physical or financial conditions of work had a foreseeable and calculable effect in terms of output unless it was connected with the psychological and social attitude of the worker. The psychological and social attitude of the worker includes the personal bond between the worker and his work, the meaning of work to the individual, the individual's integration with the group, the individual's recognition of his own goals and objectives and of those of the group and the company, and the relationship of the supervision with the individual and his group.
2. The logic of efficiency ran counter to the logic of sentiment, except in those cases where the logic of sentiment was oriented in the direction of psychological and social values that produced efficiency as a by-product. There was considerable evidence to indicate that workers will react unfavorably to any behavior forced upon them from above without their participation in shaping the decisions and understanding of objectives and means for achieving the objectives.

THE HARWOOD MANUFACTURING CORPORATION STUDY

The Harwood Manufacturing Corporation, maker of pajamas, employs about 500 workers.[3] It is regarded as a progressive company, alert to employee problems and public relations. Its policies are regarded as fair, liberal, and progressive. A high value has been placed on fair and open dealings with employees, and they are encouraged to take up any problems or grievances with management at any time. The supervisors are given help and encouragement in finding solutions to their own problems.

By most all standards, this company could be regarded as a good example of a smooth-functioning organization. However, one of the basic characteristics of the business was causing some difficulty. Competitive forces and styling changes made it imperative that jobs be changed rather frequently. The necessity of these changes was rather obvious to the entire organization, but there was evidence that employees resented and resisted changes—even though the changes were essential to the continued success of their company.

RESISTANCE TO CHANGE

Resistance to change in job methods and assignments was demonstrated by substandard production on transferred jobs, extended relearning periods, hostility to supervision, and excessive quits. The company management was interested in investigating this problem, and so a research project was set up.

CONTROL

Three groups of employees were selected so that the groups were approximately equal in production performance, amount of relearning that would be involved in a change, and the "we" feeling within the groups. The first group, used as an experimental control, was transferred to new work by the procedures normally used in the plant. A group meeting was held, the necessity for the change was explained, and the new job method and production standard explained.

REPRESENTATION

The second group was involved in developing change in work methods through representation. The entire group was called together and the importance of devising efficient production methods was dramatically presented to them. Management then proposed that the group select several of their members to help devise methods improvements, to be the subjects for time study in order to establish performance standards on the new job, to explain the new job to the other group members, and to help train the other operators. The group selected their representatives and the plan was executed as proposed. The "representatives" and the engineer developed improvements and a new production standard was established. The "representatives" of the group referred to the results as "our job" and "our rate," for they had actually participated in developing the new job. The new method and the production standard were explained to the entire group, and the "representatives" trained the other group members.

PARTICIPATION

The third group participated directly in the entire job change. A smaller group-size allowed an informal atmosphere that immediately led to direct participation of all group members. The importance of improving work methods was outlined in much the same manner as it was for the second group. The operators responded with numerous suggestions.

Through participation of the entire group, the method was improved and a new production standard was established.

RESULTS

The control group behaved about as expected, based upon past experience with job changes. They evidenced resistance to the change, aggression against management, uncooperative actions with the engineer, hostility to their supervisor, deliberate restriction of output, and 17% quits in the first forty days after the change.

The group that participated in the job change through representation performed much differently. They recovered their production level rapidly, were cooperative, worked well with the engineer, had only one incident of aggression against their supervisor, and had no quits in the first 40 days after the change.

The direct participation group performed even better than the second group. They recovered their previous production level rapidly, were cooperative, worked well with their supervisor and the engineer, had no acts of hostility, and had no quits in the 40 days following the change.

COMMENTS

Again, we have seen evidence of the logic of efficiency running in opposition to the logic of sentiment, and evidence of the power of social and psychological forces in determining individual behavior. Restriction of output, resistance to and resentment of change, and aggression were caused by the threat to individual and group interpretations of their own welfare. Their inner security was threatened by change. Frustration led to overt behavior that seemed detrimental to individual, group, and company objectives. This can be summarized as "group dynamics" in action.

Participation in job change produced dramatic results. Most problems associated with restriction of output, resistance to and resentment of change, and hostility were entirely eliminated. This also is "group dynamics" in action, but the group has been made a more active part of the entire organization. The problems of competition have been shared with the group. They have had their objectives clarified and have changed in the direction of improved productivity. Their jobs have been made more meaningful, more important, and more satisfying.

JOB ENLARGEMENT

Another very interesting and significant experiment dealing with the human factor centers around what is called *job enlargement.* The story goes that on a trip through International Business Machines Corporation's plant at Endicott, New York, I.B.M. President Thomas J. Watson spotted a young woman standing idly by a milling machine. Upon questioning, she explained that she was waiting for the machine inspector. She could not proceed with her work until the inspector had checked and approved the setup. Her job was restricted to operating the machine. A separate setup man and an inspector were responsible for the other functions. Even though she was fully capable of adjusting the machine, she could not, for it was against plant rules. Mr. Watson thought this to be fundamentally wrong, and he proceeded to change the plant rules to combat what seemed to be over-specialization. He persuaded skeptical production executives to try allowing operators to enlarge their jobs and to more fully utilize their capabilities. It worked—very successfully. The workers found their jobs to be more interesting and less fatiguing. Absenteeism decreased. Fewer "mistakes" were made. Misunderstandings and quarrels were almost eliminated, for there were fewer inspectors and setup men and the foremen had more direct contact with their workers. Productivity went up. The concept of job enlargement has since been extended throughout the I.B.M. manufacturing activities. The same concept has also been used, very successfully, within many other organizations.

One might speculate about what is really involved in the concept of job enlargement. Is it the simple enlargement of jobs that accounts for increased interest, satisfaction, and productivity? Or, is job enlargement accompanied by a better satisfaction of the need for dignity, self-respect, self-confidence, and the other requirements of the inner man, irrespective of the enlargement of the job? Perhaps it is a combination of both. Actually, it is not the simple enlargement of jobs that leads to success; rather, it is the basic human values that are more adequately treated in the new environment. In many situations, job enlargement is a valid approach to improving the working environment and treatment of the human factor, and of thus obtaining increases in productivity.

The previous examples relating the human factor and the working environment have been presented in order to develop a better understanding of human nature as it influences the problems of striving for and achieving improvement. The examples, even though dramatic, are somewhat restrictive. They pertain principally to production-type activities and are influenced by improvement efforts *within* the organization. They represent important problems relative to improvement efforts, but human nature must be treated in an even broader fashion. The same general concepts do apply at higher levels within an organization and in a broader scope. The nature of human nature can serve as a guide to effective utilization of human potential in the quest for total improvement on behalf of an organization and its members.

ESPRIT DE CORPS

These words imply a very desirable orientation and spirit within an organization. Individuals recognize their own goals and aspirations—and they likewise recognize the goals and aspirations of fellow members of the organization and of the organization itself. When this spirit is oriented toward a systematic pursuit of excellence and improvement, the organization is likely to be highly successful, particularly when the appropriate technical support is available.

The consequences of *esprit de corps* and an organization-wide striving for improvement, relating individuals to their organization and the organization to its environment, is well demonstrated by many organizations. The Matsushita Electric Co. of Japan has been selected as an example. The reasons for this selection are:

1. Matsushita is a highly successful company, with a dedication to excellence and continual improvement.
2. It reflects much of the spirit that is common with Japanese industry, which has a large part to play in the phenomenal development of Japanese industry and economy. Japan today is one of the wealthy nations of the world and an industrial leader.
3. Perhaps the success of this organization and its country will serve as an inspiration for emulation by other companies and countries—within both the economically developed and economically developing areas of the world.
4. The striving for improvement represented by Matsushita clearly illustrates that efforts must be broad, encompassing all phases of the organization and its relationship with its environment. Improvement efforts are most successful when related directly to the nature of human nature.
5. This example might possibly stimulate the reader to think critically about why some individuals, some organizations, and some peoples are so much more successful than others. What causes them to "strive" for improvement? What allows them to achieve success so far beyond the accomplishment of others? There are no simple answers to these questions, but the answers are of great significance and it is important that we attempt to understand better what is involved in such matters. We can learn much from a critical study of the successes and failures of our fellow man and of ourselves.

The story of Matsushita is drawn from a special report published by *Time*.[4]

In the sunny living room of his home near Osaka, 26-year-old Seiji Hayakawa last week contemplated his existence and found it good. Mornings, Seiji and his young wife Kumiko wake to the bubbling of their automatic rice cooker, turned on minutes before by an electric timing device. Evenings they watch *Laramie* or the samurai dramas on their television set and fight off the winter chill by toasting their feet on an electric footwarmer. So well paid are their jobs at the nearby Matsushita Electric Co. radio plant—as a foreman, Seiji makes $61.12 a month, plus a bonus of 6½ months' pay last year—that they also own a refrigerator, transistor radio, vacuum cleaner, electric iron and washer. If the expectant Kumiko presents him with a son next month, Seiji even talks confidently of sending the boy to a university. "What more could I want?" Seiji ruminates contentedly—and answers himself: "I can't think of anything."

The contentment of Seiji Hayakawa is a consequence of the biggest and most hopeful economic news out of Asia since the end of World War II: the emergence of Japan as a consumer-oriented society and the first Asian nation to approach a Western standard of living. Less than a century after its awakening from feudalism and only 16 years after the soulcrushing devastation of World War II, Japan ranks among the world's great industrial powers. Stimulated originally by liberal transfusions of U.S. aid* and propelled by the boundless energy of its people, Japan last year boosted its national output to $45 billion—four times the highest prewar level. Exporting at the rate of $4 billion a year (triple the 1951 rate), Japan today is the U.S.'s single biggest trading partner after Canada; last year Japan's exports to the U.S. hit $1.1 billion, its imports from the U.S. $2.2 billion.

What makes Japan unique among Asian nations, however, is that its growing wealth, instead of being concentrated in the hands of a small elite, is benefiting the entire nation. . . .

KING OF TAXPAYERS

Japan's energetic businessmen, freed from the military domination of prewar days, have shown themselves to be among the world's

* Largely cut off in 1952, though U.S. procurement for the Korean war brought another cornucopia of dollars into Japan.

most aggressive and imaginative free enterprisers. And of all the men who have helped to build Japan's prodigious industrial machine, none has worked so consistently and successfully to distribute its products among Japan's ordinary people as Seiji Hayakawa's boss—gentle, sad-eyed Konosuke Matsushita (pronounced Mat-*soosh*-ta), founder of giant Matsushita Electric Industrial Co.

At 67, wispy (5 ft. 4 in., 129 lbs.) Konosuke Matsushita has the self-effacing look of an elderly, underpaid schoolteacher. In fact, he is a daring manufacturing and merchandising genius who, starting out at nine as an errand boy, has built Japan's biggest appliance business from nothing. Matsushita's success has made him Japan's biggest yen billionaire; last year his personal income hit $916,000, and for five out of six years he has been Japan's "King of Taxpayers." But Japan's prosperity does not delight Matsushita merely because it fills his coffers. His hero is Henry Ford—the man who brought the automobile to the masses—and he believes that if the world can be filled with material abundance, men will at last be free to pursue universal peace and happiness. In making himself the Henry Ford of Japan's appliance industry, he has also made himself the most widely admired businessman in Japan.

. . .

Matsushita's business career began in a Japan that was still shaking off the effects of two centuries of political, economic, and international hibernation under the autocratic Tokugawa shoguns. To preserve their nation's independence, the new rulers of Japan —an uneasy coalition of military leaders descended from the old samurai and the great financial clans known as *zaibatsu*—concentrated on building Japan's industrial and military power at forced draft. The policy was in part highly successful—until World War II, Japan was the only Asian nation that had never been colonized or dominated by a Western power—but it cost a grim price. Like Communist China today, prewar Japan built its strength on the sweat of its people, had no surplus to spare for decent living conditions.

NEGLECTED CRANNY

Matsushita managed to exist alongside the grasping *zaibatsu* by slipping into a cranny of industry they cared nothing about: consumer goods. The Osaka *zaibatsu* even lent him money, with no attempt to dominate him. But his success came from introducing the Japanese to a brand of imaginative, Western-style salesmanship they had never seen. When retailers refused to believe that his battery-powered bicycle lamp would run 30 hours—ten times longer than any other then on the market—he left one turned on in each store. Before long, orders came streaming in, and Matsushita Electric was on its way to becoming big business.

By 1931, Matsushita had 600 employees, was producing appliances from electric foot warmers to radio receivers. But it was not until one day in 1932 that he realized what his mission as an industrialist was. "It was a very hot summer day," he recalls. "I watched a vagrant drinking tap water outside somebody's house and noticed that no one complained about it. Even though the water was processed and distributed, it was so cheap that it didn't matter. I began to think about abundance, and I decided that the mission of the industrialist is to fill the world with products and eliminate wants."

. . .

ECONOMIC EXPLOSION

In the past decade, Japan's steel industry has poured $1.3 billion into construction of some of the world's most automated plants, has increased its output 480%. Last year, without benefit of military spending—Japan still produces no missiles or heavy military equipment—Japanese steel production hit 27.8 million tons, enough to oust Britain as the world's fourth largest steel producer. In shipbuilding, by adopting the most modern techniques and guaranteeing quick delivery, Japan nosed Britain out of the No. 1 spot six years ago. The Japanese chemical industry, riding the crest of a demand for chemical fertilizers that has helped make Japan self-sufficient in rice, has more than doubled its sales (to $3.2 billion) in the past six years, is now going heavily into petrochemicals. Under the protection of stiff tariffs, even the long-struggling Japanese auto industry has increased its sales—virtually all domestic—from $93 million to $1.3 billion since 1951.

In this mighty surge, Japanese industry produced a managerial class that can hold its own against any in the world. . . .

THE BOTTOM

Of all Japan's industrial titans, none has brought his company so far and so fast since the war as Matsushita. Matsushita came out of the war with worn-out machinery—miraculously, the B-29s had failed to hit any of his plants—and exhausted, frightened workers. He was so badly in debt that for a time the future King of Taxpayers was billed as the King of Tax Delinquents. American occupation authorities lumped him with the *zaibatsu*, who were scheduled to be obliterated from the industrial scene. "It was the bottom, the low point, the toughest period of my career," he says.

Salvation came from an unexpected quarter: the labor union whose formation U.S. officials encouraged as a measure to introduce democracy to Japan's industry. Time after time, delegations of Matsushita workers trooped to Tokyo to tell the occupation authorities that their boss was a non-*zaibatsu* poor boy, a benevolent employer, whose aim was a better life for the masses. After three years of appeals, Matsushita's name was finally taken off the purge list and his company spared the enforced "deconcentration" that hit other giant firms. Still, the hard times forced him to lop off 30 subsidiaries and reduce his staff to 3800. Says he: "I never felt so sad about anything in my life."

THE NEW FREEDOM

Once he could operate freely in a civilian economy, however, Matsushita was in his element. He pioneered easy-payment plans, became Japan's biggest advertiser (his ad budget last year: $18 million), flooded his dealers with sales aids. His domain swelled to 89 plants, employing 49,000 workers. From $17 million in 1951, Matsushita's sales made an astounding leap to $486 million last year, and in five more years he expects them to pass the billion dollar mark. Unlike most U.S. electrical-equipment makers, he does a scant 1% of his business with the military.

To his prewar product line, Matsushita has added a staggering array of new products including television sets, tape recorders, hearing aids, mechanical massagers, electric pencil sharpeners, and electrically heated trousers; now he is developing a home freezer and a line of computers. Sold under the brand name "National" (except in the U.S., where, because of a trademark conflict, they carry the name "Panasonic"), Matsushita's products have done much to change Japanese life. His rice cooker, which automatically turns out a perfect batch of rice every time, has freed Japanese women from the need to get up an hour earlier than their husbands —and from the terrible mother-in-law's verdict, "She can't even cook rice," which once was enough to send a Japanese bride back to her parents in disgrace. Matsushita's vacuum-cleaner ad that promises women "freedom from one phase of household drudgery," introduces a notion that, though old hat in the West, marks a revolution in the status of Japanese women. Much of the old, austere simplicity—wooden blocks for pillows and floor cushions instead of chairs—still persists in Japan, but it is unlikely to survive another generation. "The old Japanese style," says Matsushita, echoing the sentiments of young Japan, "is just too uncomfortable."

"FINEST PERFORMANCE"

Unlike many Japanese industrialists, Matsushita exports only 10% of his production. In fact, he disputes the national contention that Japan, with its few natural resources and scant arable land, must either trade or die. "The government should consider ways of bringing about prosperity without depending on foreign trade only," says he. "Our ancestors did it."

But although he exports less than such competitors as Toshiba, the high quality of the goods Matsushita sends abroad is helping to erase the old image of Japan as a producer of cheap junk. In dramatic evidence of the changing international reputation of Japanese goods, New York's Macy's last week took full page newspaper ads to tout Matsushita's "world-wide reputation for finest quality, finest performance," and to boast that it had the U.S.'s first stock of his new Panasonic portable television sets. Like other Japanese industrialists, Matsushita finds the U.S. and Canada his best customers. Latin American countries are becoming increasingly important, but Europe still maintains stiff trade barriers, and Asian nations have not progressed enough to want the new, sophisticated products Japan turns out.

"HARMONY AND SINCERITY"

The Japanese are naturally hard workers and love fine workmanship, but Matsushita ceaselessly exhorts his employees anyway. From the ceilings of his gleaming white, air-conditioned plants hang signs declaring: "Quality Is Everybody's Job," "Always Think of the Consumer." And each day before work begins, Matsushita executives and their uniformed workers gather to sing with the fervor of a college homecoming crowd:

For the building of a new Japan,
Let's put our strength and mind together,
Doing our best to promote production,
Sending our goods to the people of the world,
Endlessly and continuously,
Like water gushing from a fountain.
Grow, industry, grow, grow, grow!
Harmony and sincerity!
Matsushita Electric!

So infectious is the plant spirit that even skeptical new white collar employees fresh from the universities soon join in the singing. Jobs with Matsushita are considered such plums that thousands of young men and women take examinations for them each year.

MANAGEMENT CREEDS AND PHILOSOPHIES

The spirit which characterizes the Matsushita organization, and which is largely responsible for its success, is a reflection of the creed and philosophy of the organization. This creed guides the daily operation and general conduct of business for the organization and its individual members.

The effectiveness of formalized statements of management philosophy as a guide to the behavior of an organization has been studied by the American Management Association in an attempt to evaluate their influence upon the actual operation of an organization. It seems obvious that a formalized statement of an organization's policies should serve as a guide to behavior. This may or may not be true, but a formalized statement of basic policy and management belief *can* serve as a valuable guide and stimulant to individual and organizational behavior. This is particularly true where all managerial personnel have participated in the formulation of the statement and interpretation of policy and philosophy, and thus have a personal involvement with its execution. An evaluation of the AMA study concludes that "the process of formulating the creed is often more valuable than the finished product." This implies that the personal involvement in "discovering" the goals, objectives, and guides represented in the "creed" and "philosophy" of an organization can serve to provide a strong personal identification with them. The process of analysis and discussion also facilitates understanding. These statements vary in detail and manner of expression and are not always the result of group endeavor. An example will serve to illustrate the intent and typical content of these formalized statements.[5] This particular example has resulted from the efforts of a chief executive officer to capture the philosophy of his organization as a reflection of actual managerial behavior, and his personal interpretation of *why* the organization acts as it does.

THE "IMPACT PROGRAM" (BELL & HOWELL)

William Hodge, director of industrial relations, and Elizabeth Lyman, director of public relations, discussed the formulation and use of the company creed. They explained that Charles H. Percy, president of the firm, writes a regular column in the company's periodical, *The Finder*. One of these articles, entitled "A Creed For Management," was published in April 1952 and is still used as the creed of Bell & Howell. In 1955 this creed was fitted into the company's "impact program," which is primarily aimed at creating a definite image of the company in the minds of employees and the public. Both the creed and an outline of the impact program are reprinted at the end of this case study.

In reality, the creed cannot be separated from the impact program. The creed which originated in Mr. Percy's article actually states basic objectives of the firm by introducing each one with the phrase, "we believe." The impact program states responsibilities of the company and goes on to fill in some detail. Objectives and responsibilities, in this case, seem to be much the same, as a careful reading of both documents will reveal.

Mr. Hodge explains why he believes Mr. Percy first began to spell out the company's creed in 1952: "Specific instances have frequently arisen when some of our managers asked, 'As a company, just what should our position be?' or some similar query which concerned general, over-all direction in the conduct of our business. These questions came from all parts of the business. Our creed, as far as it has been developed now, has come about from multiple needs—problems in human relations, problems relating to the community or the public, and problems in manufacturing and elsewhere which should be solved quickly as they arise by individuals acting on their own. Having our position—what we stand for—spelled out, so that each individual knows and understands, enables each of us to solve such problems promptly, consistently, and intelligently. Whether he is a foreman, a member of our top management, or an employee, an individual who has this type of understanding can be expected to live up to what might be called 'the rules of the game.' Our president feels strongly that it is important for him to communicate the *philosophy of management* under which we operate (*our* rules of the game) to all of us."

. . .

As I See It—A Creed for Management

by **CHARLES H. PERCY**

President of Bell & Howell

THERE are over 64 million gainfully employed people in the United States. One-half of these work directly for American corporations, and the other half are vitally affected by business directly or indirectly. Our entire economy, therefore, is dependent upon the type of business management we have. Business management is therefore in many respects a public trust charged with the responsibility of keeping America economically sound. We at Bell & Howell can best do this by keeping our own company's program on a firm foundation and by having a growing group of management leaders to direct the activities of the company.

Management's role in a free society is, among other things, to prove that the real principles of a free society can work within a business organization.

Our basic objective is the development of individuals. In our own present program we are doing everything conceivable to encourage, guide, assist, and provide an opportunity to everyone to improve their abilities and skills, thus becoming more valuable to the company and enabling the company to improve the rewards paid to the individual for such additional efforts.

Our company has based its entire program for the future on the development of the individual and also upon the building of an outstanding management group. This is why we have emphasized so strongly the supervisory training program recently completed by all Bell & Howell supervisors, and why we are now offering this program to others in the organization training for future management responsibilities.

But a company must also have a creed to which its management is dedicated. I hope that we can all agree to the following:

We believe that our company must develop and produce outstanding products that will perform a great service or fill a need for our customers.

We believe that our business must be run at an adequate profit and that the services and products that we offer must be better than those offered by competitors.

We believe that management must serve employees, stockholders, and customers, but that we cannot serve the interests of any one group at the undue expense of the other two. A proper and fair balance must be preserved.

We believe that our business must provide stability of employment and job security for all those who depend on our company for their livelihood.

We believe that we are failing in our responsibility if our wages are not sufficiently high to not only meet the necessities of life but provide some of the luxuries as well. Wherever possible, we also believe that bonus earnings should be paid for performance and output "beyond the call of duty."

We believe that every individual in the company should have an opportunity for advancement and growth with the organization. There should be no dead-end streets any place in an organization.

We believe in the necessity for constantly increasing productivity and output. Higher wages and greater benefits can never be "given" by management. Management can only see that they are paid out when "earned."

We believe in labor-saving machinery. We do not think human beings should perform operations that can be done by mechanical or electronic means. We believe in this because we believe in the human dignity and creative ability of the individual. We are more interested in the intellect, goodwill, initiative, enthusiasm, and cooperativeness of the individual than we are in his muscular energy.

We believe that every person in the company has a right to be treated with the respect and courtesy that is due a human being. It is for this reason that we have individual merit ratings, individual pay increases, job evaluation, and incentive pay; and it is why we keep every individual fully informed—through *The Finder*, through our Annual Report, through Family Night, through individual letters—about the present program of the company and also about our future objectives.

We believe that our business must be conducted with the utmost integrity. We may fight the principle of confiscatory taxation, but we will pay our full share. We will observe every governmental law and regulation, local, state, and national. We will deal fairly with our customers, we will advertise our product truthfully, and we will make every attempt to maintain a friendly relationship with our competitors while at the same time waging the battle of free competition.

Some business leaders, on the one hand, preach the virtues of the free enterprise, democratic system and, on the other hand, run their own business in accordance with autocratic principles—all authority stemming from the top with little delegation of responsibility to individuals within the organization. We believe in democracy—in government and in our business.

We hope that every principle we believe in is right and is actually being practiced throughout the company as it affects every individual.

THE IMPACT PROGRAM

[The memorandum which originally accompanied Mr. Percy's letter]

In considering the "impact" of Bell & Howell on all people with whom it comes in contact, the character of the company has been defined as follows:

A. *Broadly* (factors apply to all succeeding headings).
   A Company that:
   1. Manufactures quality, precision, reliable product.
   2. Has special tradition of pioneering, quality, progress, and leadership.
   3. Is growing, aggressive, sound, enlightened, friendly—conducting affairs in good taste.
   4. Operates on basis of highest integrity.
   5. Is profitable.
   6. Has stable, equitable, consistent policies.

B. *To Employees:* A good Company to work for.
   1. Good wages.
   2. Maximum benefits.
   3. Pleasant, safe conditions.
   4. Security and opportunity afforded.
   5. Fair in all relationships.

6. Nonpaternalistic.

C. *To Shareowners:* An organization providing above-average return on investment with majority of earnings re-invested in the business.

D. *To Consumers:* A Company that:
   1. Designs product to sell—with equitable profit.
   2. Demonstrates alert, aggressive, and progressive merchandising.
   3. Is fair and reasonable in all relationships.

E. *To Dealers:* A Company that:
   1. Designs product to sell—with equitable profit.
   2. Demonstrates alert, aggressive, and progressive merchandising.
   3. Is fair and reasonable in all relationships.

F. *To Community:* A Company willing to assume its responsibilities as good citizen and neighbor.

This, in aggregate, can be considered our company character. Although recognized that we have not yet fully attained all of this character goal, we shall continuously and energetically work toward this objective.

HUMAN NATURE AND MANAGEMENT SCIENCE

Improvement function activities in their broadest sense encompass all phases of an organization. The objective of an improvement function is to encourage and systematically pursue improvement. The previous examples have illustrated human nature in production settings—both restricted and organization-wide. The next example will explore some similar problems involving management. This example deals with the introduction and effective utilization of computers, the human nature problems of top management in regard to this undertaking, and suggests that the problems of the human factor are equally valid (although not quite as precise) at this level of an organization as at the "production" level. The study was not undertaken to investigate the human factor as it influences improvement activities at top management levels within organizations, but it does provide a dramatic example of this very thing.

McKinsey and Company, management consultants, undertook a study of what American industry has gained from its heavy investment in computers and of the factors which lead to success or failure in their use.[8] The results of this investigation are very significant relative to computer-management science applications and relative to reinforcing the importance of human nature in all improvement endeavors. The highlights of this investigation will be presented.

The study included 27 large firms, regarded as leaders in their industry, representing a cross-section of American industry. All of these companies have had extensive computer experience. The "typical" company had sales just under $1,000,000,000 in 1962, and began to develop its computer system in 1958. Of the 27 companies studied, it was apparent that some were highly successful with their computer and systems installation (9, which will be referred to as the "above-average" or "lead" companies) and some were not (18, which will be called "average" companies). The lead companies were making broad use of their computer systems throughout their organizations, and had already recovered the start-up as well as the current operating costs of their computer installations. The average companies were making only limited use of their computers and were still a long way from covering current outlays, much less recovering their original investment.

Analysis of the factors surrounding the successful and the not-so-successful use of computer systems in the 27 companies lead to the conclusions that success is more dependent upon executive leadership than on any other factor. No company achieved above-average results without the active participation of top management. Success was associated with the level within the company at which responsibility for the computer systems work was placed (see Fig. 15-1) and the involvement of operating management in all phases of the systems work—from initial determination of problem areas through to implementation and operation of the systems (see Fig. 15-2).

Almost without exception, the above-average companies had made broad-scale use of computer-based systems. Most of their operating divisions had major applications installed and more underway. Typically, they had set up computer applications in most major functions of the company, from production to marketing and distribution, not just in the accounting area. Unlike the average companies, whose computer systems were generally confined to routine record-keeping activities, the lead companies had put the computer to work on the crucial decisions of the business: in sales forecasting, in manpower and production scheduling, in inventory management—as indicated by Fig. 15-3—in addition to the routine office and accounting functions.

The benefits derived from computer systems applications include administrative cost reductions (savings in clerical personnel, lower accounting machine rentals, etc.), operating savings (due to lower inventories, improved scheduling, etc.), and many intangible benefits such as improved customer service, reduced manufacturing cycle time, better and more timely information for evaluation and control, etc. (see Fig. 15-4).

An analysis of the results of this study clearly indicates the importance of human and organizational factors as determinants of success in exploiting technology within the area of management. Top management participation in recognizing where new technology can assist the organization, and participation in the development and installation of these new technological-based aids to management is an important factor in their successful exploitation. Human nature is directly involved at the management level, and successful results are more dependent upon the human factor than they are upon technical factors.

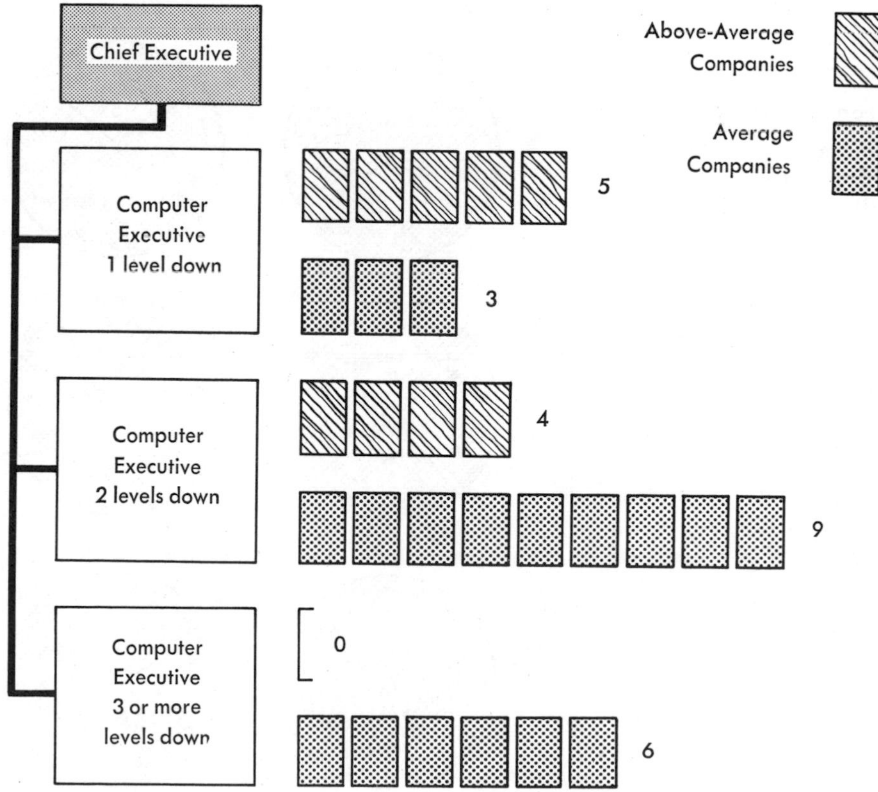

Figure 15-1. Organizational Level of the Corporate Computer Executive. (Copyright 1963, McKinsey & Company, Inc. Reprinted by permission.)

It seems obvious that intelligent management personnel would work continually and conscientiously for improvement *within their own activities,* as well as within the activities for which they are responsible. It would also seem obvious that management would attempt to be imaginative in visualizing how technological developments could assist them in the pursuit of improvement within these two areas. However, as we have seen from the analysis of factors surrounding the effective utilization of computer-management science developments, many of the same human problems were involved in improvement at this level as were involved in the production level examples previously presented.

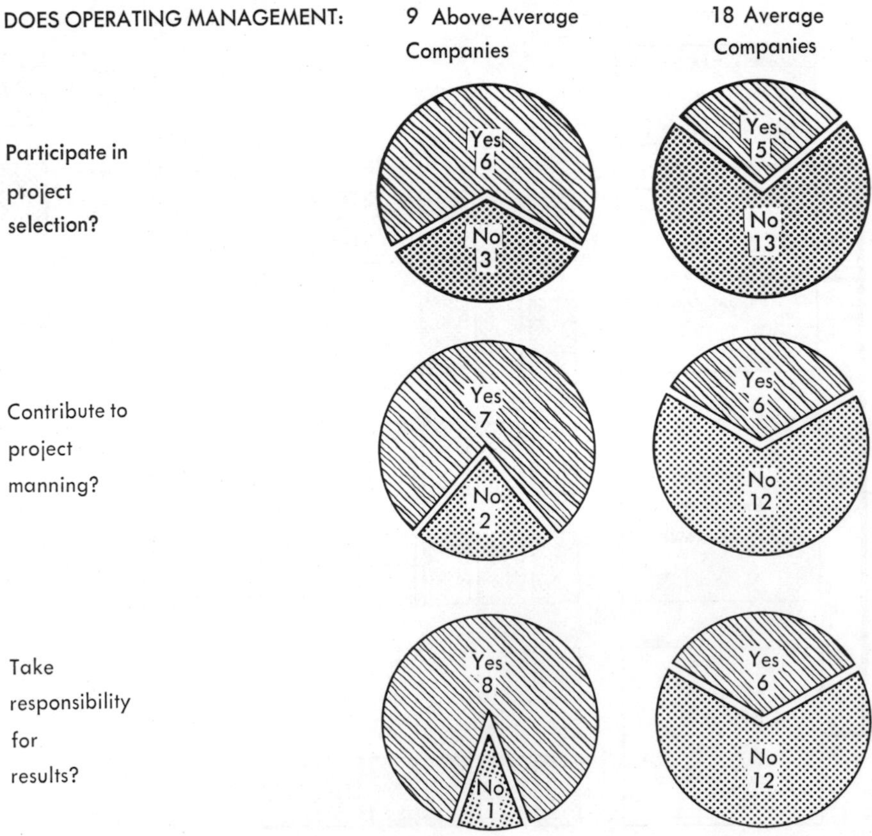

Figure 15-2. Involvement of Operating Management. (Copyright 1963, McKinsey & Company, Inc. Reprinted by permission.)

One might speculate about the cause-and-effect relationships of management leadership in the lead and average companies as total improvement efforts are involved at various levels within the organizations. As in the Hawthorne Studies, technical changes were unofficially but effectively

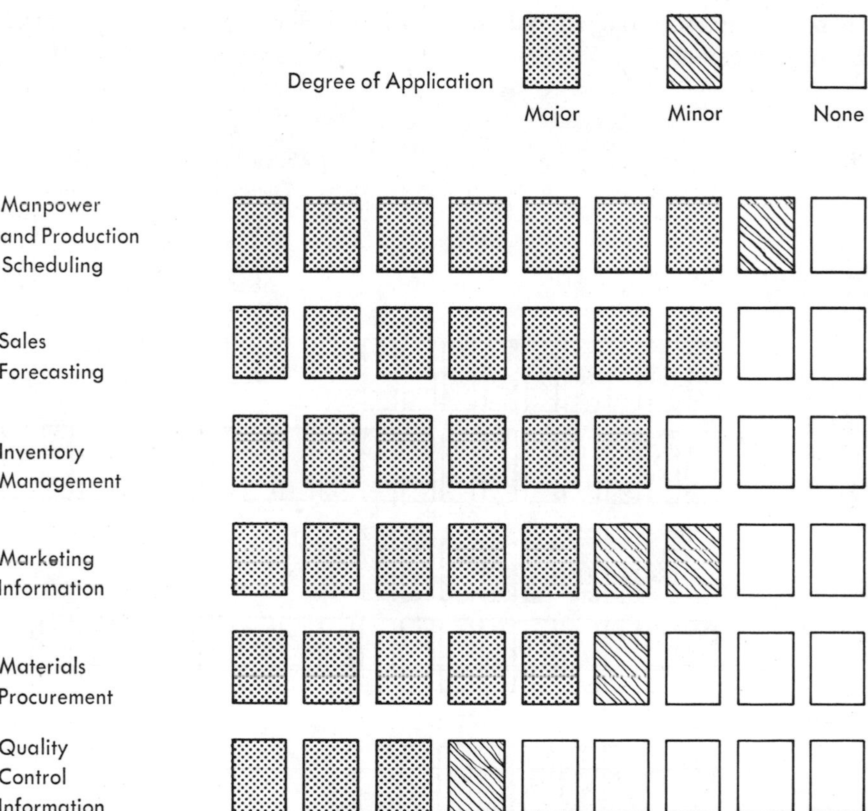

Figure 15-3. Breadth of Applications. Nine above-average companies. Decision areas covered by computer systems. (Copyright 1963, McKinsey & Company, Inc. Reprinted by permission.)

resisted by the middle management in the average companies, particularly where these changes directly affected their own work activities, What influence does this exert upon the organization as a whole?

The present example has been selected to provide food for thought concerning the human problems of pursuing improvement *within* management as a complement to the other examples which tend to emphasize the same thing relative to activities being managed. Although this study was not intended to be human factor research, it does indicate the critical importance of human and organizational factors as determinants of improvement. If management—at all levels, but particularly at the top level—cannot visualize opportunities to achieve improvement within any and all activities of the organization—including their own sphere—then the organization will fall far short of achieving its true potential for improvement.

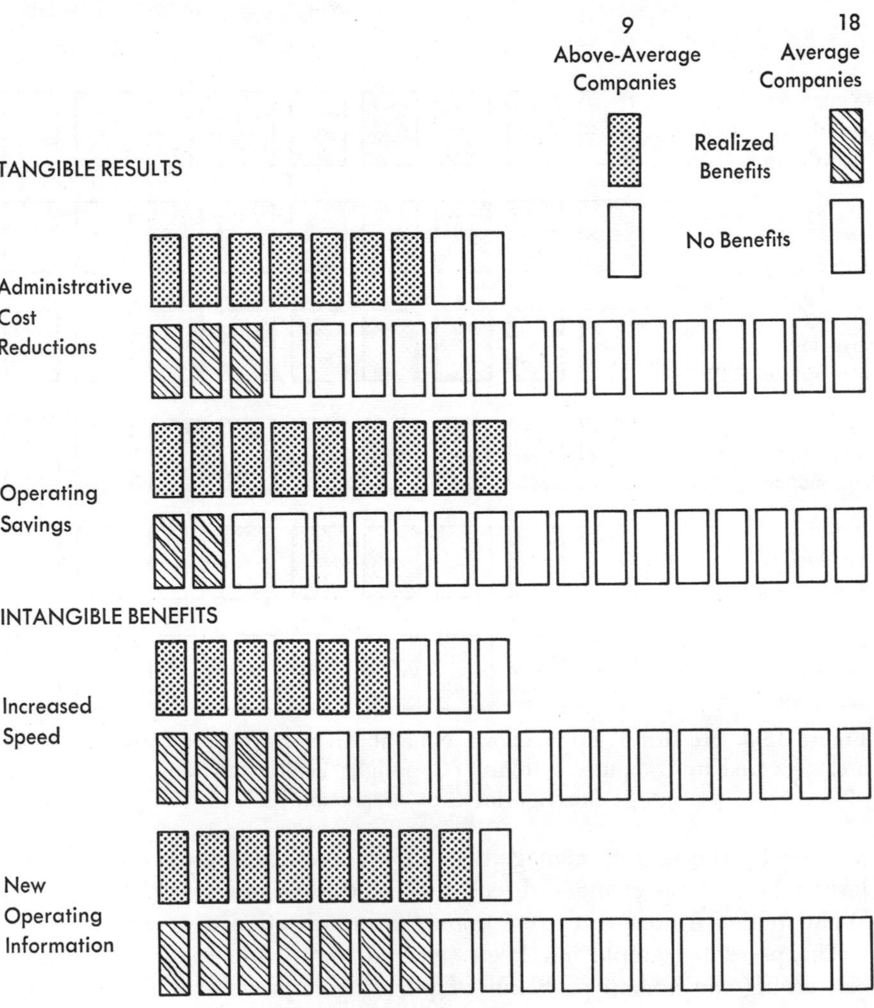

Figure 15-4. Benefits Derived from Computer Systems Applications. (Copyright 1963, McKinsey & Company, Inc. Reprinted by permission.)

PRINCIPLES OF THE HUMAN FACTOR

The case studies discussed above could be extended indefinitely to include many more and different types of situations. However, we have presented sufficient information to serve as the foundation for certain generalizations about human nature and its relationship to improvement activities.

It should be remembered that the cases discussed involved companies that regarded themselves, and were regarded by others, as quite outstanding. Even so, it was found that only a fraction of the human potential was being recognized and used. The importance of the human factor requires continuing attention in even the best organization. Properly cultivated, it can lead to dramatic success. When ignored, tremendous human potential is wasted, work becomes distasteful, and improvement endcavors are thwarted.

The myth of the "economic man." For many years the behavior of man was explained in terms of economic preservation, assuming that man guides his behavior to insure maximum economic well-being. This concept has been blown sky-high. There are other and more powerful forces that guide human behavior. These are part of the complex of social and psychological forces working upon the individual.

Group dynamics. Every individual in his work is a member of at least one social group—usually many more. These social groups exert a profound influence upon the behavior of the individual, often in a very subtle and unrecognized way. Social groups exist within every organization. These groups may have objectives and codes of conduct that are not in harmony with the avowed objectives of the organization. In fact, the informal group codes may induce actions that are detrimental to the individual and the organization.

On the other hand, the forces of social groups can produce a positive influence upon individual behavior and reinforce the objectives of an organization. Such things as job enlargement, brainstorming, and group participation in solving work problems tend to make productive use of the concept of group dynamics. The final results are in excess of the total results that could be achieved by the individuals acting on their own. Group dynamics offers a challenge to direct the dynamic social forces toward improvement within any organization.

External social groups also are important when considering on-the-job behavior. All of us are influenced by our interpretation of social values and custom. These standards do affect, and sometimes conflict with, the values and standards of behavior that are indicated by organizational and personal objectives.

Rational behavior. Human beings are capable of logical and rational behavior, but they are not inclined to act in this manner. We are more inclined to act emotionally, even though we may be able to analyze a situation on a factual basis. Our beliefs, biases, prejudices, habits, and subconscious fears guide much of our daily action. Even when the "facts of the matter" are presented to us, we may still ignore them and act in a nonlogical fashion. We may resist and resent those things which others try to do to help us. We may sabotage improvement efforts, even though they are to our advantage, to the advantage of our fellow workers, and to the advantage of our organization.

Self-esteem. We all want to feel that we count for something—that we are important, and that we are responsible. We must feel that we are true to our own values and true to the values of our "group" in order to retain our self-esteem. Change, when imposed upon us, tends to degrade and to undermine our self-esteem. Creative improvement efforts, when we participate in their development, can reinforce our self-esteem and give us a sense of accomplishment.

We see only through our own eyes. Our experiences, beliefs, values, biases, and prejudices flavor what we *see* in any situation. What we do see may be entirely different from what others see, and entirely different from the actuality, but we regard our own version as the "truth." This flavoring of our views is not a willful distortion of the truth, but normal human behavior produced without conscious knowledge. We may interpret efforts to improve work methods as personal affronts and threats to our own inner security. This must be overcome before we can enthusiastically work for improvement.

When others do not see the same things in the same situation, we are inclined to believe the others to be distorting the "truth." We regard what we see to be obviously true. We can only see through our own eyes, and this "colors" what we see. The other fellow is also human, and he can see only through his eyes. This dilemma creates very serious problems in the communications of ideas, and ideas are very important in our efforts to systematically pursue improvement. One of the basic objectives of formally stating the creed or philosophy of an organization is to achieve a more uniform understanding of the objectives of the organization and of how all individuals can effectively achieve their own personal objectives *and* the objectives of the organization through efforts to achieve greater efficiency.

Lack of information and understanding breeds antagonism and contempt. When we don't understand something, we are inclined to be antagonistic toward it. This holds true of ideas and individuals. Often, our antagonism and contempt is subtle and subconscious. It is not necessarily based on facts—for we do not always see the facts or behave rationally. It may be that we have not been informed of the necessity to develop improvements and that changes are seen by us as threats to our security and self-esteem. Maybe we haven't been consulted or involved in the development of improvements, and so we intend to protect ourselves with the simple and expedient acts of hostility, aloofness, and counteraction. This poses an additional problem to the communication of the ideas that are so important to improvement endeavors. Every man in an organization should be kept informed of "the facts of life" of daily operation. Our problem of communication does not stop at this point, for we must be sure that the facts are actually seen and understood.

Ideas can best be communicated by actions. If you keep telling a group that you're a good fellow, some of them will eventually believe it. But if you could *demonstrate* this "fact," many more people would believe it to be so. Likewise, you can tell a group that improvement and efficiency will help them achieve their personal objectives, and some of them will believe it. But if you can demonstrate the benefits, many more will believe it. Demonstration by example is an excellent way to put ideas across. In fact, we are demonstrating and putting ideas across by every action, even when we don't intend to communicate. It is extremely important to any improvement program that actions prove sincerity and the truth of the ideas involved in the program, and that no actions tend to dispute these ideas.

I recall one organization that was undertaking an "efficiency" program. This organization had enjoyed a rapid growth and the management had enjoyed high profits. The employee group had not participated in the fruits of success and they were very uncooperative in the attempts to increase productivity. The owner of the company purchased a private plane and had the company purchase a second plane. These planes were used primarily for his pleasure, and occasionally for company business. To the employee group, these two airplanes were symbols of management waste and sources of conflict relative to increasing productivity. Why should they try to save materials and time when the "boss" wasted money by such foolishness? To make matters worse, the employees were not even assured of steady employment. The "boss" expanded and contracted production at what seemed to be his whim. It's no wonder that this organization was in conflict over the concept of increasing productivity. Actions speak louder than words.

Our behavior is influenced by what we feel is "expected" of us. If we feel that we are supposed to act stupid, the chances are that we will. If we are expected to act with dignity and responsibility, we might. If we feel that we are treated with dignity and respect and that we are expected to act in the same manner, the chances are that we will act so. We are profoundly influenced by what we *feel* is expected of us. Our feelings are subject to our own interpretation of social, group, and organizational objectives and standards. If we are challenged in our daily work activities, we usually try to meet the challenges, and we derive great satisfaction from doing so. In order to continually strive for improvement, we must feel that doing so is expected of us and that efficiency is respectable and desirable.

Change is inevitable. Nothing is static. We must continually change products, services, equipment, materials, tools, work methods, and procedures in order to survive in modern business. Even when our organizational objectives are not profit, we are still faced with the inevitable necessity to change. This continual change can cause feelings of insecurity and frustration unless it is made with full consideration of the individuals involved. We seem to learn one thing well only to find that we must forget it and learn another thing in its place. Our skills are undermined. No wonder we are inclined to resist change. But do we really resist change, or do we resist the threat to our inner security, self-confidence, and self-esteem? Are we now doing the same things in the same way as we did, say, five years ago? Did we resist buying a new car or air-conditioner? I doubt it. We wanted to change. This brings us to the point where we can recognize the importance of wanting to change and of not having the changes forced upon us. When we recognize the need for change and actively participate in its development, we are usually very enthusiastic for the change.

We are creatures of habit. Humans seem to be inclined to form habits, and once these habits are formed it is very difficult to break them. Our resistance to changing our habits is often emotionally flavored. We have become accustomed to doing things in our particular way, so that in itself is good reason for not changing, even though a change might be quite "logical." This trait of habit formation can be a severe handicap to improvement endeavors. It can also be channeled into constructive use by the formation of habits that challenge and question why things are done as they are. These constructive challenging habits breed improvement and personal development. The key to changing habits is to first develop a true desire to change. If we really *want* to change, habits are of little consequence.

Self-criticism. We all tend to resent criticism—unless it is self-criticism. Changes in our work methods, when imposed upon us, are a form of criticism. These criticisms are threats to our self-esteem and inner security. Our natural defense mechanism is one of resistance, hostility, and resentment. Even when the criticism is intended to help us, we are likely to react violently and emotionally, although we usually manage to maintain an outward appearance of control and acquiescence. This can lead to frustration, antagonism, and misunderstanding. It can thwart improvement efforts.

Self-criticism can be extremely harsh and still not be resisted or resented. We don't mind challenging ourselves. In fact, our desire for novelty encourages us to criticize our own actions. Self-criticism is a very powerful tool and can be combined effectively with group dynamics. These approaches are so powerful that they can be used for subversion as well as for constructive approaches to improvement.

Need for inner security. The security we all need most is inner security. Those things that tend to undermine our inner security and our "self" values will naturally be resisted. Those things that help reinforce our inner security will be enthusiastically pursued and accepted. Adding dignity and responsibility to work and respectability to the pursuit of efficiency and improvement are excellent ways of helping to satisfy the needs of the inner man.

Participation. Participation in solving our own work problems gives us a voice in determining our own destiny. We want to be our own masters —free agents—and this is often difficult to accomplish within the imposed limitations that seem necessary in modern society. However, many problems (in fact, almost all of them) can be successfully solved by group action, as a supplement to individual responsibility. Group action can lead to better problem solutions and to a genuine sense of accomplishment for those who have participated. New methods developed by consultative or group methods are bound to have a much better chance of being successful than those developed by outsiders. There is no fear of criticism, only a sense of accomplishment and pride. The process of communication can be facilitated greatly.

A person's leader exerts a profound effect on his reaction to his job and his organization. The leaders are key figures in any organization. They represent the organization to their men in their daily, on-the-job lives. They must provide guidance and encouragement. If they cannot lead their men, they will be unable to drive them. They must stimulate and support the self-esteem and emotional security of their men. These are some of the reasons why *participational* work simplification and improvement programs are usually aimed at supervisory and management levels, and why positive management leadership is important.

Desires of the working man. Many investigations have been undertaken to determine the "wants" of the working man. Almost invariably these studies indicate that money or pay is far from being the most important desire.

One of the surveys that yielded rather concise results was conducted by Elmo Roper for *Fortune Magazine.* Roper listed the four basic desires of the working man as:

1. A steady job at reasonably high wages.
2. A chance to advance.
3. A feeling of dignity and responsibility.
4. Just to be treated like "people."

These results imply that we all desire a certain amount of security—but not necessarily financial security or the extreme amount in high pay. Security and fair pay are strictly relative matters, and beyond a certain point (which is exceeded in most jobs) these factors are of only secondary importance in their absolute sense.

When demands for increased pay arise as the primary demand from a working group, it almost invariably indicates that a more basic need has been thwarted. We seem to be unable to demand inner security and dignity, for these needs are difficult to recognize and articulate—but we can easily demand a balm to soothe our feelings, in the tangible form of more pay. This fact is often ignored.

We all want a chance to advance, to express ourselves, to be a part of the group and to progress in our own eyes and the eyes of the group. We want to know that opportunity is available, even if we choose not to take advantage of it. We want to have a share in determining our own destiny.

The concept of dignity is quite basic to human nature. Work must not be degrading if work is to be satisfying and if we are to function as *human* beings. Responsibility is related to dignity. We are basically inclined to want to be responsible for our own actions—to be individuals. But responsibility also implies control over those things for which we assume responsibility. Responsibility without authority and control leads to frustration and degradation.

In summary, Roper states that we all want to be treated like people—

as human beings. This covers a lot of ground, and it is an excellent summary. It could also be stated as the Golden Rule.

SUMMARY

We have discussed many facets of human nature as influenced by and as they influence improvement activities within an organization. Specific examples have been presented to illustrate the lack of a positive approach to improvement, the subversion by human nature of attempts to achieve improvement and efficiency, and constructive approaches to improvement built upon the nature of human nature. We have also considered the role of management in leading their organization toward improvement, and we have implied that the influence of the human factor is as significant in the areas of leadership as in those areas being led. Improvement and efficiency must be desired by an organization, and approaches to its pursuit must be developed in such a manner that the *nature* of human nature assists in the quest for improvement. This is the key. It allows for full exploitation of science and technology and a natural expression of human capabilities, for the benefit of the organization and its individual members.

REFERENCES

1. Portions of this chapter are based upon material appearing in R. N. Lehrer, *Work Simplification: Creative Thinking About Work Problems,* Prentice-Hall, Englewood Cliffs, N.J., 1957.
2. Additional information about the Hawthorne Studies can be found in the following:
   Elton Mayo, *The Human Problems of an Industrial Civilization,* Macmillan, 1933.
   F. J. Roethlisberger and W. J. Dickson, *Management and the Worker,* Harvard University Press, Cambridge, Mass., 1939.
   T. N. Whitehead, *The Industrial Worker, Harvard University Press,* Cambridge, Mass., 1938.
3. Additional information on the Harwood Manufacturing Corporation can be found in the following:
   L. Coch, and J. R. French, Jr., "Overcoming Resistance to Change," *Human Relations,* Vol. 1, 1948, pp. 512–533.
   Schuyler Dean Hoslett (ed.), *Human Factors in Management,* Harper, New York, 1946.
   A useful summary of behavioral research is presented in Saul W. Gellerman, *Motivation and Productivity,* American Management Association, New York, 1963.

4. *Time,* February 23, 1962, pp. 93–97.
5. Stewart Thompson, *Management Creeds and Philosophies: Top Management Guides in Our Changing Economy,* Research Study Number 32, American Management Association, New York, 1958, pp. 79–84.
6. "Getting the Most Out of Your Computer," McKinsey & Company, Inc., New York, 1963.

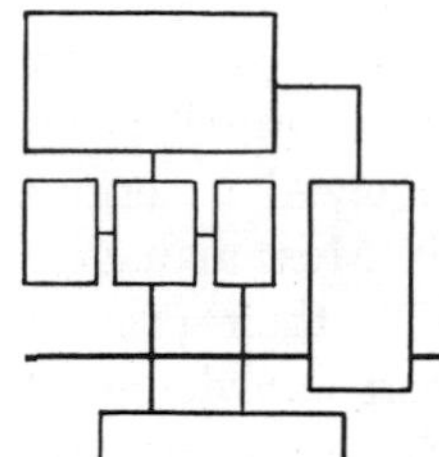

CHAPTER 16

STARTING AN IMPROVEMENT FUNCTION

MANAGEMENT, as well as staff specialists engaged in improvement activities, frequently ponders the question of how an improvement function can be started most effectively. Should a program be started in a formal way or informally? What responsibilities should be involved? What areas should be included? Where should it be fitted into the organization structure? What should be the organizational relationships? Should it start big? In essence, these questions all involve "How do we start?" "What should we do first?" "When and how should it be done?"

While there is no one correct answer, as each situation is highly individual, there are general concepts and principles that will help answer these questions. Some answers are likely to emerge from the general considerations outlined in earlier chapters. Additional questions will be answered by an analysis of how others have proceeded in introducing and developing an improvement function. The following example illustrates the starting of an improvement function and its evolution. Some parts are presented in detail, while other significant happenings have been condensed or omitted.

THE SITUATION

The ABC Company is a retail grocery chain operating about 150 retail stores served by four regional warehouses. This company has had a rapid growth and has enjoyed considerable success. In a period of 15 years it has expanded from a small operation with only 20 stores to its present size, with approximately 10,000 employees.

Rapid growth, while a cause for pride, also may carry with it many problems. Top management had become increasingly concerned about the future well-being of their company, for they recognized a serious deficiency within the management and supervisory levels. Most managers and supervisors were self-made men who progressed to their present position by virtue of hard work, determination, and expert knowledge of their previous jobs. While a virtue, their success was cause for concern. Top management came to realize that these self-made men were somewhat inflexible in their thinking, and this was cause to doubt their ability to visualize, in a creative way, what steps should be taken to insure continued success in the future. Surely, the company wanted to continue to grow and prosper. But, flexibility and creative thinking would be demanded if success was to continue.

NEW BLOOD

Top management decided that the company's future well-being could best be insured by bringing new blood into the organization. This was done by hiring a number of college graduates, including several experienced industrial engineers. The engineers were hired specifically with the idea of incorporating the improvement objective within the responsibilities of the line management positions to which they were assigned. They were experienced in staff improvement activities and had indicated potential relative to line management. They were expected to keep things running well and to develop improvements within their areas of responsibility.

The engineer-managers performed well. They fully justified the faith of top management. They were successful in discharging their assigned management duties, gradually earned the respect of their associates, were well-accepted by the personnel of the company, and achieved notable results in developing improvements within their areas of responsibility.

One of the engineer-managers was assigned responsibility for the warehouse. He developed a number of improvements in warehouse operation, one of which is of particular interest in illustrating the informal origin of a formal improvement function within the company.

He was faced with a shortage of dock space for truck receipt of merchandise. It seemed obvious that dock space was inadequate. Congestion and delays in receipt were typical. His subordinates were forceful in recommending to him that more dock space was necessary for proper operation. The main alternatives available to him were:

a. To request additional dock space.
b. To devise improvements that would increase the utilization of the presently available dock space sufficiently to eliminate the need for expansion.
c. To decrease the volume of truck receipts.

The third alternative was impractical, and not considered.

Being a thorough individual he analyzed the problem and determined that a 30% increase in dock facilities would be necessary if "adequate" capacity were to be had using the present methods of operation. This would require constructing three new dock positions to expand the present 10 to 13. This would cost approximately $12,000.

The present method of operation involved "dock delivery" of merchandise by the truckers serving the company. When a truck arrived and a dock position was open, the driver backed his truck into position. After receiving authorization to unload from the receiving clerk, the driver and his helper would open the trailer doors, position the bridge plate, and proceed to unload the merchandise by the "walk-out" method. This involved the handling of each box—picking it up inside the trailer, carrying it out of the trailer, and placing it on the dock. As the merchandise was placed on the dock, the receiving personnel would restack the merchandise onto pallets and move the loaded pallets back on the dock away from the truck position. When the unloading was completed the receiving clerk would verify the shipment, sign the shipping documents, release the truck, and authorize movement of all the merchandise into the warehouse. For a typical truck load, averaging 600 cases of merchandise, the turn-around time was 114 minutes.

The engineer-manager's approach to the problem, after he had learned what could be done to solve the problem (that is, install three more docks or decrease the turn-around time to about 80 minutes), was to consider various ways in which he might reduce the turn-around time. First, recognizing that the driver and his helper were required to carry the boxes out of the trailer and to place them on the dock, he considered requesting that the boxes be placed on pallets rather than directly on the dock floor. The objective was to save the extra work, required of the receiving personnel, of restacking the dock-delivered boxes from the dock floor on to pallets.* Then, recognizing that this was not a

* The engineer-manager later found out that this same scheme had in fact been tried out several years before. It did result in a saving of receiving personnel, but it proved to be entirely unworkable. The truck drivers did not accept the scheme as

solution to his problem about dock capacity (for it would do very little to decrease the turn-around time) he proceeded to visualize other schemes.

The next scheme was to have the receiving personnel help the driver and his helper unload and palletize the merchandise. This arrangement would involve complications relative to the rights and responsibilities of the trucker. It perhaps would reduce the turn-around time sufficiently, but it would increase the work and manpower requirements of the receiving department.

Next, light-weight roller conveyors were considered. These could be placed inside the trailer, advanced into the body as unloading progressed, and would eliminate the walking-out of the individual cases. This arrangement, however, would require warehouse personnel to be present at the dock end of the conveyor during the entire unloading cycle to remove the boxes from the conveyor and to transfer them to pallets. Additional personnel would be needed.

Loading of boxes onto pallets placed inside the truck and removing of the loaded pallets by fork-lift trucks was tried. This method decreased the turn-around time to about 75 minutes. However, the method did not operate smoothly because the fork-lift trucks were never available immediately after stacking of a pallet was completed. Occasionally, a delay of more than 10 minutes was experienced. The truck drivers were too impatient to wait, and some of them refused to use the prescribed method. Three additional fork trucks and drivers would be required to reduce the delays to an acceptable level. Even with the additional fork trucks it was doubtful that they could operate effectively because of the added congestion they would create.

The final scheme combined the best features of the other methods while avoiding their disadvantages. It was referred to as the "dolly" method. A dolly, with wheels or rollers on the bottom and retractable rollers (in the opposite direction) on the top, would be provided. This dolly would be the same size as a pallet and would allow an empty pallet to be moved into the trailer, placed next to the boxes being unloaded, and stacked until full; then the full pallet would be rolled out of the trailer onto the dock. The retractable top rollers would be raised and the loaded pallet would be shoved from the dolly onto a section of roller conveyor where it would wait until a fork-lift truck would move

---

one favorable to them, for they were slightly inconvenienced and recognized that the required dock-delivery did not imply that the boxes needed to be stacked on pallets on the dock.

it to the back section of the receiving dock. After the loaded pallet was shoved off the dolly, the top rollers would be retracted, an empty pallet placed on it, and the cycle would be repeated. This scheme would save considerable effort on the part of the driver and his helper, would minimize the work of the receiving personnel, and would decrease the turn-around time. Subsequent analysis and testing of this scheme proved it to be workable and to result in an average turn-around time of 73 minutes.

The problem of dock space was solved. The effective capacity of the dock space was increased by more than 30%. The consequences of the engineer-manager's innovations, however, extended beyond his immediate area. His developments required less manpower. He was able to transfer five men from the receiving dock to other work as a result of the "free" palletizing involved in the dolly method. The methods he developed could be used by the other regional warehouses. The net result was a savings of 20 men throughout the company (five men saved at each of four warehouses). His accomplishments were:

Dock expansion not needed: $12,000 saved
Twenty men released for other work: $100,000/year saved

The engineer-manager received considerable recognition for his accomplishments. Top management was well-pleased. Their scheme for management development was working nicely; but how could the impact be expanded? The other managers and supervisors were quite impressed by what had been accomplished and very much interested in how they might do similar things within their own areas of responsibility.

MANAGEMENT DEVELOPMENT

The stage was now set for expanding the management development efforts. The approach selected by top management was to undertake a management development program concentrating on the improvement function as a direct part of management's responsibilities. The approach was to provide training for management personnel in the concepts and techniques that would be useful in their work and to assist them in viewing their jobs in a new, more constructive manner.

Top management also had in mind a particular department where they thought improvement should be encouraged. The bakery was a source of concern. The superintendent was very likeable, had achieved a good record with the company, but he was not as progressive as desired. Top management felt that the bakery operations, while good, could do better. Comparison with other bakeries clearly showed that costs were not favorable. The bakery superintendent, however, maintained that he had achieved an excellent record and that his operation was "tops." Top management did not want to be "tough" with the superintendent. They wanted to find a way to help him recognize that he could achieve better results through a more creative leadership.

The approach to management development was through a work simplification program. The specific objectives which management had for this phase of the over-all program were:

1. To develop management.
2. To foster an attitude of "improvement-mindedness."
3. To stimulate improvements in one particular area (the bakery) and to encourage the supervisory and management personnel in this area to be more progressive.
4. To provide the background for introducing an industrial engineering department at some future date.

The program was executed by a consultant who spent one day per week with the company. He conducted a series of informal two-hour seminars at the end of the working day, and he held consultations with the individuals participating in the seminars during the other six hours. These consultations centered around informal assistance, helping the individual managers recognize the problems that they had in their jobs and developing approaches to solve these problems. A group of 20 managers and supervisors, representing all departments, participated in the program. The specific objectives of the seminar sessions and the consultation were:

1. To introduce the concept of dual management responsibilities—to get the work out without interruptions and to continually improve the activity involved in getting the work out, that is, to develop an attitude of improvement-mindedness.
2. To introduce the concepts and approaches of work simplification as an aid to better management.
3. To provide the participants with knowledge of some of the basic tools of problem solving.
4. To involve the participants in a group project where they would select a work activity within the company, study it, and develop improvements—and thereby demonstrate to themselves that they could successfully use work simplification as a tool for solving work problems.
5. To provide encouragement and assistance to the participants so that they would analyze their own jobs, determine what they should be attempting

to do to improve, and to systematically approach solutions to their problems.

The seminar sessions were informal. The consultant presented general concepts, general examples, specific examples related to the company's operations, and encouraged informal discussion by the participants. The seminar topics were:

1. Introduction to work simplification: its scope, approach, and examples.
2. The manager's job, work simplification as an aid to management, and further examples of work simplification.
3. The economic structure of the company, how it has progressed, where it stands today, challenges for tomorrow, the supervisor's and manager's challenge, areas of economic weakness, and areas of potential savings.
4. Approaches to identifying, defining, and solving problems, and the selection of an activity for group study.
5. An introduction to and practice in using selected problem-solving techniques: manpower and cost analysis, flow diagrams and the process chart, operation analysis, activity analysis (man and machine problems and crew coordination), and photography.
6. The human factor.
7. Group project.
8. Provision for a continuing activity which would encourage and assist the participants in the application of work simplification to their individual work problems.

The entire program extended over a period of three months. The informal counseling of the participants resulted in their recognition of many problems of which they had not previously been aware. In most cases, the participants did develop a more constructive attitude toward their jobs, and several of them demonstrated capabilities previously not shown. The group freely discussed their own problems during the seminar sessions and enthusiastically exchanged ideas and experiences. The group selected the bakery, with the encouragement of the bakery superintendent and his manager (who were participants), as the area of activity for their group project. The consultant and top management did some very subtle and gentle steering of the group and the bakery superintendent toward their selection of the bakery, but the choice was made freely by the participants.

The bakery activity was viewed as a whole, and one portion of the bread processing was selected as the subject for study. The problem was arbitrarily limited to the exiting of the baked bread from the oven to the point where the bread was ready for loading onto trucks for delivery to the stores.

Motion pictures, both regular movies and time-lapse, were made of all activities between the starting and ending points of the process.* These films were subsequently analyzed during the seminar sessions, and additional data were gathered. A simple record of the functional steps involved in the process was constructed.

After gathering the necessary factual data, the seminar participants proceeded to examine each part of the activity and to visualize how things might be done better. A number of suggestions for possible improvement resulted from this systematic questioning. These were carefully evaluated relative to the requirements of the work. Many were rejected as unworkable, but four main suggestions remained for further evaluation. These were:

1. To design and install a cooling conveyor. This would be a long, continuous conveyor that would allow circulation of the hot bread coming from the depanning operation until it had cooled sufficiently to be fed into the slicing machine. This would eliminate three operations (and three workers) but it would involve a capital expenditure. To request such an expenditure it would be necessary to have a preliminary design, price quotations, and a justification for the expenditure. This seemed a reasonable course of action, but time would be required.
2. To design a more suitable shipping container than the cardboard boxes now being used. Although several "better" designs were suggested, these would require careful testing to evaluate their merits and disadvantages and their costs. All of this would require additional time.
3. To combine the packing, labeling, and tying operations. All three of these operations were obviously "easy" jobs with a great deal of idle time. Their combination would eliminate two men from the process. A rough check of the idle work time for the operations indicated that a combination would require an improvement in efficiency of work methods if the combined task were to be performed within the time available. A new shipping container might influence the packing speed and help accomplish the needed methods improvement.
4. To combine the tying and labeling operations. Both of these tasks were underassigned (that is, they required less than the time available). The combined work times for both operations were slightly more than 100% of the available cycle time. A modest improvement in the work method resulting from combining the activities of both operations would allow satisfactory performance of the combined task.

* Motion pictures were used as a convenience, to "bring" the work being studied into the seminar, and to allow continual re-viewing of the activities until the analysis was completed, and also to demonstrate the use of movies as a tool of improvement endeavors to gather data, and to communicate ideas.

The seminar participants evaluated the desirability of pursuing these four possible changes. They decided to defer consideration of the first three because of the detailed studies and extended time required and to concentrate on the combining of the tying and labeling operations. A combined operation was developed and the individual acts required for performance of the dual task were listed. Considerable difference of opinion existed within the group relative to the time required to execute the new task. Some claimed that it could not be done within the available time, and others claimed that it could be. At this point the concepts of predetermined motion-time data were introduced, and a methods-time-measurement (MTM) analysis of the proposed operation was made for them. This analysis indicated that the operation could be satisfactorily performed within the available time. The group then completed the design of their new methods, evaluated what changes would be required and how much they would cost. The physical changes required movement of several conveyor sections, a modification of the tying machine guard to hold the label wetting pan, and an extension of the bed on the tying machine. These changes could all be made for $20.

After rechecking their proposal, to make sure they had not neglected any important factors, the group decided to proceed with the change. The tying machine bed was extended and the guard modified. The changes were explained to the bakery personnel * and the procedure was tied out. After a period of adjustment, lasting for about 15 minutes, the new procedure was working smoothly and as expected.

All of the seminar participants, including those from the bakery, were well-pleased with their efforts and the results achieved. With a little effort and $20 expenditure they had improved activities so that one man was now available for other work where he was needed. The gross savings were $5000 per year. The participants were sufficiently proud of themselves that they decided to edit the movies they had made during their study so that they could tell the story of a successful experience in learning how to use work simplification. This was done, and the movie was subsequently shown throughout the company. It was well-received, and the seminar participants were very proud not only of their accomplishments but also of the credit and recognition they received.

* The bakery personnel were well-informed about work simplification from the start of the seminars. The superintendent and his manager did an excellent job of passing on their newly gained knowledge from the seminars—and also of passing on their enthusiasm. More will be said about this in the following sections.

CONTINUING ACTIVITY

An important part of any improvement program is the follow-up phase, or the mechanism for encouraging a continuing use of the knowledge, skills, and experience gained during the more formal instructive phase of the program. As previously mentioned, the consultant involved with this improvement program spent one day per week working for the ABC Company. Two hours were spent in seminar activity, and the other six hours were devoted to individual consulting and counseling. The objectives of the individual counseling were to help the participants take a fresh look at their jobs, to map out a program of self-improvement (including improvement of activities for which they were responsible), and to help them develop solutions to their problems. The counseling approach was one of rendering staff assistance to line management. The consultant was the industrial engineering "staff," on a part-time basis, for the company. Individual consultation was continued beyond completion of the seminar sessions and was well used by the participants.

Additional seminar programs were undertaken, starting about two months after completion of the first program. The individuals completing the seminars continued to display untapped qualities of competency, imagination, and ingenuity. Many of them were so enthusiastic and successful that they inspired their subordinates and other managers to develop improvements, to request the opportunity to participate in one of the future seminar programs and to request the assistance of the industrial engineering "staff."

Within two years it seemed appropriate to establish an industrial engineering department. The line managers were requesting staff help to the extent that the consultant's available time was not sufficient. Top management thought the time was right for formalizing the improvement function. A new department was established and charged with the responsibility for continuing the work simplification activities and for rendering staff assistance to any request from line management.

SIDE BENEFITS

During the period following the start of the first work simplification seminar the participants developed some very worthwhile improvements. Many of these were developed in conjunction with "staff" assistance. Many others were developed exclusively by the managers themselves. Two of these improvements will serve to illustrate the character of the side benefits derived from the management improvement program.

FIRST EXAMPLE

One of the individuals participating in the work simplification seminars was in charge of the shops of the ABC Company. During the early phase of the seminars, prior to the group project, he had carefully evaluated improvement potential of the various activities for which he was responsible. One of the activities that he thought should be improved was the assembly of supports for display stands. These were welded angle-iron frames to which a wooden base and wooden back-up strips were attached. The operation had been performed by two of his workers off and on for about two years. The men had devised the work method, which involved placing the welded frame and base together in a fixture on top of a work bench. While the frame and base were held in alignment, bolt holes were drilled in the wooden base; the holes in the metal gusset plate were used as guides. The frame and the wooden base were then lifted from the fixture, bolts inserted in the holes, washers and nuts placed on the bolts, and the nuts were tightened with a power wrench. The second man placed the back-up strips on the frames. The partly assembled support was placed at the side of the work bench, with the base on the floor and the upright leaning against the bench. The wooden strips were aligned on the upright, drilled (the holes in the angle-iron were used as guides for the drilling), bolts inserted, washers and nuts attached, and the nuts tightened with a power wrench. This was repeated for all of the shelf brackets, with almost all of the work being done in a squatting position. The supports were subsequently used in the construction of display stands. Any variation in the dimensions of the supports, or misalignment of the back-up strips, required adjustment and shimming during assembly and installation.

The supervisor had ideas about what could be done to improve the operation. However, he did not want to dictate the changes to be made. He wanted the workers themselves to originate the ideas for improvement. He had previously told his workers of his experiences in learning about work simplification. He asked these two men what could be done to simplify and improve their task. The immediate reaction was one of defensiveness. They had been doing the job for over two years, and all possible improvements had long since been made. They were using power tools and a fixture to align the base and frame while the holes were drilled. The operation was already perfected.

At this point, the supervisor related several examples of improvements that had been discussed in the seminar sessions and explained more about the philosophy of improvement. He then asked them if they would think it over and see what ideas they could develop for possible improvements. Obviously, it was uncomfortable to work in a squatting position. It was difficult to accurately align the back-up strips while in this position and using a wooden rule. What could be done to improve these conditions?

The supervisor again discussed the matter with his men the next morning. They had developed a number of ideas. By mutual discussion of the pros and cons of the various ideas the three of them decided on the exact changes to be made.

A new fixture was made from a scrap piece of boiler plate. The angle-iron frame and all wood pieces were to be properly aligned by the fixture, and the entire assembly could be performed without removing the materials from the fixture. Cut-outs in the boiler plate would allow access to all bolt locations. The fixture was to be mounted on supports that would allow working in a standing position. There would be space for materials and tools where they would be conveniently accessible.

The new fixture was constructed and put to use. The entire cost of making the change, including the worker's time and the materials for the new fixture, was slightly less than $50. The results were excellent. A subsequent cost analysis showed a direct savings of $800 on the quantity of assemblies that would be made during the next year and an indirect savings, due to virtual elimination of the adjusting and shimming during assembly and installation of the stands, of more than $1000. These savings, however, were not the major gains. The pride of the two workers who had improved their own jobs, and the effect of their enthusiasm upon other workers, was far more valuable.

SECOND EXAMPLE

The second example of the side benefits resulting from the management development program occurred in the bakery. The reader will recall that top management had as one of its objectives in undertaking a formal work simplification program the stimulation of leadership and the encouragement of improvements in the bakery area. The group project of the work simplification seminar participants involved the bakery. The reader will also recall that the bakery superintendent and his manager did an excellent job of sharing their experiences in work simplification learning with their people. Improvement-mindedness had become a way of life in all bakery activities.

The bakery operated many hours of overtime, to meet production requirements. One activity that regularly required overtime operation was the production of brown-and-serve French hard rolls. The rolls were formed into individual balls of dough by a roll machine and deposited on a narrow belt conveyor. The conveyor passed the dough balls under an inclined pressure pad, where they assumed an elongated shape, and then carried them past one of two seeding stations. If the individual dough balls had touched each other while being drawn under the pressure pad or were otherwise misshaped, they passed the seeding stations, were collected in a catch pan at the far end of the conveyor, and subsequently recycled through the roll machine. At the seeding stations the individual elongated dough balls were picked up, moistened in a pan of water, and placed wetted-side down in one of two seed pans. The dough balls were then picked up, pressed into the seeds until properly seeded, and carefully arranged on baking tins, seeded-side up, and separated one from the other. When the tins were filled with 24 dough balls, the tins were picked up and placed on racks. When the racks were filled, they were moved to the proofing oven where they remained until the dough had risen and the rolls were ready for baking. The rolls were then prebaked, packaged, and shipped to the retail stores. Yearly requirements were 390,000 dozen rolls. This required a nine man crew to work a total 1300 hours, much of which was on overtime.

Improvements in this activity were principally accomplished by the lead man who was in charge of these nine workers. He received encouragement and assistance from the superintendent and manager, but he is due credit for recognizing the problem, visualizing a solution, and actually developing, testing, and successfully installing the solution.

A machine called a Pan-O-Mat was used for making hamburger buns. This machine received the dough balls formed by the roll machine and placed them in trays containing four pockets. The dough balls were subsequently deposited onto baking pans, arranged in rows of four each. The lead man visualized taking advantage of the machine's ability to align dough balls. If he could figure out some way to elongate the dough balls and to have them deposited, in rows of four, onto baking tins, then perhaps this machine could be used. The seeding could perhaps be done after the dough had been proofed, just prior to baking.

Seeding of the rolls after proofing was tried. The raised dough was moistened with water spray, and seeds sprinkled over the tops just prior to baking. The results were excellent. The quality was improved.

The Pan-O-Mat machine was equipped with an inclined pressure board, and after some adjustment and testing, the new scheme worked nicely. Now all that was left to do was to rearrange the process and give it a real test. This was done by attaching the roll machine to the Pan-O-Mat and feeding baking tins onto the pan conveyor. One man tended the machine, a second fed baking tins onto the conveyor, a third and fourth checked the elongated dough balls on the tins to make certain they did not touch, and a fifth man placed the full tins on the racks. Rolls were being produced at the rate of 1360 dozen per hour compared to 300 dozen per hour by the old method.

The racks, after being filled with trays of dough balls, were moved to the proofing ovens as before. After the dough had risen, the racks were moved to the oven where the tins were placed on a table so that the rolls could be sprayed with water, sprinkled with seeds, and then fed into the oven.

The test was a success. The new scheme was adopted as standard and put to regular use. Needless to say, the bakery superintendent, manager, and (in particular) the lead man were all extremely proud of the new arrangement for making brown-and-serve French hard rolls. Nine men were required by both methods, but the new method was so much more rapid that overtime operation was almost entirely eliminated. Roll quality was improved and yield increased.

In order to communicate the results achieved in improvement endeavors to top management, and also throughout the entire organization, the consultant was available to assist in preparing improvement reports. These reports summarized the original situation, defined the problem area and objectives sought, presented recommended solutions, summarized how the proposed solution would be effected and the results that would be obtained, and analyzed the cost consequences. The reports were frequently used to request authorization of specific changes in operating procedures, as well as a device to report improvement accomplishments and to credit the proper persons. Typically, the reports included the following, supplemented by sketches and photographs:

1. Identification of the activity, department, and (most important) the individuals responsible.
2. A statement of specific objectives.
3. A brief description of the present method.
4. A listing of proposed changes.
5. A brief description of the proposed method, how the changes will be made, and how the new method will operate.
6. A listing of comparative data for the old and new methods.
7. An evaluation of the proposed method, usually involving determination of the savings resulting from the new method.

WORK SIMPLIFICATION REPORT

DEPARTMENT: Bakery DATE: December 1954

ACTIVITY: Making French Hard Rolls.

ANALYZED BY: C. W. Rowe, J. T. Mitchell and M. H. Scarborough.

REASONS FOR ANALYSIS:
1. To decrease overtime
2. To improve roll quality
3. To increase yield and decrease rework
4. Cost reduction

PRESENT METHOD: (See the layout sketch for the present method) The rolls are discharged from the roll machine onto the conveyor, where they pass under a pressure board, and onto Station 1 or Station 2. They are picked off the conveyor, dipped in water and placed in pans of seed. Rolls that "double" are allowed to continue on the conveyor past Stations 1 and 2 to the end of the conveyor where they fall onto a catch-pan. These "doubles" are periodically returned to the roll machine and reworked. The rolls that have been place d in the seed pans are picked out of the pans, rolled in the seeds if necessary, and placed on sheet pans, 24 rolls per pan. When these pans are full they are carried to racks and placed on the racks. When full, the racks are pushed to the proofing box, and placed in the box until ready for baking. The racks are then removed from the proofing box, pushed to the oven, and loaded into the oven for baking.

The net production by the present method is about 300 dozen rolls per hour. A considerable amount of reworking is required. A nine man crew is required for the work steps outlined.

PROPOSED CHANGES: A pressure board attachment on a PAN-O-MAT would allow a considerable increase in the speed with which rolls could be made and placed in the pans. The seeding could be done at the oven just prior to baking, without handling the individual rolls. Rolls are to be wetted by a water spray, and the seeds applied by sprinkling over the top of the rolls. These changes not only will increase the speed of making rolls, but will improve the quality.

PROPOSED METHOD: (See the layout sketches for the proposed method) The rolls are discharged from the roll machine directly into the PAN-O-MAT. The machine operator checks the loading of the pans, removes "doubles" and fills any empty pans. The rolls are fed through a pressure pad, and discharged 4-at-a-time onto sheet pans. The rolls are straightened on the pans, and the pans

Figure 16-1. The Improvement Report.

are transferred to racks when they are fully loaded with 24 rolls. The racks are pushed to the proofing box when full. After proofing, the racks are pushed to the oven where the pans are removed and placed on the seeding table. The rolls are sprayed, seeds sprinkled over top of them, and they are then fed into the oven.

The net production by the proposed method is 1,360 dozen rolls per hour. The same nine man crew is required. Rework is almost entirely eliminated. The roll quality is considerably improved.

COST ANALYSIS:

Production by present method = 300 dozen rolls per hour

Production by proposed method = 1,360 dozen rolls per hour

Nine men required by both methods

Yearly requirements are about 390,000 dozen rolls

Time required to produce yearly requirements by present method is 1,300 hours for nine men, or 11,700 man hours.

Time required to produce yearly requirements by the proposed method is 287 hours for nine men, or 2,583 man hours.

At $1.50 per hour, the cost by the present method is $17,550

the cost by the proposed method is $ 3,875

SAVINGS: $17,550 - $3,875 = $13,675

COST OF CHANGE: The only expense involved in the change is for a pressure board attachment for the PAN-O-MAT. This costs only $20.00. The PAN-O-MAT is available.

OTHER ADVANTAGES OF THE PROPOSED METHOD:

1. Overtime work to make French hard rolls is almost entirely eliminated.

2. Rework is almost entirely eliminated.

3. Roll quality is greatly improved.

LAYOUT FOR IMPROVED METHOD --
MAKING FRENCH HARD ROLLS

ROLL MACHINE

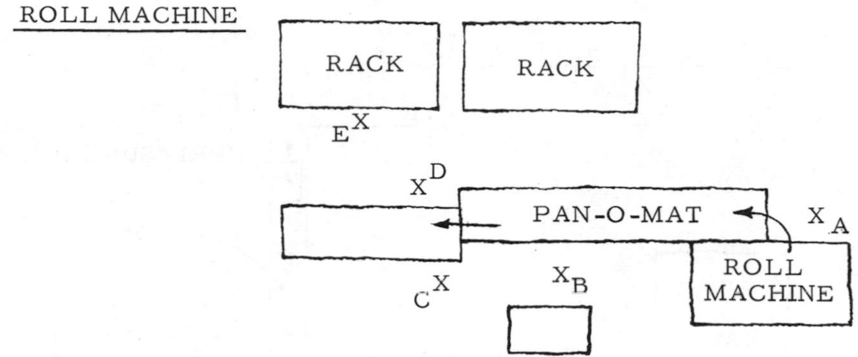

WORKER A OPERATES THE ROLL MACHINE AND PAN-O-MAT

WORKER B FEEDS SHEET PANS INTO THE PAN-O-MAT

WORKERS C & D STRAIGHTEN THE ROLLS ON THE SHEET PANS

WORKER E CARRIES SHEET PANS TO THE RACKS

OVEN

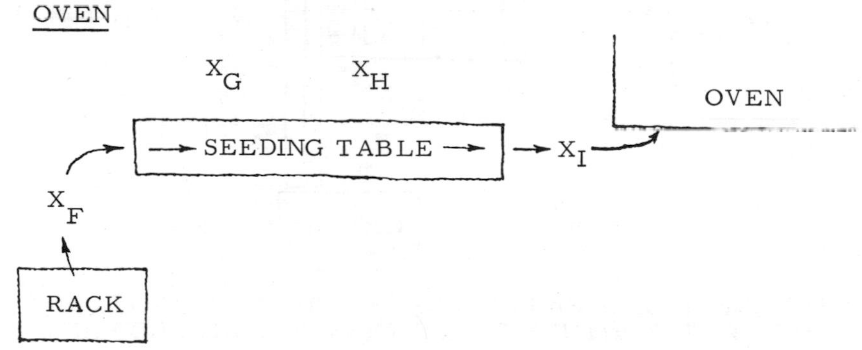

WORKER F REMOVES THE PANS OF ROLLS FROM THE RACK AND PLACES THEM ON THE SEEDING TABLE

WORKER G SPRAYS THE ROLLS WITH WATER

WORKER H SHAKES SEEDS ON THE ROLLS

WORKER I LOADS THE ROLLS INTO THE OVEN

9 MEN REQ'D. -- PRODUCTION 1360 DOZ. /HR.

LAYOUT FOR PRESENT METHOD --
MAKING FRENCH HARD ROLLS

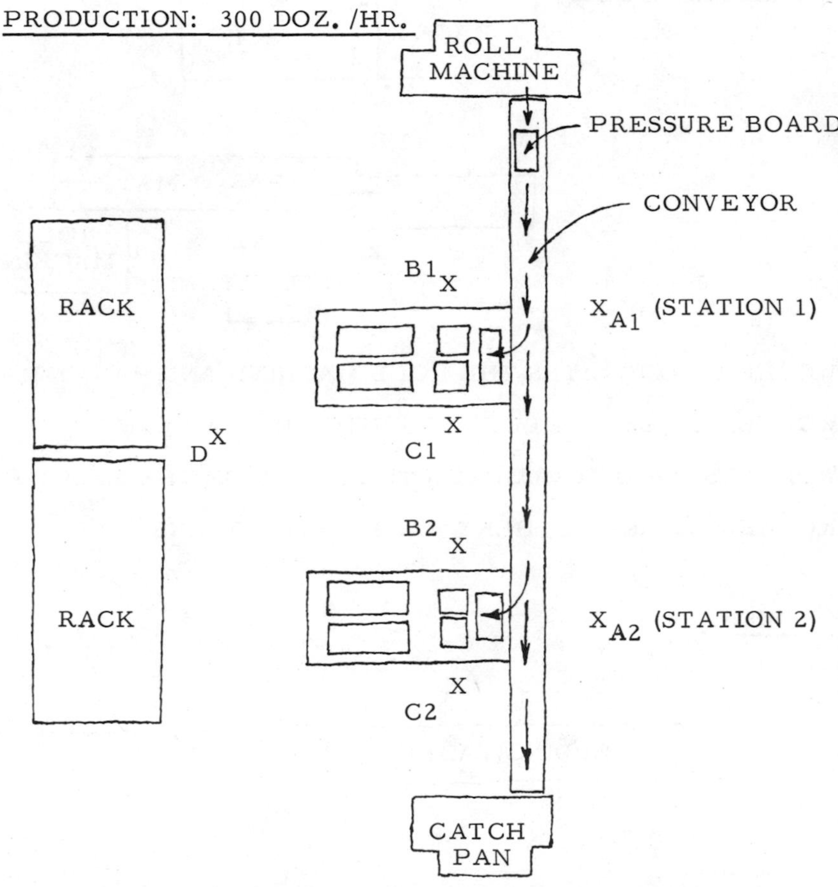

WORKER A1 & A2 PICK ROLLS OFF THE CONVEYOR, DIP THEM IN WATER & THEN PLACE THEM IN THE SEED PANS.

WORKERS B1 & C1 OR B2 & C2 PICK THE ROLLS FROM THE SEED PANS & PLACE THEM ON SHEET PANS.

WORKER D CARRIES THE SHEET PANS TO THE RACKS.

2 MEN REQ'D. AT OVEN -- A TOTAL OF 9 MEN REQ'D.

8. A statement of the costs of adopting and installing the proposed method.
9. A listing of other significant advantages associated with the proposed method.

A report was prepared for the roll production improvements (see Fig. 16-1), consisting of two pages of descriptive material, and two layout sketches—one for the old method and one for the new.

MORE CONTINUING ACTIVITIES

Management and supervisory personnel gradually accepted the idea of improvement as one of their prime responsibilities. They also accepted the concept of staff assistance to help them devise ways to do their jobs better. The staff assistance was helpful, complemented their own individual efforts, and resulted in full credit for accomplishment being given to the line people who had the problems that were solved.

Following the first seminar, the other ideas for improvement in bread processing, which were suggested during the group project, were investigated. A cooling conveyor was designed, justified as a worthwhile installation, authorized, installed, and placed in operation. This change resulted in releasing three more men from this activity. Several new shipping containers were designed and tested. These did not possess sufficient advantage over the present containers to justify a change, so none was made. The combining of packing, tying, and labeling, which was somewhat dependent upon improvement of the shipping container, was further considered and judged to be unworkable.

Many of the problems that the seminar participants identified, with the assistance of the consultant, were subsequently solved—some by the individuals and some with the help of the consultant. The participants requested staff help in undertaking a variety of additional studies, many with very worthwhile results.

As the work simplifications seminars were repeated and extended to all areas of the company, similar individual improvement activities developed. The newly created industrial engineering department became increasingly active and gradually expanded in size. It was invited to engage in a wide variety of special project studies.

OPERATIONS RESEARCH

About four years after the start of the work simplification program, top management became increasingly concerned about several problems of their own. These were:

1. A tight money situation and the need for additional working capital to accommodate store modernization and expansion activities underway.
2. A need for expanding warehouse capacity.
3. A problem of how to effectively utilize a computer that had been ordered without a complete analysis of how it would be put to use.
4. Continual problems of out-of-stock and over-stocked conditions.

The executive vice-president and the controller had started to think about operations research as a means of solving these problems. All of the problems seemed to center around the buying-inventory function. Perhaps the computer would offer opportunities for routinizing some of the buying-inventory decisions.

A preliminary investigation by the executives of operations research applications in similar situations in other organizations was less than satisfactory assurance that O.R. was the right answer. It was their decision to undertake a "pilot" study to determine the potential utility of O.R. and what could be done. The specific objectives of the pilot study were:

1. To investigate O.R. and its applicability to the problems of the company.
2. To investigate how the computer, which was on order, could be successfully put to use.
3. To determine if some buying function decisions could be made routine and incorporated into the computer-data processing system.
4. To develop better coordination in the buying-inventory area.
5. To determine if warehouse expansion might be avoided by decreasing inventory levels.
6. To determine if additional working capital could be freed by better inventory management.
7. To determine the consequences of a coordinated program of inventory management.

The pilot study was executed by the industrial engineering department with cooperation and support from the functional areas involved, direct participation by members of the controller's staff, and with guidance and technical assistance from outside consultants. The study extended over a period of three months.

PHASE ONE

The first phase of the pilot investigation involved preliminary study to determine the exact nature of the problem and the extent of the project. The buying-inventory area was examined to determine typical buying procedures and the factors which were of significance in these decisions. The scope of the investigation was limited to include only the warehouse, thus excluding any inventory problems within the retail stores.

The preliminary investigation revealed that the buying-inventory decisions were being made without adequate consideration of all significant factors and the consequences of these decisions upon other related areas.

The buyer's task was a difficult one. Each buyer was responsible for several hundred items. He was furnished regular reports for each item giving the average of the demand for a six week period, the demand for the most recent full week, the present inventory level, amount on order, and the amount received during the current week. He would relate this information with his expert knowledge of market conditions and of special item sales promotion in making his decisions of when to order and how much. Very close coordination with the transportation department did exist, and minimum transportation costs were realized in most cases by mixing carload lots and pooling orders.

The effect of buying decisions on warehouse and receiving operations, however, was not considered. The motivation of the buyer was to attempt to insure sufficient stock on hand to prevent out-of-stock conditions, even if this required a larger inventory than was really necessary. The buyers were unaware that receipt of truck shipments was less costly than receipt by rail. (Rail receipt required unloading and palletizing by company personnel.) They did not know of the cost reductions achieved by the dolly unloading method previously described.

Various factors influencing the total costs of the buying-inventory system were identified. The more significant ones were:

a. *The price-quantity relationship:* large quantity orders would usually result in lower per unit costs.
b. *Transportation costs:* full carload lots, pooled orders, and selection of the correct mode of transportation all influenced the cost of transportation. In general, large orders would result in minimizing transportation costs.
c. *Cost of ordering:* decreasing the frequency of orders by means of fewer and larger orders would decrease ordering costs.
d. *Cost of physical receipt:* rail or truck receipt result in different costs. Costs would also be influenced by the quantity relative to multiples of full pallet loads, for the handling of a partly filled pallet is almost the same as for a full pallet.
e. *Cost of space occupied:* larger order quantities require more warehouse space. Smaller orders, placed more frequently, would allow reduction of warehouse space for individual items.
f. *Cost of money tied up:* investment in inventory requires working capital. The larger the average inventory the higher the costs associated with investment, tax liability, and insurance.

g. *Cost of stock-outs:* being unable to fill a store order because of an out-of-stock condition is undesirable. Management policy is to discourage out-of-stock situations, which results in an inflated inventory.

The main factors considered by the buyers when deciding about orders included:

a. The price-quantity relationship.
b. Transportation costs.
c. Cost of stock-outs.

The principle influence of these considerations was to encourage large quantity orders and a large inventory. Past experience with out-of-stock conditions inclined the buyers to avoid reoccurrence. All significant factors did not receive a balanced consideration.

PHASE TWO

After the preliminary investigation, the nature of the inventory was considered relative to what might be done to formalize the buying decisions and to have all of the previously mentioned factors considered. The inventory was first analyzed to determine which items were most important and secondly which items were amenable to formalized treatment.

As with most inventory situations, it was found that a limited number of items were responsible for a major portion of the inventory problem (that is, they were high volume, high value, or high inventory cost items). These items were the ones most deserving of detailed study, for they represented the largest potential savings. There was also a limited number of items having just the opposite characteristics, for which little savings could be realized through formalized inventory control.

The inventory items were next considered relative to the predictability of demand. Three general categories were established:

a. Steady demand, which could be projected for the future on the basis of past experience.
b. Seasonal demand, which fluctuated according to some pattern and could be projected if past experience provided the pattern of fluctuation.
c. Random or unpredictable demand, where past experience provided no sound basis for predicting the future.

The steady demand items were the ones most suitable for formal analysis and routine handling. The high value items were the ones most likely to yield larger savings from formalized treatment. Seasonal demand items presented substantial difficulties in establishing the patterns of fluctuation and in obtaining sufficient valid data with which to work. The buying-inventory decisions for low-value steady-demand items, while potentially not as important as those for the high-value steady-demand items, could be formalized with ease.

One of the most formidable problems encounteed in the study, which is a problem quite frequently encountered in O.R. work, was the acquisition of the necessary data. Great quantities of data were available, but not in the form needed for the study. These data were historical working data and accounting data not intended for the new use. The inventory-control study required gathering much original data and the analysis and reinterpretation of past records.

PHASE THREE

Emerging from the preliminary phases was a plan for the balance of the pilot study. It was decided to concentrate upon development of formalized inventory control for steady demand items, considering high value and low value items as separate groups. Formal handling of seasonal demand items did not seem practicable and economic at that time. Formal handling of random demand items was impossible. Both of these could best be left to the experience, skill, and judgment of the buyers. Formalization of the steady demand items would minimize the need for attention from the buyers and allow more time to be devoted to the items that really needed attention. Detailed analyses were made for selected items that typified the inventory system.

REORDER POINTS

Reorder points were established by analyzing the demand data for the past two years, establishing trend lines, and analyzing the reorder-replenishment cycle time. Variability of demand and of the reorder-replenishment cycle were considered, and the reorder points established. This was done to hold the risk of an out-of-stock condition to an arbitrarily established probability value, which was acceptable to management. Calculation of the quantity which would result in the desired probability value (risk) of the demand (during the reorder-replenishment cycle) exceeding the supply (reorder point quantity) determined the reorder points.

The demand data was obtained by reanalyzing available records. The reorder-replenishment data was also available, but required detailed analysis of several sets of records in order to determine when items were first requested and when these items were received, placed in inventory, and available for filling store orders.

ECONOMIC ORDER QUANTITIES

Economic order quantities were established by relating the significant cost factors previously listed (see Phase One) in a cost equation, and then manipulating this expression to determine what quantity would result in minimum cost. Some of the factors favored large order quantities (that is, the price-quantity relationship, transportation costs, and ordering costs) while the other factors favored small order quantities (that is, cost of space occupied, cost of money tied-up). Some factors were influenced by the specific conditions associated with the order and the item (that is, mode of transportation, rail versus truck receipts, multiples of full pallet loads, size of "line" position allocated to storage of the item). The cost equation allowed each factor to be properly considered relative to its influence on total costs, and the determination of the order quantity that would result in a proper balancing of all factors to achieve minimum total cost.

MONITORING SCHEME

The next phase of the study was to determine how the formalized inventory control procedures could be integrated with the data-processing system and how the computer would be related. A punched card system was currently in operation. As store orders were received, inventory cards were removed from the card files; the ordered quantities were deducted from the item master cards and the individual item cards used for warehouse ordering and accounting. Weekly summaries of inventory and movement data were furnished to the buyers. No formal reorder points existed. The buyers would decide in their own fashion what was to be ordered, in what quantities, and when.

The formalized inventory control procedures could be incorporated into the punched card system with little difficulty. After the store orders were deducted from the item master cards, an additional operation of checking the balance against the reorder point would detect the items that should be reordered. This information could be furnished to the buyers, or with the computer it could be used to produce a purchase order which would subsequently be checked and approved by the buyer. In effect this would routinize the buying-inventory decisions for all items that were handled in a formalized manner and allow the buyers more time to concentrate on the items where their skill was really needed.

Provisions were also made to facilitate monitoring of the system by the buyers. The formalized decision rules were not intended to replace the buyers, but to simplify their complex task. This was done by routinizing that portion of their work that could be satisfactorily routinized. The buyers were still as important as ever, and would need to know if and when any of the factors that were built into the formal decision rules changed. Periodic auditing of the cost factors would help, but it also would be necessary to check continually on shifts in the demand rates. Demand data would still be furnished to the buyers, but it would be supplemented by statistical analyses to detect changes in the rates. A visual display in a modified form of an $\overline{X}$ & R quality control chart could be furnished for any item that the buyer desired to examine. This display would use a punched card with the center row scaled to represent the average demand rate and the next to the top and the next to the bottom row scaled to represent plus and minus three sigma control limits. Weekly demand data would be punched into the card relative to the average and the control limits. Points falling beyond the control limits, or a significant run of points above or below the center line, would signal that a change in the demand characteristics had likely occurred and that the situation merited examination. The cards could also be used to visually check the fluctuations in weekly demand.

EVALUATION

The final phase of the pilot study was to evaluate the work relative to the original objectives of the study. The applicability of operations research to the problems of the company was clearly demonstrated. In addition to the inventory problem area, several other significant problem areas where O.R. would be useful were located during the pilot study. Plans for future use of O.R. were formulated.

The problem of how to put to use the computer that was on order was also solved. The computer would allow consolidation and extension of the punched card system covering all inventory control and accounting. It would also allow effective routinizing of many buying decisions, thus supplementing the skills of the buyers and freeing them for concentration on items demanding their attention.

Lack of coordination relative to inventory matters was clearly evident. The formal decision rules forced coordination by means of properly weighting the various significant factors incorporated into the determination of reorder points and economic order quantities. The process of gathering data for these determinations resulted in the development of a keen awareness throughout the company of the importance of close coordination that had not previously existed.

Formal inventory control was applicable to about 60% of the inventory items. Analysis of typical items indicated that formal control of this

60% would result in a substantial reduction in the required warehouse space. Most items would be carried in lesser quantities, but a few items would have their inventory levels increased. The indicated reduction was more than adequate to offset the additional space that had been requested. A warehouse expansion was not really needed. Reductions in inventory would release a considerable amount of working capital for other uses. A savings of $500,000 per year was indicated as possible with inventory control.

The results of formalized inventory control of two items is presented in Table 16-1. Both items are steady demand items: one is a high

TABLE 16-1

Comparison of Inventory Cost for Two Steady Demand Items as Affected by Formal Inventory Control

	High Demand Item		Low Demand Item	
	WITHOUT	WITH INVENTORY CONTROL	WITHOUT	WITH INVENTORY CONTROL
Average Demand per Week, in Cases	180	180	9.6	9.6
Variation (Standard Deviation)		12		.8
Reorder Point	Not used	350	Not used	25
Expected Number of Stock-Outs per Year	Unknown	0.2	Unknown	0.2
Reorder-Replenishment Cycle	Equal Probability of 6, 7, or 8 days			
Economic Order Quantity	Not used	117	Not used	45
Average Order Size	180	117	12.5	45
Number of Orders per Year	52	80	40	11
Ordering & Receiving Costs	$62.92	$70.40	$35.20	$9.77
Average Inventory, in Cases	390	197	25	33
Average Inventory Value	$865.80	$437.34	$122.50	$161.70
Cost of Money Tied Up	$82.25	$41.55	$12.90	$15.38
Transportation Cost Penalty	0	0	0	0
Warehouse Space Costs	$11.00	$8.25	$2.75	$2.75
Total Annual Relevant Costs	$156.17	$120.20	$50.85	$27.90
Ratio of Total Annual Relevant Costs to Annual Sales Value, %	0.75	0.58	2.08	1.14

demand item, while the other is low. Total annual relevant costs are reduced from $156.17 to $120.20 for the first item and from $50.85 to $27.90 for the second. Expressed as a percentage of the sales values of these items this is a reduction from 0.75% to 0.58% and from 2.08% to 1.14%. The percentage values are particularly significant, for net profit is considered to be good if 1% of total sales. Relative to profit, the costs affected by inventory control are quite sizable. It should also be noted that the most economical inventory policies require a decrease in average inventory for one item and an increase in the other.

SUMMARY

In this chapter we have seen the gradual development of a formal improvement function, starting with top management recognition of the need for improvement and progressing to a staff department serving various levels of management with both traditional and the modern industrial engineering technology. The developments have been presented in a modified critical incidence manner in order to highlight some of the important occurrences that had a significant influence upon the decisions and reactions in regard to the development of the improvement function within the organization.

Several concepts that are significant in their influence upon the developments should be re-emphasized:

1. Recognition by top management of the importance of management development and strengthening of the line organization.
2. Recognition by top management and the entire organization of the importance of management responsibility for continual improvement within their areas of responsibility, and the importance of recognition and reward for successful achievement of improvement.
3. Gradual recognition by management and supervisory personnel of the benefits of staff help.
4. Demonstration by the "staff" that they could effectively assist when called upon to do so.

The development of the improvement function was step-by-step, geared to the needs of the organization. The key to success was creation of an awareness of a need for help, and then rendering the service effectively. Each of the incidents discussed had substantial influence in developing the environment necessary for a viable and formalized improvement function. The entire cycle from first recognition by top management that the organization needed better management and supervision until the staff was serving all levels within the organization with modern improvement technology, as well as the traditional, occupied a period of almost seven years.

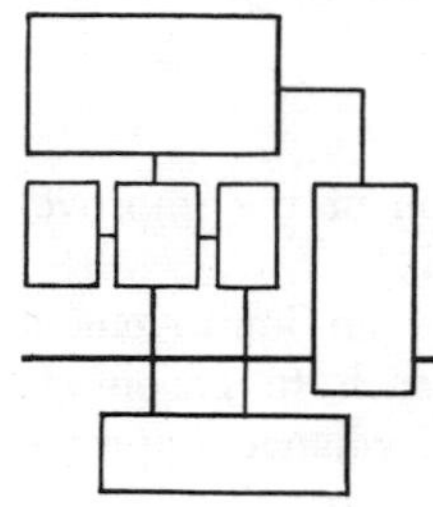

CHAPTER 17

EVOLUTION OF AN IMPROVEMENT FUNCTION

THE GENERAL THEME that we have frequently referred to stresses the importance of incorporating the improvement concept within all managerial and supervisory jobs, and of providing the individual manager and supervisor with staff assistance in pursuing improvement objectives. The nature of staff assistance and the scope of the improvement function as a combined line and staff responsibility will depend upon the needs of the organization, the abilities and strengths of the individuals involved, and the recognition of ways in which needs can be satisfied. Successful improvement endeavors are the result of evolution. They are in response to the dynamic and changing needs of an organization. They are greatly influenced by developments consciously and laboriously borrowed from other seemingly unrelated areas. The approaches, the organizational patterns, and the functional responsibilities are continually changing in an attempt to better satisfy a need and develop better service strategy.

Our next example of a broad improvement function is within a very progressive company producing a broad line of packaged consumer goods and industrial chemicals—Procter & Gamble.* The formalized improve-

* Appreciation is expressed to The Procter & Gamble Company and, in particular, to Mr. Richard A. Forberg, for furnishing the information upon which this chapter is based.

ment function is most evident in the industrial engineering division at the corporate level, and in the associated industrial engineering departments at the plant level. This particular organization has been selected as an example because:

1. It is an outstandingly successful company.
2. The industrial engineering function, as a manifestation of the improvement function, is broad and progressive—and successful.
3. It provides an excellent example of the evolution of an improvement function, particularly relative to the team-goal approach to encourage management participation in cost reduction and performance improvement.
4. It clearly shows the importance of research and development within the improvement function directed toward improving the effectiveness of improvement function activities.

Prior to a detailed examination of the development of the team-goal approach, some introductory comments on the organization of the industrial engineering function are in order.

THE COMPANY

The company is large, with more than 33,000 employees, over 60 plants located throughout the U.S., Europe, Central and South America, and Asia, and has current annual sales in excess of $1,600,000,000.

The company operates on a decentralized basis. Separate operating divisions for product groups, and individual plants, enjoy a fair measure of autonomy in their operation. Their main responsibility is satisfactory performance and profitable operation within a framework of general policy and procedure guides.

The company has long been a leader in the area of industrial relations, having introduced profit sharing in 1885 and guaranteed annual employment in 1923. Responsibility for these programs, and for job evaluation and industrial relations in general, rests with a special organization group. Quality control also lies outside of industrial engineering because of its early organization as a specialized function.

IMPROVEMENT FUNCTION

Industrial engineering activities were first introduced into the company in 1928 when time study was used to establish performance standards to be used in conjunction with wage incentive systems in various areas of manufacturing. Industrial engineering gradually expanded its area of operation, still within the manufacturing activities, until the present organizational arrangement emerged in 1958. This function now is composed of a centralized activity, the industrial engineering division reporting to the vice-president of manufacture, and industrial engineering departments reporting to the managers in plant organizations. In addition, there are industrial engineering activities in buying, traffic, sales, advertising and in the production engineering and field construction activities of the engineering division.

The improvement function, initially centered in manufacturing but extending its influence considerably beyond the common interpretation of manufacturing, has been extremely successful—and extremely progressive. New developments in operations research, management sciences, behavioral sciences, etc., are continually evaluated relative to their utility within the organization. Considerable continuing attention is given to evaluation of the improvement function relative to what it is accomplishing, what it should be attempting, and how it can render better service to the company. Operations research was used early as a complement to the more traditional industrial engineering technologies. Computer applications and their effect upon managerial performance have been researched, and basic concepts from the behavioral sciences have been incorporated into procedures for stimulating continually improving performance.

The general corporate organizational structure is shown in simplified form in Fig. 17-1. The organizational position of the industrial engineering division is shown in Fig. 17-2.

OBJECTIVES

The specific objectives that guide the industrial engineering function are first a reflection of the company's strong concern for the well-being of their personnel, extending the pioneer work of profit sharing and guaranteed annual employment into the present situation, and secondly a dedication to render effective staff assistance to line management to help them do their jobs well and to pursue continual improvement. These objectives are:

1. To assist in designing jobs and working environment in keeping with the needs and abilities of the "whole" man. This requires working with the research and development division (which has design responsibility for products and processes), with the engineering division (which has design responsibility for process equipment, services, and structures), with the line organization (who, as the users, contribute to design decisions),

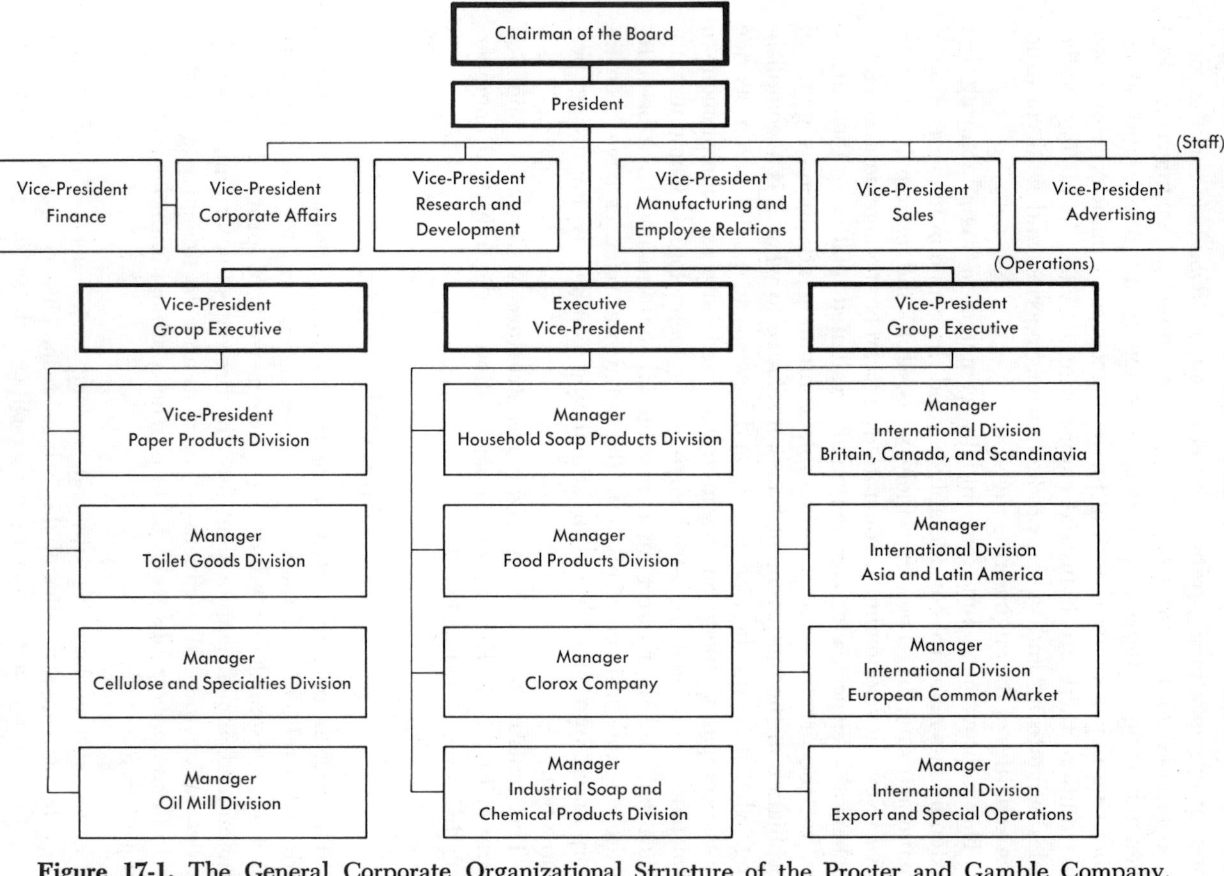

Figure 17-1. The General Corporate Organizational Structure of the Procter and Gamble Company.

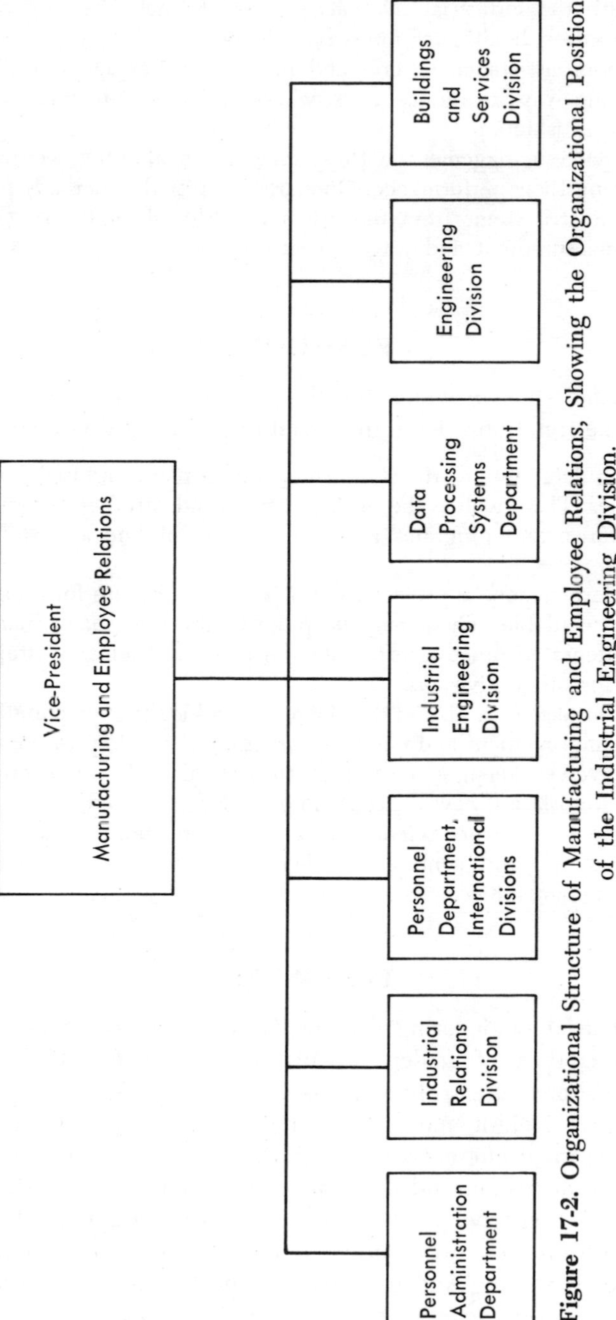

Figure 17-2. Organizational Structure of Manufacturing and Employee Relations, Showing the Organizational Position of the Industrial Engineering Division.

and with the industrial relations division (which has responsibility for worker safety, health, and industrial relations).

2. To render assistance to line and other staff personnel in finding and evaluating ways to reduce costs, while maintaining or improving quality and job satisfaction.
3. To provide management with systems for evaluating, controlling, and improving their performance. One large part of the methods for pursuing this objective stems from the original industrial engineering activity of work measurement and wage incentives.

FUNCTIONS

The specific ways in which the three objectives are pursued are embodied in the functions of the industrial engineering division. These are:

1. To stimulate, guide, develop, and control plant industrial engineering activities. This involves the design of plant industrial engineering policies, procedures, and programs and the auditing of line and staff execution of them.
2. To undertake special project work of a systems nature for which no other staff is available. These may be projects affecting many plants, dealing with integrated process, information or service systems, or projects undertaken for other divisions.
3. To undertake research and development, and long range planning, relative to the improvement and effective extension of the improvement function. This involves keeping abreast of theoretical and professional developments, translating new concepts into workable procedures for use in improvement endeavors, selective recruitment and professional development of personnel, and continual evaluation of improvement activities and service opportunities.

PERSONNEL

The industrial engineering division is composed of about 80 persons and is organized into four departments as shown in Fig. 17-3. A majority of these personnel are technically educated: nine have industrial engineering degrees; eight, mechanical engineering; six, chemical engineering; two, electrical engineering; two, other engineering or science; nine, business administration and economics; and four, mathematics or statistics. Eight of these people have advanced degrees, two of which are Ph.D's. In addition to formal education, all of these individuals have received special training and experience opportunities to round out their knowledge and understanding of industrial engineering as viewed and practiced by the company. Many of the individuals are active in professional organizations.

In keeping with the third basic function of the industrial engineering division—to undertake research and development, and long range planning, relative to the improvement and effective extension of the improvement function—approximately 50% of the efforts of the 80 people in the division are devoted to research and development.

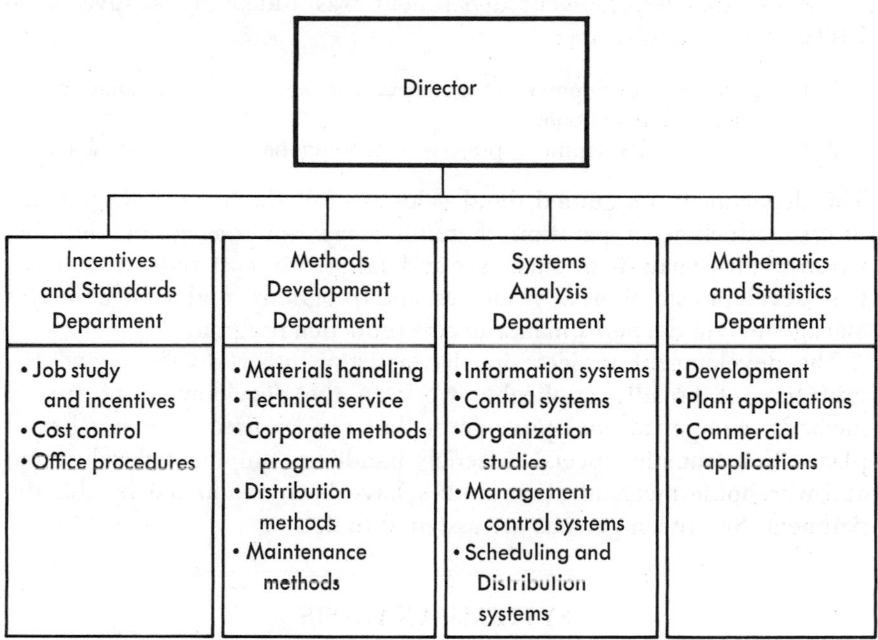

Figure 17-3. Simplified Organization Chart of the Industrial Engineering Division. Total personnel: 79 (technical staff 49, administrative 8, nontechnical 22).

The central industrial engineering division is the main concentration of improvement function activity within the company. However, the efforts of the central group are supported by approximately 400 individuals within the plant industrial engineering organization and by line management. Approximately 5% of the time of line supervisors—of which there are more than 2000—is devoted to improvement activities.

INCENTIVES AND STANDARDS

The incentives and standards department is the oldest in the division, emerging from the first industrial engineering activities, started in 1928.

It is divided into two sections: job study and incentives, and cost control. Each section is responsible for the development of plans, programs, policies, procedures, and the auditing of their execution at the plant level within their area. Eleven people are assigned to this department.

METHODS DEVELOPMENT

The methods development department was added to the division in 1943 and is responsible for:

1. Research and development of concepts and methods for stimulating cost reduction and innovation.
2. Execution of development projects extending beyond individual plants.

This department has guided the development of the team-goal approach to cost reduction, preparation of training aids, interchange of ideas between plants, analysis of successes and failures in cost reduction activities, development of new strategies and programs, and evaluation for management of the performance of cost reduction programs.

The development projects involve assisting other divisions, and the execution of broadly applicable work in the development of special methods, equipment, and procedures that can be used by a number of plants. For example, special materials handling equipment development and warehouse mechanization studies have been conducted by this department. Seventeen persons are assigned to it.

SYSTEMS ANALYSIS

One of the significant changes that has taken place in industrial engineering in the past ten years has been a broadening of the scope of concern away from narrow and isolated problems toward concern for the systems opportunities for improvement. This shift has been stimulated by awareness of the importance of systems interactions and the development of analytical problem-solving techniques in systems engineering and operations research.

The systems analysis department was established in 1953 to supplement the traditional job analysis approach, long associated with industrial engineering, with the systems analysis approach to design and cost reduction. Following are examples of some major projects which are currently occupying the attention of the department:

1. Mechanized information systems to provide management with the basic, timely knowledge necessary to manage their assignment.
2. Studies to determine marketing strategy, to measure effectiveness thereof, and to make tactical decisions of a timely nature as the market reacts. Information systems are an essential part of such studies.
3. Extensive studies of the distribution system to establish controls for sales and traffic management.
4. Control systems, dealing with such things as production scheduling systems, inventory control, and simulation of system performances.
5. Process systems, dealing with such objectives as decreasing down time, determining optimum processing cycles and evaluating differences in operating practices between units for a variety of processes.
6. Building analysis, concerned with the long range needs and planning for construction, renovation, and service facilities.
7. Management study, concerned with research of management processes and the development of new systems to improve management effectiveness.

Twenty-three people are assigned to the systems analysis department.

APPLIED STATISTICS

The applied statistics department was established in 1956 in response to the needs for expert mathematical and statistical assistance arising from various systems analysis problems, and to provide training and assistance in the basics of operations research for staff and management personnel. In addition to extending the skills of the systems analysis department and advising on mathematical approaches to problem solution, this group has assisted in training personnel within the industrial engineering division, the research and development division, and the engineering division. Fourteen people are in the department.

MAINTENANCE AND CONSTRUCTION

The procedures for applying methods study, planning, estimating, scheduling, and follow-up to maintenance work in all plants originates from the industrial engineering division. The execution of the program at the plant level has been assigned to plant engineering. The same general procedures are also used in field construction activities with some construction contractors. Considerable effort is directed toward innovation in methods, materials, and tools, as well as to a systematic preplanning of work activity. Eighty people are involved in this work in plant engineering departments.

OFFICE METHODS

Industrial engineering was originally concerned with manufacturing, with primary concentration on improving the efficiency of manufacturing operations. Gradually, the scope of industrial engineering has expanded to one of concern with improvement of all activities. The growing complexity of forms, reports, and paperwork in general, as well as the development of data-processing equipment and computers, has caused many organizations to devote special staff attention to developing improvements in the office area. Prior to 1958, the manufacturing office methods department was the direct responsibility of the line organization. With the transfer of responsibility to the industrial engineering division, this area of activity now receives the broad range of industrial engineering attention for forms control, procedures analysis, and methods improvement. Mechanization and computer applications are the responsibility of the data processing systems department. One person works with these problems at the present time.

PLANT ORGANIZATION

Industrial engineering at the plant level reports directly to the plant manager. Its main function is to provide local management with the tools and methods to execute their jobs and develop improvements. A major share of industrial engineering effort is devoted to execution of the programs formulated by the central industrial engineering division. The balance of their time is available for special project work of a local nature, frequently requested by the plant manager. Approximately 400 persons are involved in plant industrial engineering. The departmental size varies from 5 to 40 people. The plants have from 125 to 1400 employees, with 20 to 220 persons in various management positions.

Organization of the industrial engineering departments is indicated in Fig. 17-4. The departmental responsibilities are divided into three main sections, and in some of the smaller plants include a fourth—office management. These sections are work measurement, cost control, and methods improvement.

Work measurement and cost control have long been the mainstay of the plant industrial engineering activity. Installation and maintenance of wage incentives, cost analysis, and economic justification of capital expenditure requests are old responsibilities for the department.

These activities were gradually supplemented by work associated with the cost control program and supervisory bonus. Substantially all departmental management personnel have performance standards established for their work. Such factors as direct wages, indirect labor, repairs and maintenance, yield, loss and depreciation of raw materials, steam, power, etc., are measured for the specific operating conditions and "ideal" standards are established. Management personnel receive their bonus on the

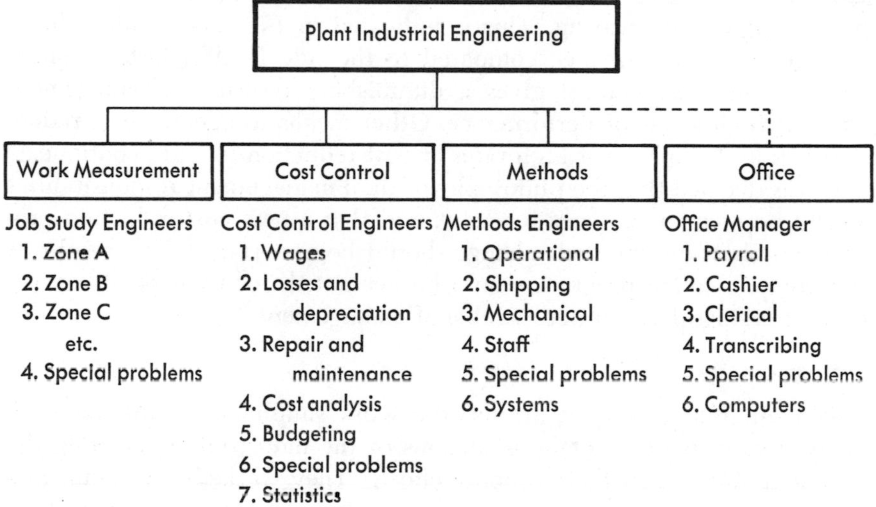

Figure 17-4. Industrial Engineering Organization at the Plant Level.

basis of performance relative to the standard. Because of the ability of industrial engineering personnel to predict from their cost control and work measurement data, the responsibility for preparation and control of budgets was placed with the department.

The most recently added responsibility is methods improvement. This activity concentrates on all activities having an indicated potential for improvement and cost reduction. Methods engineers, using the typical approach and techniques of motion and time study, have studied and improved a wide variety of operations throughout the plants. Training in the techniques for cost reduction and the introduction of work simplification was offered to supervisory and management personnel. Starting in

1945, a program to encourage continuing and active management participation in methods improvement and cost reduction was inaugurated.

NEW APPROACH

It will be recalled that the central industrial engineering division is responsible for long range planning, research and development, and better improvement strategies. Also, this company stresses the dual responsibilities of management—to accomplish results and to achieve improvement. The continual evaluation of improvement endeavors indicated that by 1945 steady progress had been made, but that the relative rate of improvement was decreasing. This is indicated in Fig. 17-5, which shows average plant performance compared to the "ideal" after installation of cost control. Cost control gives a diminishing return for management effort at high levels of performance. Other means to achieve cost reduction required emphasis if high rates of cost reduction were to continue.

It was decided that the philosophy of dual management responsibilities should be recognized more formally, and that a new cost reduction program emphasizing methods change should be undertaken. The results of this company-wide program would be evaluated, for each plant, on the basis of savings per year per member of management.

THE SPECIALIST

The program was built around the work simplification programs already underway. The methods sections of the industrial engineering departments intensified their training efforts. They worked with plant and management personnel, as experts, to analyze problems recognized by management. During the first year of the program the average savings per member of management was $700. The savings for the following year were approximately the same.

THE COORDINATOR

The results achieved by the new approach to management participation in cost reduction were encouraging and worthwhile. Even so, it was felt that they were not as substantial as they should be. It was recognized that human nature inclines one to resent implied criticism, and the specialist approach did imply criticism of past management practices; therefore a new approach was adopted. The main change in the program was a shift away from the specialist approach to a coordinator approach. This required an entirely different attitude, and perhaps personality also, on the part of the methods engineers responsible for executing the program.

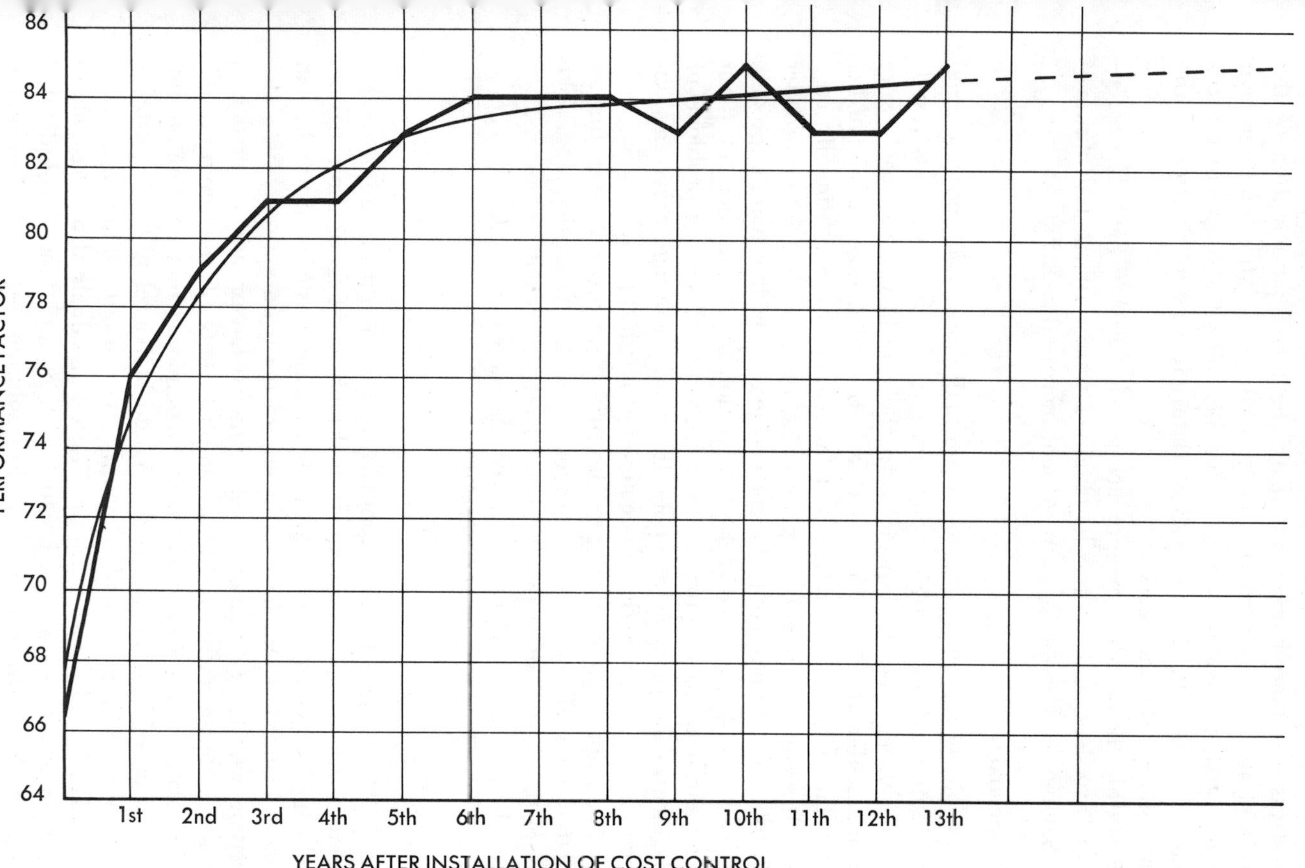

Figure 17-5. Performance Improvement Relative to "Ideal" Performance after Installation of Cost Control.

More stress was placed upon obtaining the direct participation of the supervisors and managers in the recognition and solution of their own problems, with the coordinator stressing his role of assisting in the coordination, gathering, and analysis of data. He was to function as the personal staff for the managers.

The shift to the coordinator approach was initiated in 1949. The reception was excellent, and the results obtained were a substantial improvement. Savings per member of management increased to $2300.

TEAM APPROACH

The results of this program were continually examined and evaluated by the central industrial engineering division. The improvements resulting from shifting from the specialist to the coordinator approach were significant. Other modifications, to take better advantage of human behavior relative to cost reduction and innovation, were continually considered. It seemed as though cooperative action, extending into a broader area of plant operations, could be encouraged by using a team approach. This would enlist a more direct participation of all members of plant management in a broad approach to identifying and solving problems of significance to the plant as a whole. It would encourage a systems approach as a supplement to the job-centered problem approach.

The team approach was adopted in 1952. The program was further stimulated, and all levels of management actively participated. The nature of the improvement problems involved underwent a change. They became broader and the resultant savings increased to an average of $3000 per member of management per year.

ONE PLANT AN EXCEPTION

The shift from the specialist approach to the coordinator approach resulted in a substantial improvement in the effectiveness of the program. The change in strategy was in keeping with the basic nature of human behavior. The shift from the coordinator to the team approach was also in keeping with the fundamentals of human behavior, and resulted in a substantial improvement in the accomplishments of the program. All levels of plant management were now participating in a cooperative improvement endeavor. Each individual could better relate the importance of problems within his area of responsibility to problems affecting broad sections of the total plant operation. These individuals also were able to develop an awareness of the broad problems and how a coordinated approach by key individuals would allow solution. Again, the fundamentals of human behavior had been built into the approach to encourage creativity and innovation on a broader front. The role of the methods engineer would be even more important as a coordinator, as well as a skilled resource, to help in data gathering, analysis, and implementation.

Consideration of extending the group dynamics approach of using teams included the possibility of incorporating team goals. Ideally, these goals should represent the improvement potential within a plant that could be realized by the teams if they performed well. To be a valid motivational device not only must the goals be realistic and realizable by the teams, but they must also be accepted as such by the teams and by management in general. The coordinator, representing the industrial engineering department and plant management, could be very instrumental in establishing goals and areas of endeavors—but the teams, and management in general, must accept them as their own.

The team-goal approach was tested in one plant. The goals were established in terms of specific problem areas, results desired, and savings sought. Over-all goals became a summary by top management of the subgoals established by the operating managers and supervisors. The coordinator continued to function strictly as a coordinator and advisor. The results achieved were excellent—$5000 savings per member of management in 1954. This was substantially better performance than being achieved by the other plants using only the team approach.

TEAM-GOAL

The team-goal approach was extended to other plants, with complete coverage in effect by 1957. The improvement program performance increased from an average of $3900 savings per management member in 1954 to $6000 in 1957. Since then the team-goal approach has performed exceptionally well, increasing the savings of each management member per year from $6000 to $10,200 in 1959, and to $15,500 in 1962. The cost of the program compared to the saving is approximately 1 to 10.

SUMMARY

This company has been a highly successful, progressive organization. Recognition of the desirability of a formal improvement function goes back many years. Profit sharing was initiated in 1885; guaranteed annual employment in 1923, and industrial engineering (as a formal improvement function) in 1928. The improvement function has continued to be important within the company and has gradually expanded to its present scope. It is primarily centered within the industrial engineering division at the corporate level and within the industrial engineering departments at the plant level.

Even though the improvement function is effective and successful, attention is continually directed toward ways in which it can be made more effective. Research and development, within the function, is directed toward this objective. This concern for improving the improvement function resulted in the evolution of the team-goal approach to encourage management participation in a broad scale improvement endeavor. These developments complemented other improvement activities and increased

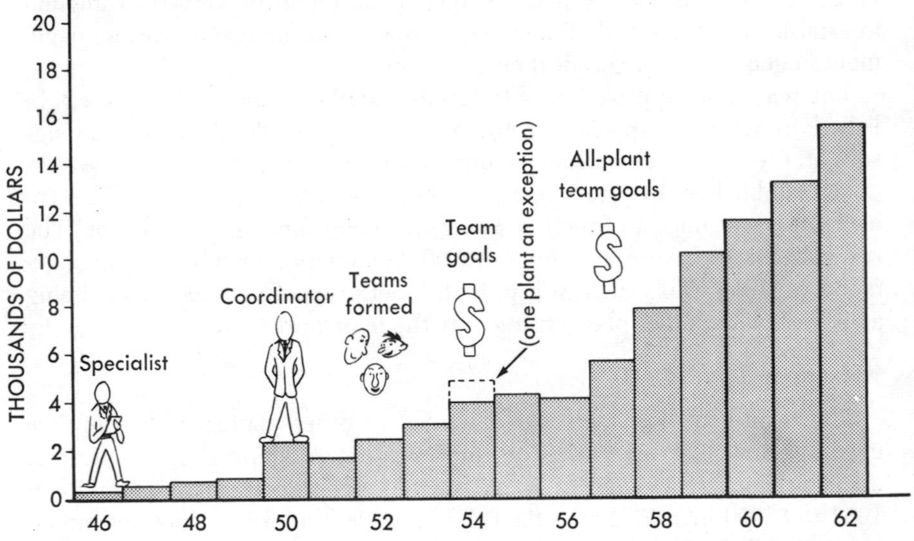

Figure 17-6. Yearly Savings per Member of Management during the Evolution of the Team-Goal Approach.

the effectiveness of the total organization. They illustrate the importance of continual efforts to search out service opportunities, adapt basic knowledge from other fields, devise new strategies to serve management and the organization, and to encourage an evolution of the improvement function in keeping with the needs of the organization and the abilities of the personnel involved with the improvement function to serve these needs. As a reminder of the evolutionary development of the highly successful team-goal approach to expanding the impact of the improvement function, the yearly accomplishments throughout its development are presented in Fig. 17-6.

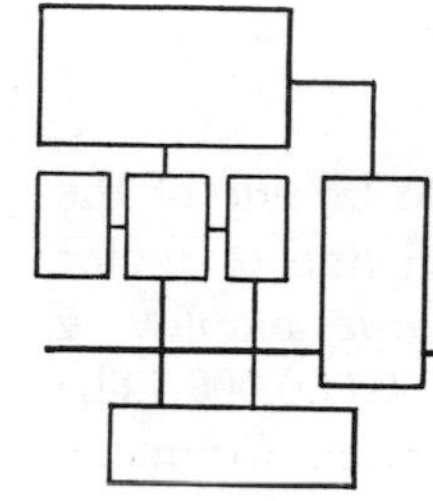

CHAPTER 18

STARTING A PARALLEL IMPROVEMENT ACTIVITY

MANY ORGANIZATIONS are coming to recognize the need for a broad-scale, company-wide improvement function. Within some organizations this recognition has been caused by natural expansion of previously limited improvement activities. This is the evolutionary approach, which has been demonstrated, and very frequently is an expansion of a production-based improvement program.

Within some organizations, however, it does not seem desirable to broaden the improvement efforts by expansion of a manufacturing-based program. It may be more expedient and efficient to establish parallel improvement activities and thus allow the manufacturing-based program to continue to devote its attentions to only the manufacturing sphere. When this approach is followed, great care is necessary to insure adequate coordination of efforts. Frequently this coordination does not exist, and fragmentary approaches are made to the exclusion of the true systems needs. Much beneficial work may be done, but the total effectiveness of the scattered approaches fall far short of the actual need for improvement.

Our next example has been selected to illustrate the starting of a parallel improvement activity—concentrating on systems of managing—which complements existing improvement activities within the manufacturing area. It relates the establishment of a new staff function called systems and data services within the International Harvester Company.*

THE COMPANY

International Harvester Company (IH) is considered to be one of the "blue-chip" American companies, producing a diversified line of motor trucks, farm, construction, and military equipment. It is large, employing about 100,000 people, with plant investment of over $750,000,000. The company has had an active industrial engineering program for many years, at both the plant and corporate levels. This activity has been successfully concerned with traditional industrial engineering problems, processing, and manufacturing research. The modern developments of operations research, automation, computers, etc., have had a substantial influence—but primarily in relationship to the manufacturing area.

The development at IH of operations research related to management problems as such and the development of management information-control systems has emerged outside of the industrial engineering activity. This can be explained partially in terms of "jurisdictional" prerogatives, partially in terms of the manufacturing area requiring the exclusive attention of the industrial engineering activity, and partially in terms of the boom in technology coming so rapidly that its impact upon all parts of the organization was not properly anticipated and planned for.

THE PROBLEM

Had IH previously had a broad-scale improvement function not confined to manufacturing, then perhaps the development of a parallel improvement activity would not have been necessary. However, by 1958 the top management of IH recognized that a problem existed—regarded mainly as one centering around the effective application of computer-information system technology and the management of information. Formal support for study and resolution of the problem came from the president and the controller and resulted in the establishment of the systems and data services (SdS) function throughout the organization—at the corporate, divisional, and operating levels.

Activities of other organizations were carefully studied, the opinions

* Appreciation is expressed to the International Harvester Company and, in particular, to Mr. John E. De Mots, for furnishing the film strip and the information upon which this chapter is based.

and needs of various management people were evaluated, and current activities related to computer systems and information-decision making activities were assessed. It was found that considerable activity throughout the company did exist—with seven computers and with tabulating installations in all manufacturing operations, in sales, sales accounting, and in the parts system and the material system. Equipment rentals for the year exceeded $3,250,000.

Clerical work simplification programs were active in many areas. A forms standardization and control program was being executed under the direction of the forms standardization section of the general accounting office. Systems activities were found in many areas—engineering, sales, sales accounting, manufacturing, and supply and inventory. One hundred twenty management people were engaged full-time in various aspects of systems work. However, the people responsible for directing this activity had other jobs to do and could provide guidance and direction only on a part-time basis. There was strong indication of variable understanding of the role of systems activities and the relationship of activity carried out in one department to those in other departments.

SYSTEMS AND DATA SERVICES

The study of computer, data processing, and information-decision making activities throughout the company led to the recommendation to establish a new staff function—systems and data services—to furnish specialized skill and handling of all activities having to do directly with the analysis, design, improvement, and installation of information-decision making systems and to operate all data-processing installations throughout the organization. Its primary objectives were to plan and manage the flow of all information not within the scope of the controller's function and to study and improve the application of such information for greater operating effectiveness. SdS was originated as a service organization, to provide advice, coordination, and control in all activities having to do with information-decision making activities. It was intended to provide additional staff help to enable management to devote the same kind of careful and expert knowledge and attention to the management of business information as they were directing toward the management of men, money, materials, and facilities. SdS was to make available to the entire corporate, divisional, and operating management the amalgamation of computer-related technology and management science as a means of achieving better management of information—and thus better management and more efficient operation.

SCOPE

The new function was intended to serve the entire company, to deal with information and improvement, and to supplement the activities of the controller's function as well as the manufacturing-based improvement activities. The controller and his staff would continue to be responsible for the evaluation and interpretation of the results of operation, the safeguarding of assets, the determination of financial position, and compiling estimates of future operations. These responsibilities encompass the audit and control of the acquisition, recording, and preparation of the data necessary to discharge the controllership responsibilities, the preparation and presentation of financial statements, and the verification of fiscal correctness of appropriation requests and proposals for changing policies. The manufacturing-based improvement activities were to continue to function as in the past. Both the controllership and the manufacturing functions were to utilize the services of SdS and were to provide assistance and support to the new function: for example, production standards personnel were to perform clerical work measurement services for SdS.

The corporate level SdS activity was to report to an executive vice-president. The divisional SdS activities were to report to the executive head of the division. The new function at the operating unit level was to be accountable to an official in the unit with unit-wide responsibility, for example, the works manager, the divisional manager of engineering. Each level of SdS was to exert functional influence over the next lower level, with responsibility for consultant services from outside the corporation reserved to the corporate level of SdS. The new function was to operate in a staff capacity at all levels, with operating responsibility for all data-processing installations.

INTRODUCTION OF SdS

The SdS function was made operational in 1959 and has since become increasingly active and influential. The new function was introduced by means of management meetings throughout the company—with a key SdS man outlining the SdS story, followed by an informal discussion. A 35 mm. color film strip was used to supplement the presentation. As a further illustration of the scope and organization of a parallel improvement activity and the approach to its introduction throughout an organization, the film strip (based on 1958 statistics) is reproduced, along with the general oral explanations which were informally presented with each picture. The meeting was opened with comments similar to:

> I'm sure you have recently read announcements or have heard about the formation of a staff function in IH called systems and data services. Also, I'm sure that most of you are wondering what systems and data services really is —what is its program, its scope, and its objectives. Probably you are also wondering how SdS will affect you. This film strip presentation, which we are showing today, has been developed for the purpose of explaining these points to you. If, following the presentation there are any points not clear to you, please ask questions. We will attempt to answer all of them, but if we don't know the answers, I can assure you that we will obtain them for you.

This was then followed by Fig. 18-1 through Fig. 18-43 and comments similar to the captions.

Figure 18-1. As you are all well-aware, there is an increasing need for information. We all need it, and when we have to make *some* decisions, we are even pleading for it. We say "information please!"

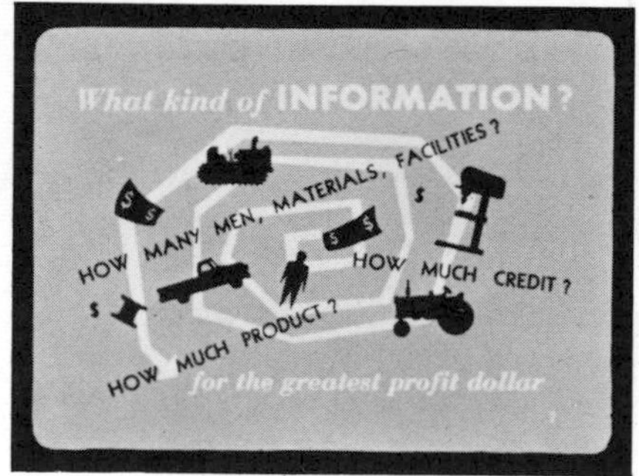

Figure 18-2. What kind of information are we talking about? We're talking about business information: how many men, how many materials, how many facilities, how much product, how much credit, and how to get the right information from all of this maze to obtain the greatest profit dollar? That's the kind of information we're talking about.

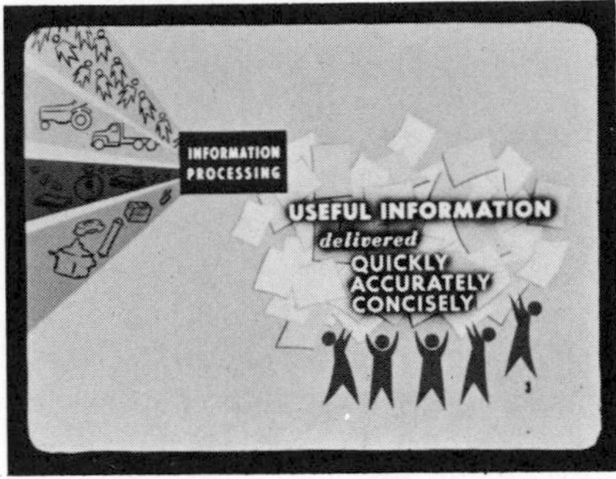

Figure 18-3. All of us are asking for better and more useful information. We are anxious to have information delivered quickly, accurately, concisely—information about men, products, money, or materials.

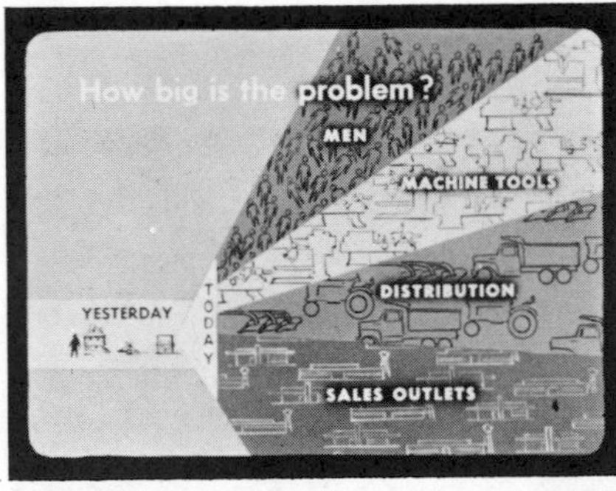

Figure 18-4. How big is the problem —our information problem?

Yesterday we had few machines, few facilities, limited materials, and few men who could communicate manually with each other.

Today, we have 100,000 men at IH and about $500,000,000 invested in facilities. The variety of products is tremendous with wide distribution. A variety with which you fellows are well-acquainted. And finally, we have sales outlets all over the world.

This all adds up to a tremendous information problem—a problem so large our present mechanical methods do not permit us to keep up.

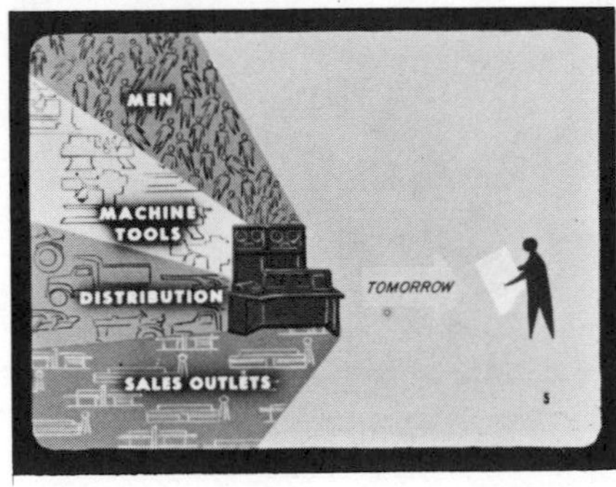

Figure 18-5. We must join the electronic age so we can reduce our information problem to a manageable size. Many of you undoubtedly realize, as I do, that missiles and space age rely heavily on mathematical techniques and on computers, which has permitted tremendous strides in this field. The thing we don't realize is that these techniques can be made available to us if we are smart enough to find a way to use them.

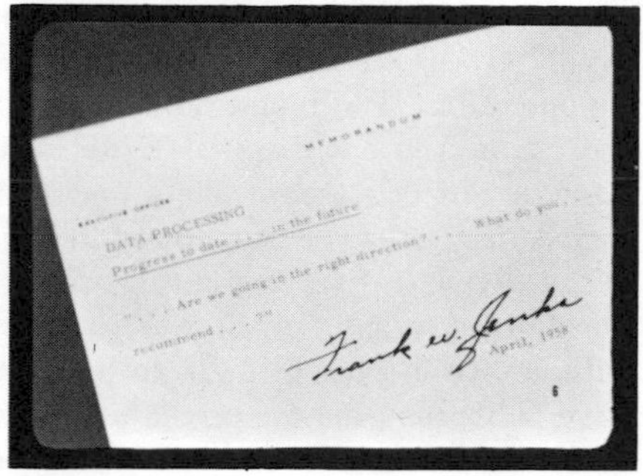

Figure 18-6. This is what prompted Mr. Jenks over a year ago, April 1958, to ask about data processing: What is the progress to date? What is the future? Are we going in the right direction? What do you recommend?

This lead to an inquiry conducted over a period of several months. Examined during the course of the inquiry were important items such as our existing effort, our existing goal, our existing programs, and our future: What was our potential? What was the opportunity at IH? What was the opportunity for our customers?

The testimony and impressions of more than 140 IH people in the field or in management generally, as well as many outside companies were evaluated and re-evaluated. It was found that some of our competitors were making significant strides in the field of information management.

It was the consensus of the testimony that IH should organize a new staff function.

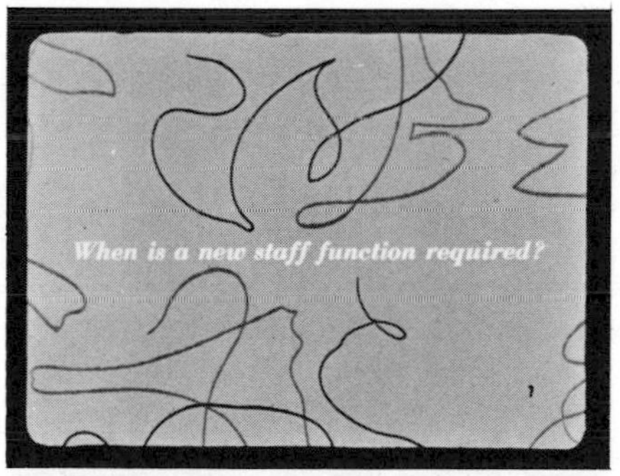

Figure 18-7. You may well ask, as was asked in the inquiry, when is a new staff function required?

Authorities in the field generally say there are certain signs to look for when a new staff function is required.

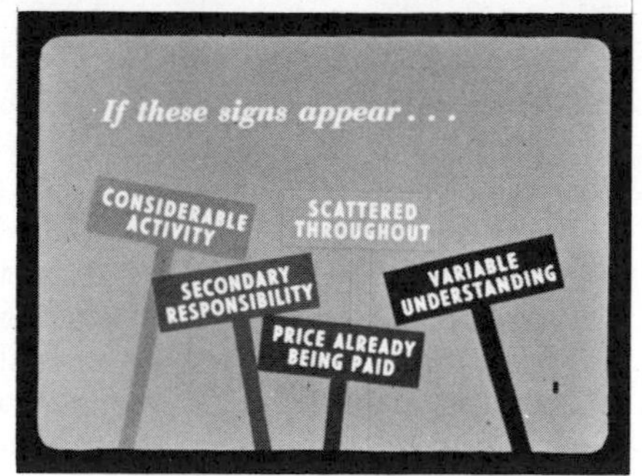

Figure 18-8. If these signs appear, then consideration should be given to a new function: considerable activity, scattered throughout the company, secondary responsibility, variable understanding, and the price already being paid.

What do we find in IH when we look for these signs?

Here are some of the things we found about "considerable activity" and "scattered throughout the company." We found seven computers, five 650 medium-sized computers and two large 705 installations. We found tabulating in almost all of our manufacturing operations. We found tabulating in sales and sales accounting, in our parts systems, and in our materials systems. We found clerical work simplification in many of our operations. We found systems activity going on at all fronts—in engineering, sales, manufacturing, sales accounting, and supply and inventory.

The people responsible for directing all of this activity had other jobs to do. Their primary assignment was in other fields. As the over-all importance of this activity increased it got to be a question of which of the two masters to serve. This new master or the job to which they were primarily hired or primarily qualified.

There was variable understanding as to how big was the potential; what were our abilities; what were our goals; what was the relationship of systems activity that was being carried on in one department or operation to those in other departments and operations.

Finally, the price was already being paid. Our IBM rentals in 1958 exceeded $3,250,000. We found 120 management people engaged full time in systems work. In addition, there were many people, probably including some of you in this room, who were spending some of their time in this field.

Yes, it was found that these signs appeared in IH—more than enough to consider the establishment of a new staff.

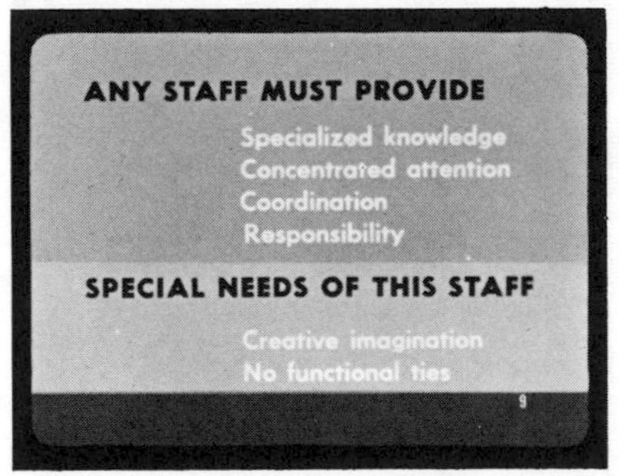

Figure 18-9. The question then was asked, "What should a staff provide?" Any staff must provide specialized knowledge, concentrated attention, coordination, responsibility. In addition, there are special needs of this staff: creative imagination, no functional ties.

Let's analyze what we mean by specialized knowledge. I believe an analogy is in order. Twenty or thirty years ago, in our shops, the foreman decided which machine tools to use, the various processes to be performed and their sequence, and how the material would flow within his department and into and out of his department. As these skills and tools became more and more specialized, it became necessary to establish a planning department for the shop—a planning department to develop route sheets, tool layouts, and material handling information. Just as this change was necessary in the shop, it is now necessary to make a change in the office. Certainly our machine tools are specialized whether they be computers, tabulating machines, or what have you. There are specialized methods regarding the way the office should be performing, and the way paper and information should flow from one department to another. Yes, we need a planning department for the office to develop tool layouts and route sheets and to become specialists in planning our office activity.

Why concentrated attention? Certainly if these people are to become specialists and educated, they must devote their full time to this activity. It must become their primary interest, permitting them to become professionals in this field. They no longer should have to choose between two masters.

You have heard discussions about how to integrate data processing and how information must flow freely between departments. This is just one example of planning and coordination. Consideration of objectives, plans of action, potentials and opportunities—all require coordination.

The next requirement is responsibility. I believe you should be interested in this consideration. In the inquiry it was found that where there was direct accountability in this field, good results had been made. In most instances, however, systems work was a job for all of us and the responsibility of none of us. One of the functions of a staff is to accept responsibility and accountability for costs, progress, and results in its field.

Then there are special needs of this staff. Just as with any staff, which must provide planning and do research and development, this staff must also provide creative imagination—the uninhibited perception to investigate traditional ways of doing things to see if computers, mathematical techniques or other means can give us better information with which to manage our particular function.

What about functional ties? It has been agreed that information management should be a new function—not an extension of an existing function—if information is to flow freely across functional lines. The facilities that are managed by this new function should be equally available to all.

With these questions answered, we then go on to the next question.

Figure 18-10. Where do we go from here?

We find ourselves currently on a modern hard top two lane road going in the right direction. Just as this road is the backbone of our country's transportation system, so it is also the backbone of our company's communication system. We find that we must maintain the backbone of the company's communication system.

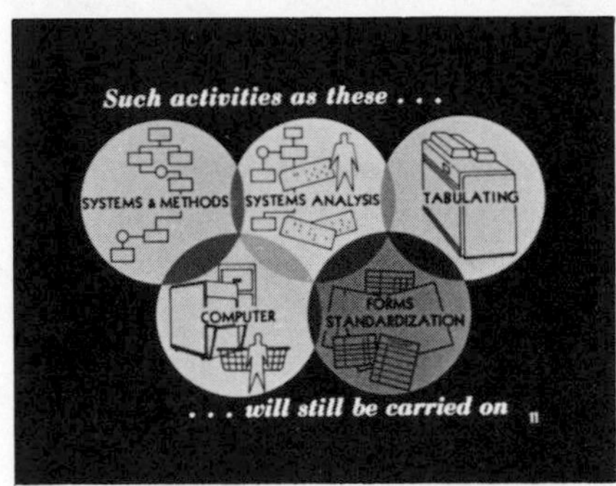

Figure 18-11. Such activities as these will still be carried on—systems and methods, systems analysis, tabulating, computer, forms standardization—as well as clerical work simplification. These tried and true techniques provide all kinds of opportunities, and tremendous potentials exist from the extension of these basic methods.

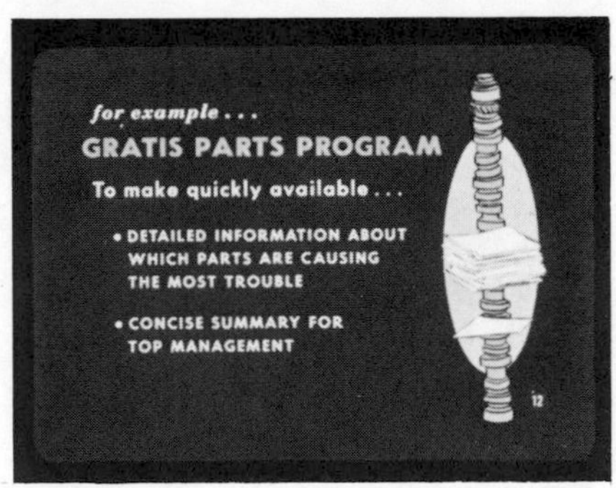

Figure 18-12. A good example of an existing application is the gratis parts program. In this particular application we punch IBM cards which indicate responsible manufacturing source, responsible engineering source, date assembled, length of service, frequency, cost, cause of failure.

Based on frequency and cost, this information is recapped, and exception reports are furnished to different levels of management based on the amounts involved. These standard approaches are good, and we must continue the momentum that we have in developing them. They are good as far as they go, but. . . .

Figure 18-13. Are we on a fast enough track to reach our goal—which is to obtain more profit per sales dollar?

We believe that we are not—and this brings forth the question. . . .

Figure 18-14. How do we get on the fast track?

If we are to cross over and get on this fast track, there are several approaches necessary such as: integration planning, concept development, operations research, model simulation.

These are imaginative new techniques which require further explanation.

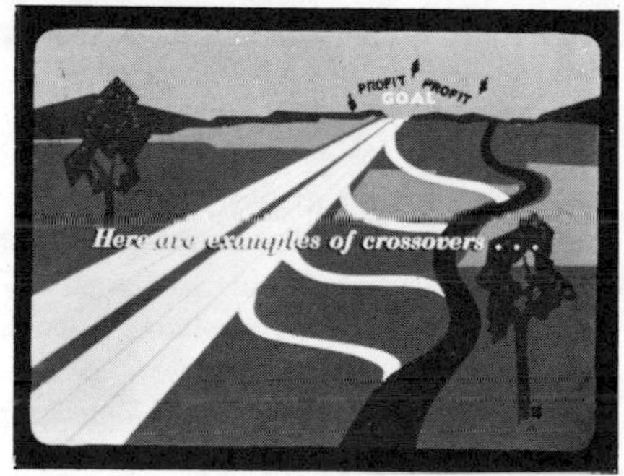

Figure 18-15. Here are examples of crossovers.

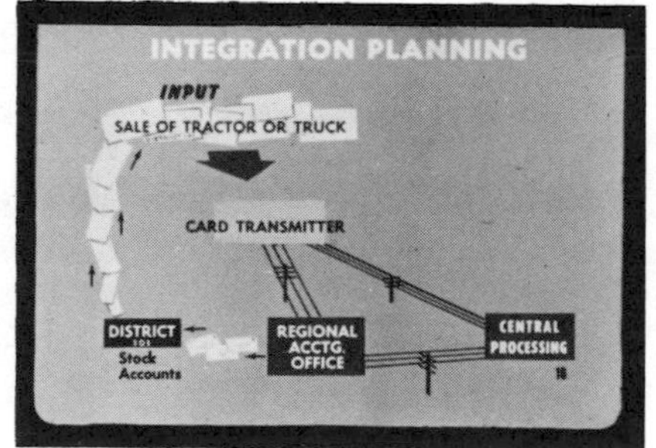

Figure 18-16. Integration planning—by integration planning we mean that from a single source of information, multiple outputs are provided to furnish information to a great many people in various functions to permit them to better manage their particular responsibility.

From a single output such as a sale of a tractor or truck, we transmit the information concurrently to the regional accounting office and to central processing. At the regional accounting office, we develop stock control activity for districts and regions, and accounts receivable information which can be returned to the district for their own use.

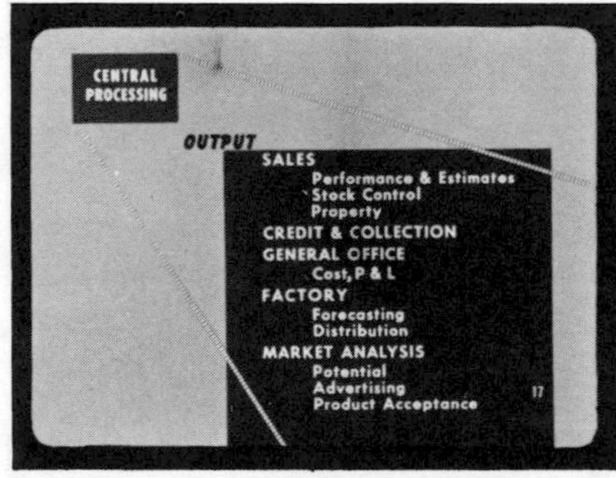

Figure 18-17. Concurrently with that, the information is sent to central processing, and again from the single input of tractor or truck sales, we can get information for all of these various outputs.

We can obtain sales information such as performance activity by districts and regions for the country as a whole, better information for sales estimates, stock control reports and property accounting—what do we have on hand and the value of it.

In the area of credit and collection, we find that when we sell a tractor, and get it out of our inventory, nine times out of ten it becomes a note receivable in our credit and collection department. As an output for the parent company, then, it is an input for this particular operation.

The information is available to general office for cost and profit and loss purposes.

At the factory level, we can develop information for better forecasting and better distribution. In this regard one of the things we are thinking about is that presently forecasting is based on plant shipments. What's happening at the dealer level? What is he selling? We feel that if we can find out actually what the dealer ships to the customer, we will be in a better position to anticipate future dealer requirements and company sales. How do we obtain this record of dealer sales? One way would be to use by-product information from credit and collection for this purpose.

Market analysis—what is our potential? What is the result of advertising campaigns? What about product acceptance?

Integrated planning is not new. Many of you people have worked with an example in the area of receiving. When something is received, information flows freely through accounting, materials control, and follow-up people. This is an example of multiple use of information from a single input.

So on to the next crossover. . . .

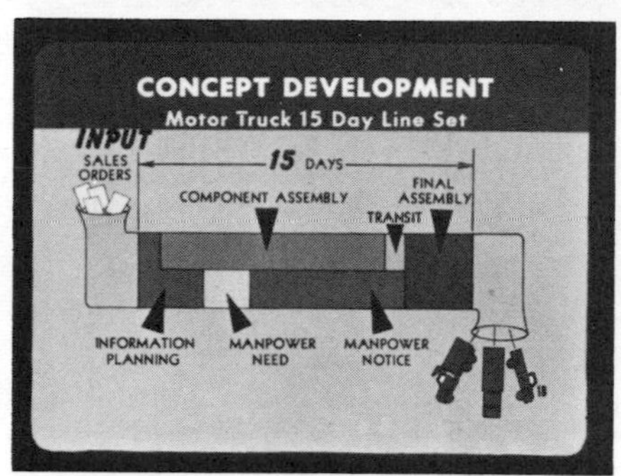

Figure 18-18. Concept development —What do we mean by this term?

Concept development refers to the way of doing something—investigating the way to do something—determining by the use of computers and mathematical techniques related to business administration if there is a better way to do something. In many instances it may mean a fresh approach away from our traditional way of doing business.

Such an approach is the particular example shown on this chart. We refer here to a proposed Motor Truck Division program called the 15 day line set.

Our traditional way of doing something in the area of forecasting in all of our plants, including the Motor Truck Division, is to base a forecast on history of plant shipments. In most instances we schedule, build, and receive from suppliers, components and assemblies ahead of receipt of orders. When an order comes in we try to match it against inventory. This necessitates maintaining a large inventory that is relatively inflexible. For example, for a model 190 truck there are 75 different types of axles, made up of 15 different part numbers, with the axle differences consisting primarily of gear ratios.

As a different way of doing things, it is proposed that instead of stocking 75 different axles at the head of the assembly line, to develop what we need before assembly, and maintain stock as 15 parts until after the order is received. Axles will be assembled, then based on definite order specifications. This will materially reduce our investment, materially increase our flexibility. It is proposed to accomplish this by taking advantage of the speed of obtaining information from computers plus the introduction of a longer period of firm line set —15 days. Now we are not saying that we can eliminate entirely the use of history information for forecasting. This will always be required. But we are saying that we propose to keep inventory in the simplest possible form and in the smallest amount until required to build a definite order.

You will also notice that the chart refers to manpower. Here again by combining the use of the computer with 15 day line set, it is proposed to determine manpower requirements far enough in advance of production of motor trucks to enable the assignment of the right number of people on the line for the assembly of these trucks.

This is a research project, fellows. We are not sure this will all work out. It is a different way of doing something—concept development. It is something that will have to be worked out with materials control, planning, and manufacturing people.

We do know, however, that the project offers tremendous possibilities. The plants were asked to study and report what they could realize from this kind of program.

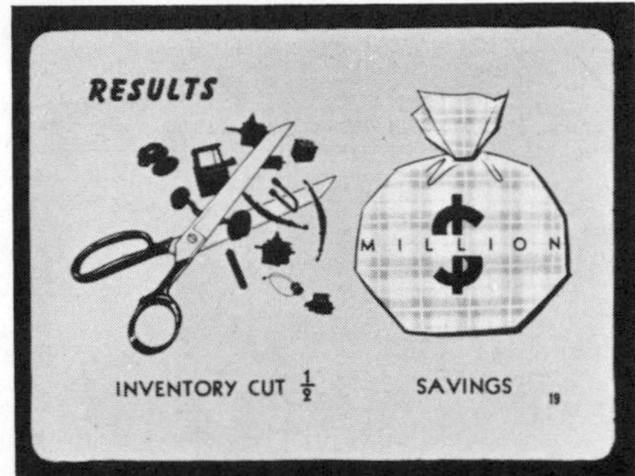

Fig. 18-19. The plants reported that they could cut their inventory in half. This represents upwards to $20,000,000 in inventory reduction, and the plants further reported that they could realize savings into seven figures. This is a result of what we call concept development or investigating the way of doing things.

Now, here is still another crossover.

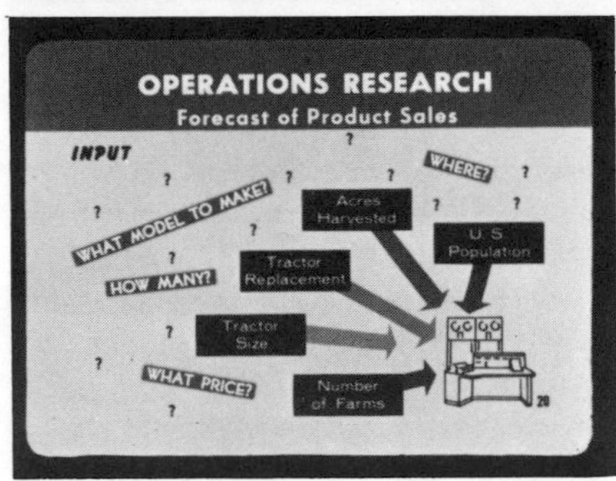

Figure 18-20. Operations research—What do we mean by operations research?

Operations research is a term applied to investigations, when problem solution is accomplished by combining both specialized knowledge of people and the mathematical approach.

Let's look at an example of an operations research problem—forecast of product sales. We desire to know the answers to these kinds of questions: What models to make? How many? What prices? Where should they be made?

By assigning values to such input factors as acres harvested, tractor replacement, tractor size, number of farms and U.S. population, by using people and computers, and by developing and establishing interrelationships mathematically, we end up with a solution like this. . . .

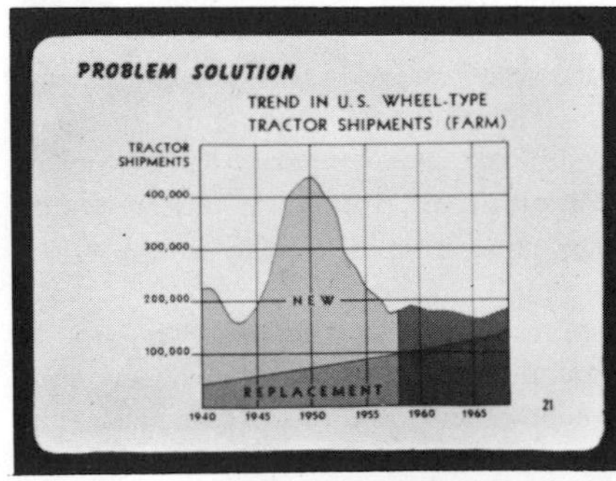

Figure 18-21. . . . which shows the trend in U.S. farm wheel-type tractor shipments for the period 1940 through 1970.

We notice that from now to 1970 U.S. farmers' annual purchases of tractors will not change appreciably. This indicates that our present facilities for production of tractors are probably adequate for this period. Second, we notice that our future market will come primarily from the replacement field. This means that our sales and advertising activity should be directed toward this replacement market.

Other factors not shown on the chart indicate that tractor sizes will be larger with corresponding higher prices per tractor.

This same type of mathematical approach is available to work out problems in engineering, manufacturing, and sales areas.

Figure 18-22. Here is the last crossover: model simulation.

Model simulation is a procedure whereby an actual condition or situation is imitated or reproduced in a computer. By varying different inputs into the system, the model will determine the results that can be expected under these varying conditions.

This particular example of simulation is from the Construction Equipment Division. It is a construction job cost estimate, prepared by the division, as a service to customers.

Various input factors such as job site, machine specifications, labor rate, fuel price and job specifications are placed in the computer. The computer, then, is programmed to imitate the actual conditions of the job. You actually imitate the equipment running up and down the road—How many tons, how many trips, how much labor, how much fuel?

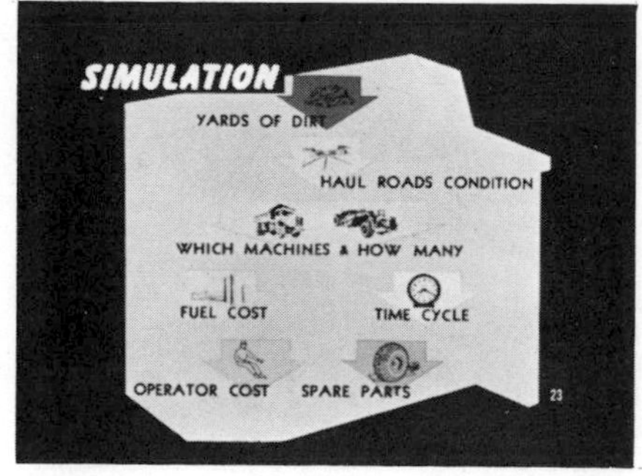

Figure 18-23. Concurrently the computer is determining the yards of dirt that have to be moved, the haul roads condition, which machines and how many, the fuel cost, the time cycle—shifts—etc., the operator cost, and the spare parts required.

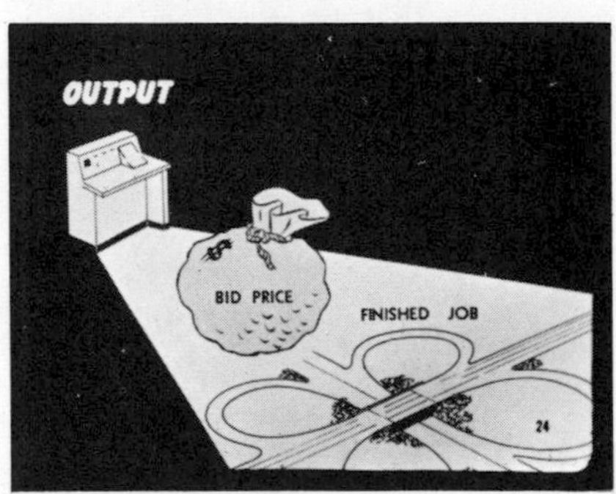

Figure 18-24. Based on this estimate, we suggest to the customer what his bid price is for this particular construction job. Not only what his bid price is but what his manpower is. What his machine load is. What kind of equipment he should have, and how he can utilize it.

This is simulation—imitating what actually goes on ahead of time—predicts what you can expect to find.

These four crossovers to the fast track—integration planning, concept development, operations research and model simulation—plus the present company activities on the modern two lane road—plus the full time concentrated attention of a staff responsible for information management—were all presented to Harvester management as the results of the investigation of the inquiry group.

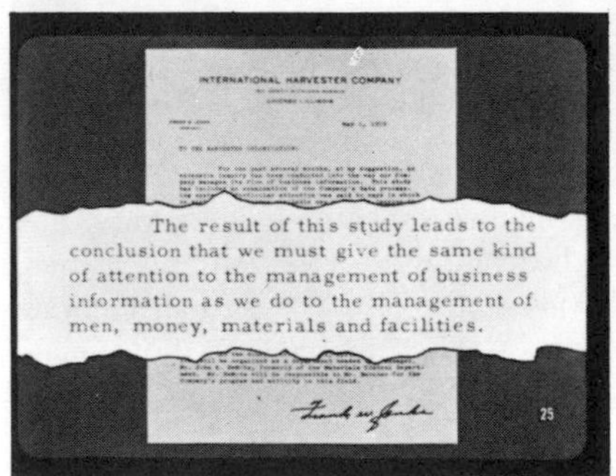
INTERNATIONAL HARVESTER COMPANY

The result of this study leads to the conclusion that we must give the same kind of attention to the management of business information as we do to the management of men, money, materials and facilities.

Figure 18-25. Based on the results of this study, then, on May 1, 1959 the company announced a new policy that ". . . . We must give the same kind of attention to the management of business information as we do to the management of men, money, materials, and facilities."

What does it take to start a business —to run a business? Facilities, materials, money, men, and information. This is what it takes to get the job done, and they all should be given equal attention.

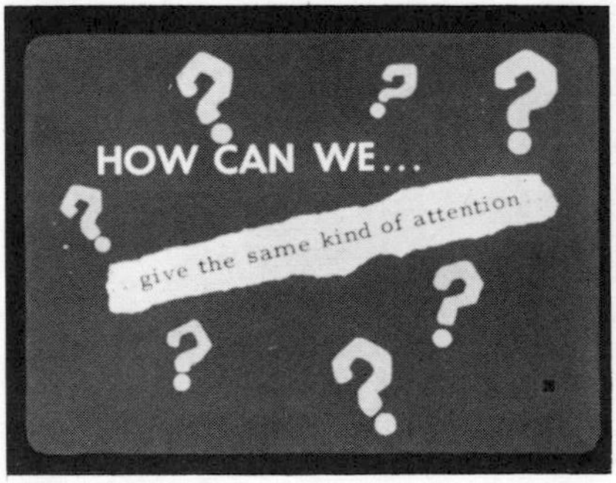

Figure 18-26. How can we give the same kind of attention to the management of business information as we do the management of materials and men?

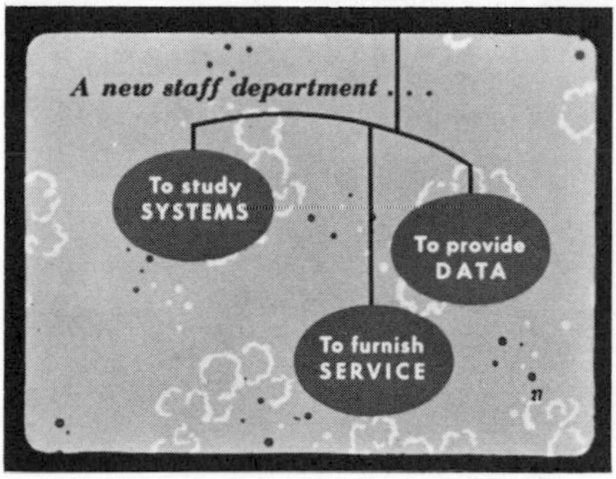

Figure 18-27. By creating a new staff department to study systems, to provide data, to furnish service.

A new staff department that will study all kinds of systems—the manpower systems, the material systems with all its flow, the money systems, the information flow in the manufacturing systems, the planning systems, the engineering systems, etc.

A new staff department that will provide data—the right amount of information, at the right time, at the right place, at the right price.

A new staff department that will accept the responsibility of furnishing service to you—an organization that you can rely on to work with you in solving your information problems.

Figure 18-28. So this is the way this new function has been established. The new department is S . . . D . . . S: systems and data services.

It is our privilege to serve you at the corporate, divisional, and operating levels of the company.

Up to this point in the presentation you have been shown the job to be done in information management. We have discussed the present scope of activities and have outlined what must be done in the future to keep on a fast enough track to reach our goal. The question remaining unanswered is "How do we get the job done?" or to state it another way. . . .

Figure 18-29. How will SdS work?

We certainly are not going to stop thinking, but we are going to emphasize the primary job of SdS—that of providing service to you.

Systems and data services is dedicated to serving the information needs of all of you—by approaching each problem with full time attention, with an open mind, and by applying specialized knowledge and techniques, including a thorough study of the problem.

Figure 18-30. SdS will operate only with the concurrence and cooperation of any department head affected by a project.

In many cases ideas originating in one department will extend to or will affect several departments. Each idea will be developed only with the full knowledge and concurrence of each department involved.

Figure 18-31. Our motto then is SdS at your service. What'll you have? Tell us your problems. Let us study the method, equipment, and personnel required. Let SdS make the detailed investigation of your ideas. This is SdS's job.

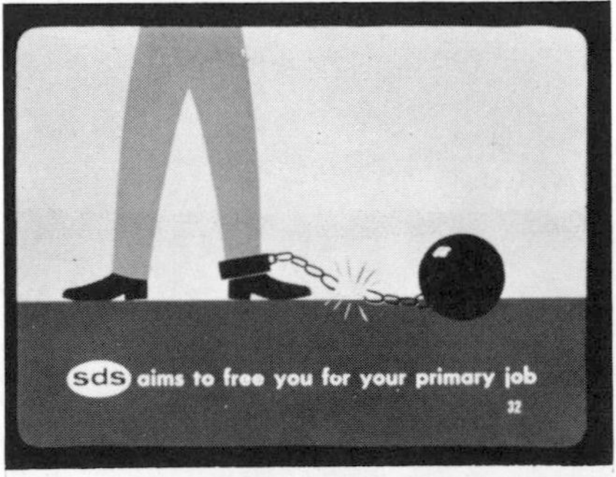

Figure 18-32. So SdS's aim is to free you *for* your primary job by accepting the responsibility of investigating and developing your ideas regarding information flow.

For example, you may have a particular problem that involves not only your department, but other departments as well. Currently, an investigation of this problem would require a lot of your time to find out the right people to talk to, to contact these people, and to collect and analyze all of the facts. This is the type of job that SdS will be able to do for you—by making the investigation and presenting the results to you for consideration.

As stated before, tell us your problems.

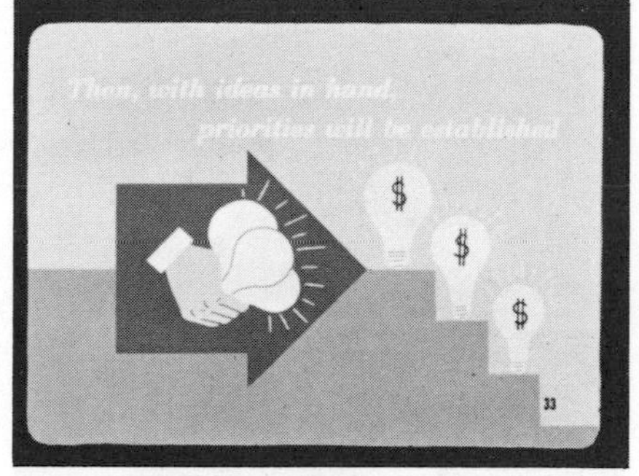

Figure 18-33. Then, with ideas in hand, priorities will be established. As to the priority of investigating, other things being equal, projects will be ranked in order of net benefits to be gained. For example, assume that two projects are under consideration—your project which we will call A and another project which we will call B. Your project A will result in such-and-such savings, but project B will give us twice the savings of A. I'm sure you will agree that project B should have priority over your particular plan. But here again the final decision will be determined with the concurrence of the department heads affected.

This will not prevent attention to projects with urgent reasons for immediate action, such as changes in SEC regulations or changes in labor contracts which require payroll changes. These mandatory programs will be placed ahead of any project that we happen to be working on.

To summarize, then, after your ideas have been screened and priorities established. . . .

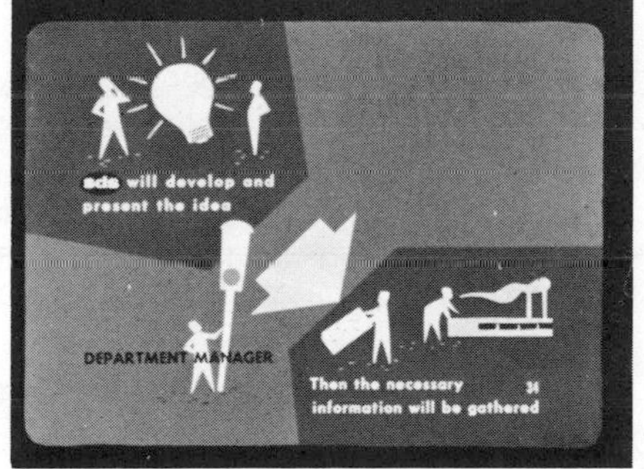

Figure 18-34. SdS will develop and present the idea to the department manager. After the department manager has accepted the proposal and has given SdS the green light to proceed, then the necessary information will be gathered and processed in the most economical manner and in the best form that will be useful to you.

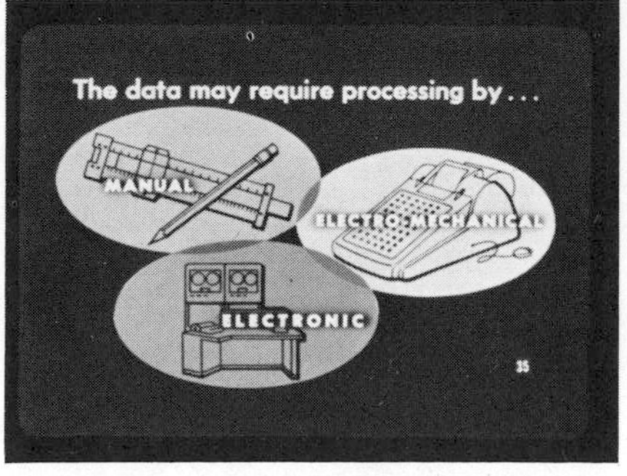

Figure 18-35. The data may require processing by manual, electromechanical or by electronic means.

The analysis may show, for example, that the processing should be done by manual methods—listing, copying, or calculating by hand.

A larger amount of data might be best processed by electromechanical equipment such as comptometers, calculators, or tabulating machines—sorters, collators, reproducers, etc. These are all types of machines that are fed or loaded manually but are electrically operated.

In many instances, because of large mass of data, speed with which results are needed, or large number of calculations to be made, it will be most desirable to do the data processing by means of electronic computers.

Figure 18-36. Now the output of most of these types of processing can become very large in volume unless we take steps to reduce it. No one enjoys having some one come in with a big stack of paper, pile it high on his desk and say, "Here are your answers." What you are really interested in knowing is the items requiring attention—not pawing through reams of paper looking at those items that are OK.

One of the jobs of SdS, then, will be to analyze the mass of data to be processed to determine if this mass can be distilled into concentrated form—to spotlight only those items needing attention. This is known as reporting by exception.

This can probably be best explained by an analogy. In the quality control program you set upper and lower limits for dimensional tolerances. As long as your product is within that band, no one is concerned and no attention is required. The minute the product falls below the lower limit you investigate to determine what is wrong. We can do this same thing in the business information field. We can establish limits or controls and print out only those items that are *not* within those limits. The gratis parts program mentioned earlier in this presentation is an example of reporting by exception.

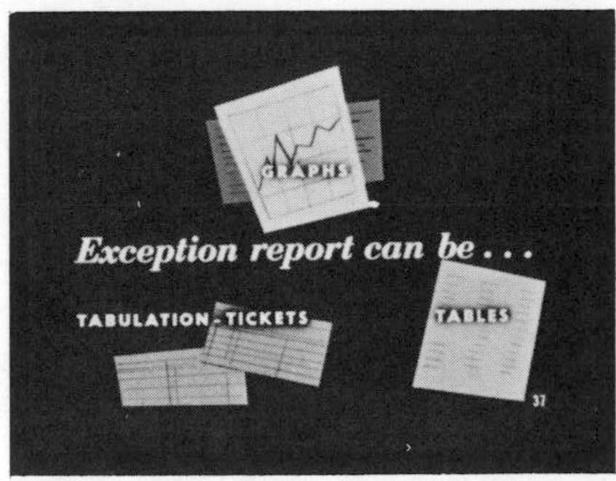

Figure 18-37. Exception reporting can be in the form of graphs, tables, tabulations, tickets, or other forms. The important thing to remember, regardless of form, is that exception reporting will show only those items needing attention.

Figure 18-38. One of the aims of SdS, then, is to deliver information ready for use—to deliver useful information quickly, accurately, concisely.

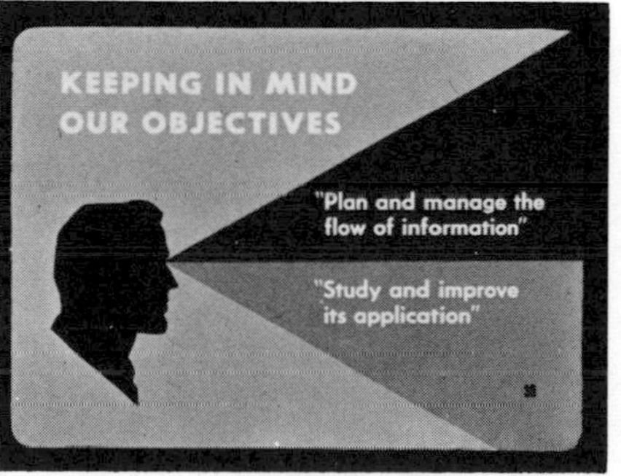

Figure 18-39. So much for the means of processing and presenting data. Let us again review and keep in mind our objectives, as outlined in Mr. Jenks' letter of May 1, 1959: (1) Plan and manage the flow of information. (2) Study and improve its application.

This then, is the responsibility of SdS, of all management. It is the reason for creating this new staff department with emphasis on concentrated attention, creative imagination and specialized knowledge.

But in order for these objectives to be achieved. . . .

Figure 18-40. SdS specialists will need ideas with which to work. Some of these ideas will come from the SdS staff, but most of them must come from all of the various departments of the company—and particularly from you.

You are in a better position than anyone to know the information needs of your department or operation.

Submit your ideas—let's all work toward the two objectives outlined in the policy announcement.

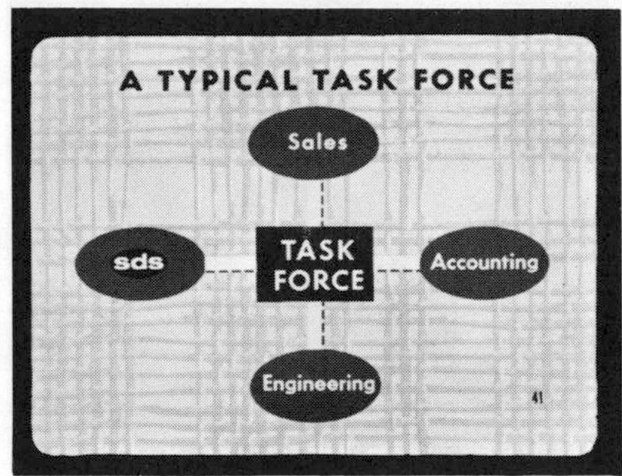

Figure 18-41. Here's one of the ways we can work together to obtain a solution to your problem. It is called the task force approach.

A typical task force might consist of a representative from SdS, from sales, from accounting, from engineering, and from manufacturing (why the chart maker forgot to include manufacturing I do not know). Another typical task force might consist of a representative from SdS, from cost accounting, from planning, and from materials control. Who should be members of the task force will be decided based on the nature of the problem.

The SdS specialist will contribute broad experience and knowledge in information management and will give concentrated attention and continuity to the task force. The other members of the task force will be given this assignment by the various departments involved *only* for the duration of the project.

The purpose of the task force will be threefold. (1) To give concentrated attention to this project. (2) To set forth your own practical ideas and knowledge of the project. (3) To take advantage of the best way to obtain information through the specialized services of a SdS representative.

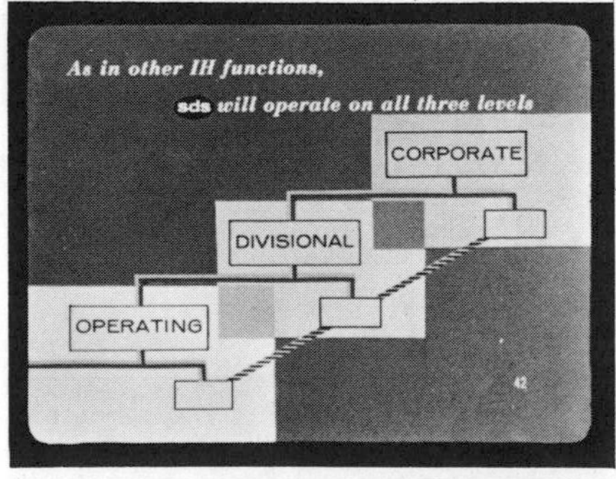

Fig. 18-42. We have answered in considerable detail the question, "How will SdS work?" The question still remaining unanswered is "What form will the SdS organization take?"

As in other IH functions, SdS will operate on all three levels: corporate, divisional, and operating.

Systems and data services is organized in the same way as other IH functions such as industrial relations and supply and inventory—with personnel at each of the three levels.

At the corporate (general office) level, the manager of SdS will have on his staff specialists in sales, sales accounting, works and general accounting, manufacturing, materials control, engineering, parts depot system, order and distribution, estimate and order review, and data processing equipment. These specialists will be available to help and advise all levels of the organization.

At the divisional level, the divisional manager of SdS will have a staff to coordinate the operating units within the division.

At the operating level, the SdS organization will vary depending upon the type of operating unit—works, engineering departments, regional accounting offices, parts depots, etc.

Particular attention is called to the strong cross-hatched line, shown on the chart, connecting the operating level to the divisional level to the corporate level. We must maintain this strong line in order to get coordination and flow of usable information at all levels. The reason why this coordination must exist among all levels is illustrated by the example of integration planning previously outlined in this presentation. You will recall it was proposed that a single input, tractor sales, be used in many and varied outputs—by the district, by the regional accounting office, by sales, by credit and collection, by the general office, by the factory and by market research. I'm sure all of you will recognize that *only* through strong cooperative ties among operating, divisional, and general office levels can such a program be made to work.

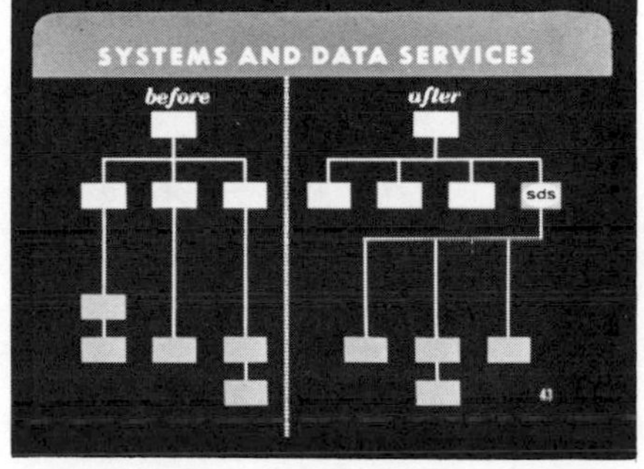

Figure 18-43. It was mentioned before that the organization of SdS at operating levels will vary depending upon the type of operating unit. To show how simple and logical this formation of SdS is through the operating levels, let's look at an example of systems and data services before and after at a typical operation.

The (lower) blocks refer to SdS activities. The *before* chart might include systems people and computer programmers reporting to one head. It might include a tab room reporting to another head. It might include other systems people (or another tab room) and the clerical administration program reporting to a third head.

Now the *after* chart merely consolidates all of these SdS activities under one man whose responsibility it is to direct *only* systems and data services. This organization frees each of the three department heads for his primary job, and at the same time places more emphasis on information management by making one man—the SdS supervisor—responsible for this entire function.

Summarizing, what does all of this mean to you? How will SdS help you?

1. You will have access to the crossovers to the *fast track* through the services of SdS specialists—people trained and qualified in this field. This all adds up to better information to aid you in making your decisions.

2. SdS will free you for your primary job by providing service in all information management activities. Your ideas will be investigated and placed into effect by SdS specialists.

3. You can be assured that information obtained for your use will be delivered quickly, accurately, and concisely.

4. Emphasis will be placed on reports by exception—providing reports of *only* those items needing attention.

5. You will know that information provided for you will not be in conflict with the needs of other departments, other works or the division.

6. You will have some one responsible and accountable for progress and costs in the area of information management.

This, then concludes the formal presentation of the scope and organization of the new department, systems and data services. We would now like to open the meeting up for a discussion of opportunities that you might foresee for uses of this service or the way this function will work with and assist you in carrying out your responsibilities.

The meeting is now open for any of your comments, points needing clarification, or questions.

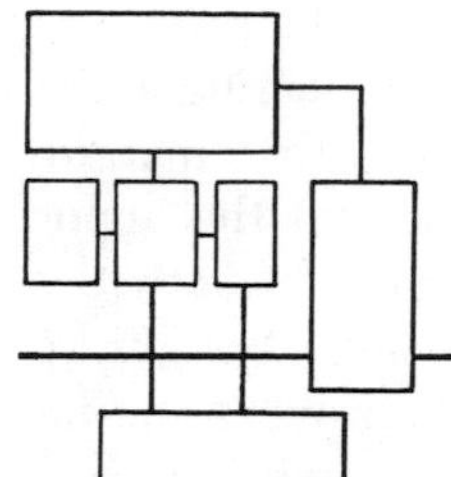

CHAPTER 19

PROFILE OF A BROAD IMPROVEMENT FUNCTION

United Air Lines is recognized as being a very progressive company and a pioneer in many ventures. One of their pioneering endeavors is associated with their highly successful use of industrial engineering and the development of a broad improvement function sparked by the industrial engineering groups.

The following materials are based upon a presentation[1] by the director of industrial engineering to a symposium sponsored by the American Society for Engineering Education and the American Institute of Industrial Engineers. The theme of the symposium was "Industrial Engineering in 1975." The intent was to stimulate interchange between education and industry relative to consideration of the changing nature of the profession and ways in which future developments could best be pursued.

It has previously been mentioned that the last ten or so years have seen an explosion of the technology affecting industrial engineering and improvement endeavors. United Air Lines has been very aggressive in finding ways to profitably put this new technology to work. They have provided leadership in demonstrating how it can be done, and have in many cases been well ahead of education in recognizing the practical importance of new developments.

The presentation is made in three parts. The first is a brief review, in five year increments from 1940 to 1960, of the development of industrial engineering within the company. The second section considers the changing nature of the profession during this same period and explains the practical integration of new technology and knowledge. The success of United in this venture has had a substantial influence upon the profession and its growth and upon the development of industrial engineering activities within other organizations. The third section considers the emerging frontiers of the profession and among other things points out the importance of research and development as a part of improvement activities. Although not specifically mentioned, United Air Lines also strongly believes in research and development directed towards improving the improvement function activities themselves, which has been highly successful in helping them to achieve their outstanding results.

Industrial Engineering Frontiers of 1975

by **WARREN R. MELLIN**

Director of Industrial Engineering, United Air Lines

THE temptation to draw aside a veil and peer into the murky fog of the future represents an almost irresistible challenge for most of us. Through the centuries this desire has been the mission of the soothsayers, palm readers, star gazers, mystics, and those expert at interpreting tea leaves. Far be it for me to resist this urge! However, rather than rely upon these somewhat less than scientific techniques for a view of the future, perhaps our comments should be based upon an understanding of the development of industrial engineering in the past 15 or 20 years and the state of the art today.

With these frames of reference, perhaps we will be better able to predict future activity and areas of greatest potential with a higher level of confidence. No doubt many educators participating in this symposium will discuss industrial engineering from the viewpoint of many different industries, the over-all economy, and perhaps the nation as a whole. Therefore, it would seem that the particular role of a practitioner in industry would be to cast this forecast in the mold of one company's experience. Thus, it will be our mission to review the birth and emergence of industrial engineering in United Air Lines and the new image of the industrial engineering function.

With this practical foundation as a launching pad, perhaps we can project a vision of the future. In order to telescope United's 20 years of industrial engineering experience so that only the highlights are stressed, our glimpse of past events will be expressed in terms of a cross section every five years.

THE EMERGENCE OF INDUSTRIAL ENGINEERING

1940. Back in the thirties, a key individual in United Air Lines gradually developed an interest in the science of business management. This basic interest led, in the fall of 1940, to the first surveys of an industrial engineering nature undertaken in United Air Lines. These surveys were largely concerned with time studies and methods improvements in passenger handling activities, as well as improvements in layouts of facilities and equipment. These efforts were innovative and designed to improve methods and ways of doing business, while at the same time following traditional approaches in industrial engineering. The success of these studies and the interest generated led United's President, W. A. Patterson, on February 15, 1941, to establish a new department known as work analysis. In his memorandum to company officers and supervisors, Mr. Patterson established the following philosophy:

> "Although this department technically will come under my office, the entire organization should feel free to work directly with it in connection with their problems. You should use these services whenever a particular problem presents itself which requires concentration and scientific study. I consider this department essential because it is only natural that we become so involved with day-to-day problems that certain practices are permitted to develop—not because we believe them to be proper, but because we haven't time to give them concentrated attention."

Acceptance of this philosophy by operating management meant an increase in demand for services, and during the next few years the work analysis nucleus of the current industrial engineering department began to expand its activities. Typical of accomplishments were:

Inauguration of a job methods training course and introduction of work simplification principles to nearly 1000 supervisors.

Studies of space needs and functional layouts for building projects.

Standardization of company forms.

Conduct of special projects, including the first standardized ticket counter, a revised airplane routing system, establishment of production lines and a production planning system at the Cheyenne modification center, and improved methods for ticketing of passengers.

1945. By this time the embryo of the industrial engineering department had developed significantly, coincident with the beginning of rapid growth on the part of air transportation and United Air Lines. The work analysis division reported administratively to the vice-president–economic controls. Other related functions reporting to him separately were the regulations division, concerned with centralized editing and distributing of company regulations, and the organization planning and control division, charged with the responsibility for organization planning, job analysis, and job evaluation.

The work analysis division in 1946 consisted of 12 individuals allocated to one of four units—methods improvement and standards setting, functional specifications (for facilities), forms control, and special projects.

The growing acceptance of the assistance that work analysis could provide was creating a significant backlog of projects. Much of the effort of the division was spent in developing temporary corrective measures rather than more permanent solutions to problems. This situation, plus a decision by management to develop and use work standards for manpower control, meant that it was necessary to expand to a complement of 24 individuals, including the establishment of a regional office in San Francisco. Important at that time was a reiteration of the philosophy of using manpower of the requesting departments on specific studies. This approach was based on the concept that work analysis was to supply highly skilled talent to serve the primary purpose of training and guiding supervisors' effort when technical industrial engineering skill was considered necessary in achieving problem solutions.

In this period the work standards program was gradually developed and expanded, with installations in areas such as ground operations, airport counters, flight kitchens, and reservations offices. The initial phase provided only after-the-fact performance measurement, and the next step in development was to use work standards in the translation of volume forecasts into manpower needs.

When United Air Lines established its operating base in Denver in 1947, work analysis personnel also were placed at this point in order to continue to provide industrial engineering services to the operating organizations based in Denver.

Representative of the highlights during this era were:

Development and installation of a work standards program leading to the forecasting and control of 50% of United's total employees by 1949.

Development of functional layouts and specifications for building projects.

Continued efforts directed towards simplification of all company reports and forms.

Completion of special projects, such as the utilization of private-line telephone circuits between major reservations offices, reorganization of flight dispatch offices, establishment of a centralized operations concept and use of a briefing room for review of systems operations, methods improvements in aircraft line maintenance activities, and an integrated plan for cleaning aircraft exteriors.

1950. The next few years saw increased expansion of the department's activities as demand for air transportation mushroomed. Extension of work standards to cover the overhaul of aircraft at the San Francisco maintenance base was undertaken. Later in the year a new regulations and forms division was established, reporting directly to the vice-president–economic controls. It was formed by combining the regulations function with the reports and forms function of the work analysis division.

In December of 1951, the establishment of an industrial engineering department was announced, including two major divisions—work analysis and organization control.

A year later the work measurement program was expanded to include specific applications for clerical personnel. Also, the function of quality control was added to the department, with responsibility for the over-all direction and development of quality control concepts throughout the company.

In 1953 the regulations and forms division became a part of the industrial engineering department, adding a third major division to the growing responsibilities of the department.

During this period, pioneering studies were made in the use of work sampling to determine time distribution of mechanics and supervisors in the maintenance base. These studies were a beginning in the endeavor to simplify work measurement, while at the same time obtaining insights into the operation and the nature of factors that were susceptible to improvement.

Exploratory meetings were held relative to the possible use of operations research techniques in solving company problems. There came to be a growing awareness of the significance of variability in predicting needs on the part of the company for both facilities and manpower. In 1954 the first operations research study by the company was undertaken. This pioneering study, utilizing the team concept, was concerned with the development of a model that would simulate the actual operation of a company aircraft maintenance station. It also was believed that the results of this study would enable our management to more properly evaluate the operations research approach from a practical standpoint.

Major activities during this period included:

Further extension of the coverage and scope of the work standards program.

Continued emphasis upon the need for functional requirements in determining building size, work flow, and relationship of activities.

Completion of a number of organization studies, continued emphasis upon job analysis and evaluation, and a major revision to United's salary structure.

Completion of special projects, such as a survey of aircraft maintenance requirements for the Convair, economic analysis of flight simulators, and possibilities for increasing aircraft fleet utilization.

Pioneering applications in quality control, such as statistical control of reservations turnover, and the settlement of billings between airlines on a statistical sampling basis. This latter approach, adopted and used by the accounting department, was an innovation in this field.

At the end of 1954, personnel in industrial engineering totaled 85 individuals—40 at San Francisco, 20 at Denver, and 25 at Chicago.

1955. Late in 1955, with the jet age on the horizon, two new functions—applied mathematics and applied statistics—were established within industrial engineering.

The pioneering study in operations research concerned with the simulation of aircraft maintenance, programmed in the latter part of 1956, was successful. This study demonstrated the practicality of simulating a business or operating system. It was to have far reaching effects in emphasizing a more objective and quantitative approach to many of United's operating problems.

During this period another long range and innovative study was begun for the purpose of determining the best system of utilizing and controlling the sale of seat space for the next 10 to 15 years. The many phases of this study developed over a period of several years, ultimately resulting in United's signing a contract for $17,-000,000 in order to lease equipment for the achievement of a completely electronic reservations system.

Increased use of applied mathematics and statistics and further extensions of the quality control effort led to more precise measurements and greater understanding of processes and their control. Practicality of some of the so-called newer techniques—probability, work sampling, and queueing—was demonstrated. In some cases these techniques were used to augment previous traditional work standards approaches, and in other cases these techniques replaced previous tools. These approaches enabled the development of a series of quantitative alternates, so that various levels of reservations and ticketing services could be "priced-out" as a basis for management decision in policy determination.

The large payoff resulting from a long range and advanced study of major systems was beginning to be recognized, and additional efforts were being directed to this channel. Also, advances in information systems and data processing systems were beginning to have an impact, and much additional effort was being allocated to these areas.

As the jet age dawned, it was hoped that these approaches and advances would assist operating management in assuring the finest quality of service at the lowest cost consistent with this quality.

In addition to adoption and practical use of statistical and mathematical techniques in the area of work measurement, and greater emphasis upon the need for a long range study in systems analysis and design, other major activities during this period were:

Gradual revisions to United's organizational structure and procedures in order to keep pace with the new and changing demands of the jet age.

Further work in the area of special projects, including a comprehensive test in early 1956 of the merits of a preloaded cargo container system for the DC-8. Another major mission was the development of functional specifications outlining space needs for a new executive office building. This building was built on a 51-acre plot in Mount Prospect, Illinois. Other studies were concerned with the location of key reservations offices, a review of the total system for ground handling of passengers, procedures for checking in and boarding of passengers, a review of specialized equipment for ticket issuance, and the need for improved flight information to passengers.

As United's markets and schedules expanded, total company personnel increased, and by 1959 the complement of industrial engineering personnel at San Francisco, Denver, and Chicago totaled 103 individuals.

1960. With United's rapid endeavors to develop an all jet fleet—Douglas DC-8's, Boeing 720's and 727's, and the Sud Aviation's Caravelle—it was difficult to have progress on the ground keep abreast of progress in the air. Special projects in industrial engineering continued at a rapid pace.

In 1960 an appraisal was made in order to more effectively determine the needs of United Air Lines in the work measurement area. This study has resulted in significant changes in work standards philosophy. Studies also were begun with reference to a linear programming approach for the determination of the number of domiciles for pilots and stewardesses, as well as the number of individuals assigned to each domicile. Guidelines were established for the evaluation of capital investments, and major studies were completed at San Francisco relative to the inspection system and the supply system. In these studies the role of industrial engineering was to be of greatest possible assistance to management in obtaining quantitative information as a basis for management decision and policy formation.

Prior to the merger of Capital Airlines into United on June 1, 1961, a great deal of planning was necessary in order to achieve a smooth transition. The role of the industrial engineering representative on the merger planning committee was to coordinate assignments relative to facilities planning and consolidations, manpower allocations, issuance of regulatory material, and the development of organization structures for all departments to most effectively meet the needs of the merged company.

With specific reference to the industrial engineering organization, United has decentralized the activities of industrial engineering, while at the same time providing over-all coordination at the corporate staff level. Thus, in addition to the 45-man corporate industrial engineering department at the executive offices in Chicago, there are six industrial engineering staffs within the operating administrations, with a total personnel count of 55 individuals. The latter staffs report to operating line management from an administrative standpoint. For example, the manager of industrial engineering at United's maintenance base at San Francisco reports administratively to the vice-president–base maintenance. However, industrial engineering activities are coordinated by the director of industrial engineering through the establishment of written objectives once a year, and a periodic follow up of performance in relationship to objectives throughout the year. Organization of the corporate staff at Chicago is shown in Fig. 19-1.

THE NEW IMAGE OF INDUSTRIAL ENGINEERING

It is hoped that this brief resume of the development of industrial engineering within United Air Lines will be more than a mere recital of history to the reader. Indeed, those of us having the opportunity to be with United during this period of dramatic change consider this a fascinating story in the history of the company and industrial engineering. Woven through this review there have been certain threads or factors that have emerged. These threads have created and developed the image of industrial engineering within the company, and no doubt many of them are at work in other industrial organizations. These threads are interwoven and not mutually exclusive. Some of the more significant elements that have gradually evolved and guided us in our endeavors have been the following:

1. *Philosophy and Climate.* The basic philosophy that President Patterson established in 1941 has had a tremendous impact upon the acceptance of the industrial engineering function within the company. Even though many, many individuals within the department have made significant contributions over an extended period of time and these contributions have been recognized, it is essential to stress and fully credit the climate created by our President. The over-all atmosphere, his alertness and expectation of innovation and progress, and his communication of ideas for continued growth and forward momentum to all vice-presidents have been prime factors in whatever contributions may have been made by other individuals.

2. *A Service Approach.* All of us recognize the fact that industrial engineering is and should be a staff department. In United, the department has certain continuing responsibilities with operating departments, such as responsibilities related to work measurement, quality control, forms design, job analysis, and job evaluation, for example. In other cases emphasis is on planning and development, with the functions of organization planning, facilities planning, systems engineering, and research and development serving as illustrations.

The department also serves as an internal consultant to the operating departments in problem definition and solution. This last mission

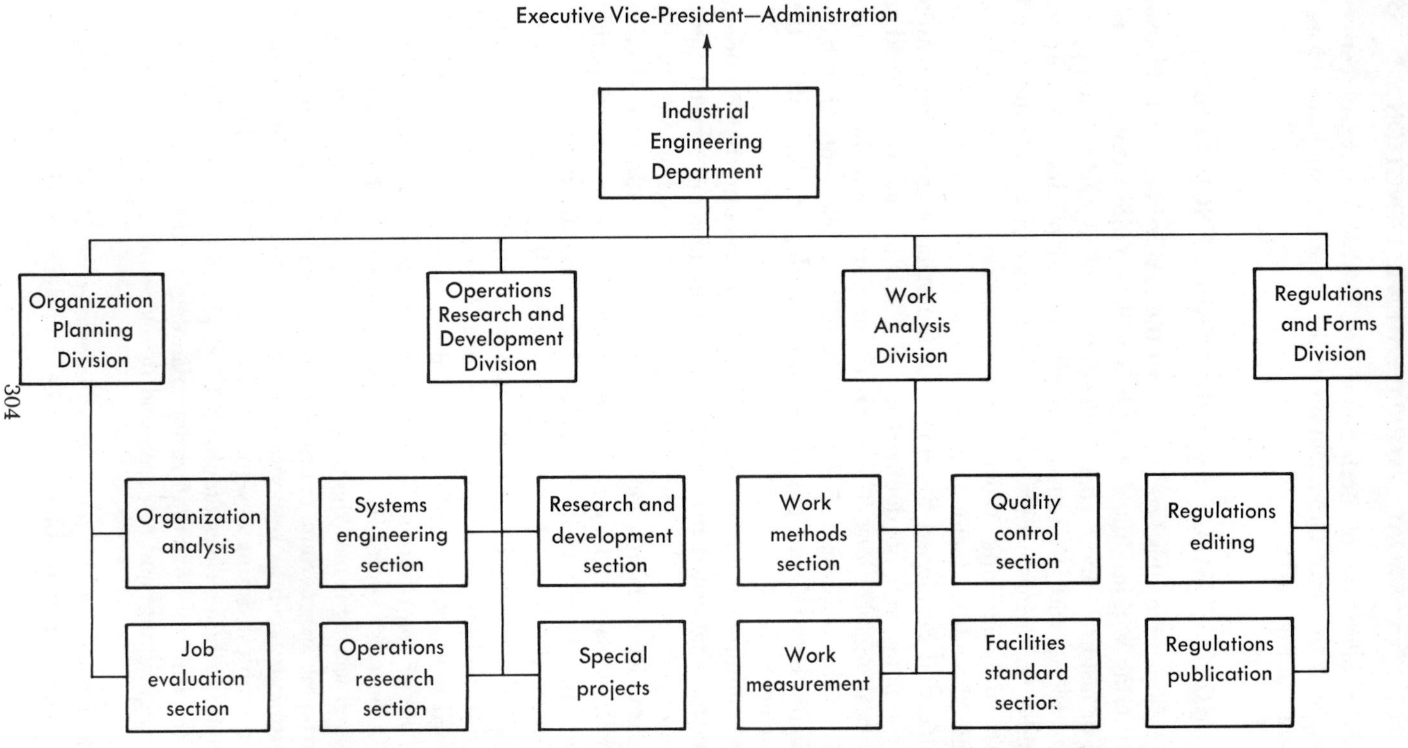

Figure. 19-1. Organization of Corporate Industrial Engineering Staff, United Air Lines.

is particularly related to the areas of special projects, and the use of some of the mathematical and statistical approaches. In all areas this desire to be of assistance closely follows the over-all philosophy established for the department, and it has enabled very close working relationships with representatives of operating departments.

3. *Personalities.* The gradual shaping of the department over an extended period of time has been a recognition of the basic functions that should be a part of an industrial engineering effort. At the same time, the manner of organization, and the changes gradually made, have reflected the personalities involved and the extent to which they may have stressed different aspects of the over-all operation. At any point in time, the organization of industrial engineering, and the functions included in its scope, may have been to some extent a short range and necessary step toward long range goals. On other occasions, rapid progress and penetration of new areas in a short time span have been due to the unusual abilities and advanced outlook of key individuals, together with participation and acceptance by operating personnel.

4. *Total Operation.* There has been an increased awareness of the existence of the total systems in operation, whether they be manufacturing, distribution, or reporting systems, for example. There is still a need to understand each part of a system, but there is increased emphasis on the need to comprehend the interaction between parts and between systems as well. In this understanding of a total system, there is a growing emphasis on the need to predict and influence what will happen rather than merely to account for it on an after-the-fact basis. Results from many systems and simulation studies have emphasized the total cost concept. Certain previous concepts in work measurement, directed toward minimizing manpower, have been questioned. There is recognition that specialized efforts in individual areas of an operation may have a tendency to suboptimize the operation. Thus, there has been more emphasis on the need for drawing together all of the parts of the total system so that results, in terms of total service and costs, can be optimized at the corporate level.

5. *Improved Tools and Electronic Computers.* Better tools and techniques have become available in terms of ability to gather data, develop measurements, and predict results. The development and increased use of statistics and mathematics, and the growth of management sciences are well known to us. Some of the newer concepts in the areas of probability, queueing, and work sampling have made

it possible for us to achieve a deeper explanation and understanding of the underlying nature of problems, as well as unlock answers and develop alternative solutions to problems.

The development of electronic computers is an important breakthrough. The computer, apart from its ability to process data faster than ever before, has enabled us to use linear programming approaches and simulation. The computer makes it possible to measure, manipulate, and predict in advance the effect of possible changes of input into a system. These inputs may be in the nature of policies, methods, facilities, inventory, and manpower. Measurement of the variance resulting from alternative inputs has led us to known and predictable outputs in terms of quality and quantity of product, or service, together with associated costs.

6. *Communications.* The need for improved communications has demanded recognition. The flow of information within a system and between systems is being recognized, as well as the need of management for timely and appropriate types of information necessary for decision-making. Varying levels of management require different types of information for operational and control purposes. The growth of industry and risks associated with less than the best decisions now demand adequate facts as a basis for understanding. Improvement in communications and information flow should greatly increase the probability of the right decisions.

7. *Long Range Planning.* There has been greater emphasis on the significance of research and development and the need for imagination in long range planning. There is a need to anticipate problems associated with growth and the changing characteristics of the business scene. Contributions have been made jointly by industrial engineers and operating personnel leading to the development of totally new concepts. Thus, the need for creativity and innovation has been highlighted. There is a continuous challenge to develop totally new systems and different ways of doing business.

8. *Policy Evaluation.* In many instances, the use of some of the so-called newer techniques has made it possible to quantitatively define alternatives as a basis for management policies. In these areas the varying costs of different systems, or procedures, or equipment can be weighed against the benefits to be derived from varying levels of service to the public. As a result of the practicality of new approaches, management gradually has begun to see the industrial engineer in an emerging role. He is being given a new image as an individual that is an aid to management. This change has been a

subtle and gradual process, and it has resulted in a better climate and atmosphere in which an industrial engineer may work.

NEW FRONTIERS

In our review of the past two decades, progress in the field of industrial engineering has been rapid. This has been a period of dynamic growth and a period of most interesting transition.

Many individuals who have been pioneers in certain areas have been somewhat impatient with the length of time that it takes to achieve acceptance and application of new tools and techniques. This impatience is both desirable and understandable. At the same time there needs to be assurance that a company continues to produce today's product or service in order to serve today's market.

Thus, in visualizing the industrial engineering frontiers for 1975, there is a need to recognize on a realistic basis that some time will pass for totally new concepts to achieve acceptance in most industries. This means that some of the very real challenges for 1975 may not consist of totally new concepts but rather will be a gradual unfolding and development of certain concepts begun in some companies and relatively embryonic in others. In all cases, there still appears to be a vast potential of challenge for the future, and included in this challenge are three basic areas.

Systems Analysis, Design, and Engineering. This area constitutes a real challenge for all of us. The need to understand each part of a system and how it interacts is significant, but the goal of optimizing an entire system is paramount. The goal in systems engineering is to balance all ingredients in correct proportions. Essential components would include work methods, work organization, facilities and layout, manpower, equipment, tools, and total inventory of parts and material.

At any given point in time there are many different systems in operation. For many valid reasons it may be necessary or desirable to study only certain systems and deliberately suboptimize the entire result. However, in the final analysis it will be necessary to balance all systems from the over-all corporate standpoint. Proper balancing will then achieve control of a given product or service so that desired qualitative and quantitative objectives may be achieved at predetermined costs.

Related to the physical systems, and an integral part of each, is the information flow or communications system that welds all of the components together. The significance of adequate and timely information flow is necessary not only within each system but also for interaction between systems. In addition, it is essential to take cognizance of the human factors in the operation of a system. Often a critical ingredient is understanding of worker motivation, and the perception and attitudes of individuals. It is essential to recognize the varying abilities of individuals to communicate and work with others.

In the systems approach, the need for recognition of variability is stressed as well as the need for understanding the probabilistic nature of both the inputs and outputs of a system. The proper design, control, and feedback from a system, both in-process and as a result of the complete cycle, must consider the need for predicting results in advance. We must consider the extent to which we can manipulate parts of a system, perhaps through simulation, to design a system that will achieve optimum results. We need to have less emphasis on after-the-fact measurements and more emphasis on before-the-fact control and direction.

The first time or two that we draw back and take a look at a total system should result in "gold nuggets," as far as significant improvements and savings are concerned. Many years from now, after a system analysis approach has been utilized many times, we may be "panning" for gold, and it may take a long time to accumulate a small pile of gold dust, but the first time or two we will be reaching and finding "gold nuggets."

As the systems analysis approach is activated and projects are undertaken, the results should further widen the door for more work and broader scope in the future.

Research and Development. The second challenge is the area of research and development. The need for more research and development effort relative to products is generally recognized; but the need for research and development in regards to business systems is frequently overlooked. There is a critical need to devote attention to the long range plans for developing totally new and imaginative ways of doing business. We need to be sure of having at least a few individuals in this effort that are insulated from the fire-fighting projects that must be done now. At the same time insulation is provided to them, we must somehow build a bridge so that they have contact with real life and so that the results of their efforts may have meaning and practical application on a long term basis. The establishment of a research and development effort should be a continuous long term effort, and might well foster a cleaner break point in some of the short range projects as to the extent of the depth that is desirable.

Any individuals set up for this mission must have the freedom to pursue ideas and concepts without any expectation on the part of management for an immediate return from their efforts. These men should be able to explore the frontiers, and their personality should lead them to be inquisitive, with a perspective and bent for innovation. From time to time there may be some merit to having them participate on certain projects with representatives of operating departments to enable them to retain touch with current problems. There is a need for balancing effort between work to be done for others and work that we must start for ourselves in the area of research. Even if the initial effort is only 2 or 5% of the total amount of industrial engineering time, it is a beginning.

The research and development effort should be relatively broad in scope and there should be little or no limitation on the channels to be followed in research. Some research may lead to a questioning of management policies. The research may be unrelated to traditional areas of industrial engineering. The effort may well lead to improved understanding in greater depth of financing concepts, rate of return on investment, depreciation concepts, market penetration, consumer reaction, location of plants and warehouses, inventory determination and control, distribution concepts, economic analysis of facilities and equipment, or related broad spectrum topics or problems affecting not only a given company but also the industry in which it is located.

Management. Third, the need for assistance to management appears to be a fertile field and one with real challenge for industrial engineers in future years. Management needs a timely and meaningful flow of selected information for decision-making. Management is certainly not looking forward to having all possible facts accumulated by a computer, processed more rapidly than ever before, and resulting in a three-inch thick report on a weekly basis for review. However, management is looking for the significant information flow that will be helpful to them for control purposes. In several companies thought is being given to the merits of establishing a management information center where pertinent data is available for decision-making. This concept may have excellent application for certain types of companies. In essence, management is looking broadly for a way to optimize gains in all areas and minimize risks. Management wants a quantitative picture wherever possible in balancing costs and all other factors associated with decisions.

The industrial engineer is in a position to develop alternative policies for consideration by management with each policy having a related cost. The balancing of policies and costs is possible in product quality, and especially in levels of service to the public where waiting lines are involved, for example.

There is a need for all of us in industrial engineering to recognize and be sensitive to the needs of management. Should the industrial engineer make significant contributions to management over a period of time and achieve acceptance of efforts in areas other than those associated with industrial engineering, as such, there may be a need for a change in the industrial engineering title. Perhaps a title such as industrial and management engineering, or management engineering services would be appropriate in some companies to best describe the functions performed. However, this change, if and when it occurs, will follow contributions and acceptance rather than be established in advance of them.

In many areas the industrial engineer can serve as a catalyst, a communications link, and an adhesive that can weld together divergent factors and provide coordination at a level below that of the president. The industrial engineer can serve the needs of management by penetrating the departmental barriers that exist. In this area the industrial engineer should avoid competition with operating staffs. Instead of attempting to compete, he should serve to complement and weave together varying skills, experience, and know-how into a composite pattern for management decision and understanding. Fundamental to all of these endeavors is emphasis on economics, the need for achieving a fair return on invested capital, and the maximization of profits on a short and long range basis.

SUMMARY

Participation in endeavors such as these will further enhance the image that is being formed by management of industrial engineering. In the final analysis, the industrial engineer will be judged not by what we define industrial engineering to be. Rather, management will judge the industrial engineer by what he does and the contributions he makes on a practical and timely basis.

REFERENCE

1. Warren E. Mellin, "Industrial Engineering Frontiers of 1975" presented to an AIIE–ASEE Symposium, Detroit, Michigan, May 10, 1961.

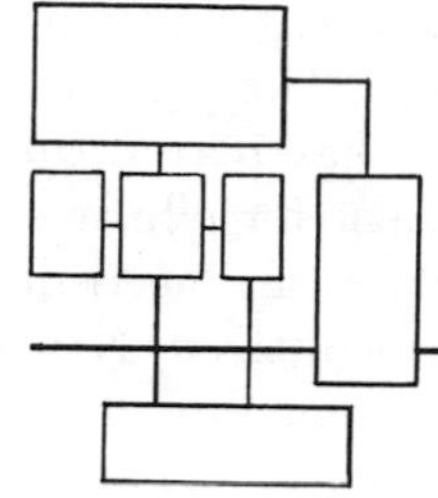

CHAPTER 20

IMPROVEMENT ACTIVITIES IN SMALL ORGANIZATIONS

IMPROVEMENT can be cultivated and managed within the small organization—both the nonprofit and small business organization—in much the same manner as within larger organizations. The improvement function can be pursued in a systematic fashion, but the degree of formalization may be much less. The pattern for improvement should reflect the needs of the organization—but this is true for any organization regardless of size—and each organization will have its own unique needs which should be fulfilled in a unique manner. Even so, the fundamentals of improvement, which have been presented, retain their validity for the small organization.

In many cases the owner-manager (or man-in-charge) must be the moving force *and* actually execute the quest for improvement. In other organizations the improvement responsibility and activity can be shared throughout the organization, even to the extent of having staff support available. In all cases the primary responsibility for orienting and organizing efforts directed toward continual improvement must rest heavily upon the man-in-charge. He should become a student of improvement, and should be aware of the many ways in which he himself can develop improvement, stimulate his organization to become more efficient, and secure the expert assistance of professional "staff" services. The main hindrance to organized improvement within the small organization is a lack of conviction on the part of the man-in-charge that improvement is desirable *and* attainable within the organization and that it is necessary.

Many small organizations grow their own problems as a by-product of their success. As a measure of success is achieved, these organizations tend to expand and their problems become more complex. The personal attention of the founder-owner-manager, which usually has played an important part in the initial success, is no longer sufficient for effective solution to changing problems. More formalized procedures are needed. Changing needs and new problems are frequently not recognized. New approaches are needed. It is frequently at this point that some organized improvement endeavor is recognized as being desirable—but all too often the organization is at a complete loss as to how it should proceed. The answers are simple and straightforward and are implicit in the fundamentals of improvement function activity presented in Chapter 3. For summary, these key points can be boiled-down to:

1. A dedication to achieving continual improvement on the part of management and the entire organization.
2. Stress on the systematic improvement of management.
3. A continual search for effective ways to obtain needed "staff" assistance as a means of further improving the effectiveness of line management.

The basic concept of dual management responsibilities (that is, to achieve results and to achieve improvement) is fundamental. The problem is how this can be done effectively.

APPROACHES

The man-in-charge is the key individual in improvement activities within the small organization. If he lacks conviction that improvement is necessary *and* achievable within his organization, then it is likely that improvement will either not take place or it will be far less than it should be. If, on the other hand, the man-in-charge is convinced that improvement is essential, it is likely that his leadership will inspire his entire organization. His conviction will enable him to approach improvement in an organized manner, allowing for the uniqueness of his organization and its problems, and will provide an example to his entire organization to seek improvement also.

Conviction that improvement can and should take place within any specific organization can be derived from knowledge of the development of mankind and the many examples of successful improvement endeavors within a variety of organizations to be found in management, trade, and professional publications. However, this conviction must be based upon an understanding of management philosophy and improvement approaches rather than upon specific gimmicks and improvement techniques. The man-in-charge should become a student of these subjects. There are many excellent books, pamphlets, and periodicals available, ranging from general management publications, to industry and professional publications, to those of the Small Business Administration of the U.S. Department of Commerce. Any individual performing as a professional manager, particularly of a small organization, should be familiar with a representative number of these publications. Many highly successful managers make a hobby of being well-informed and of becoming experts on the philosophy of management. Success is usually associated with a broad philosophical background upon which specific improvement approaches are built.

Further insight into the process of management and improvement can be obtained from participation in professional management societies (such as American Management Association, Society for Advancement of Management, and The Academy of Management), trade associations, and university seminars, conferences, and short courses. Association with related professional societies is also often stimulating and beneficial. Such organizations as the American Institute of Industrial Engineers, The Institute of Management Sciences, and Systems and Procedures Association of America usually welcome interested nonprofessional members. Their meetings provide an excellent opportunity to learn what these professionals are doing and to exchange thoughts about specific problems.

As the owner-manager acquires a familiarity with the art of management and the wide range of improvement techniques available, he will probably attempt to improve the solution of his organization's significant problems. As his understanding of management and improvement broadens, his view of his organization's problems will also broaden and he will recognize important areas which were previously not regarded as improvement opportunities, and he will want to expand improvement endeavors beyond his own efforts. This may be done by management and supervisory development and/or by providing some form of "staff" assistance.

MANAGEMENT IMPROVEMENT

Once top management has recognized the importance of pursuing and achieving continual improvement and has passed the enthusiasm for doing so on to their entire organization, they must provide some positive direction to improvement endeavors. The first steps should be to encourage development of their management and supervisory personnel. This can be done in a variety of ways—ranging from the encouragement of self-help to formal programs designed to meet the needs of the organization. Self-study should not be dismissed lightly, for there is a wealth of useful information available at little or no cost. Self-study combined with discussion, either on a formal or informal basis, almost always results in a better appreciation of the importance of self-development relative to the individual and his role within the organization. Self-study can be supplemented by attending trade-professional meetings, university short-courses, etc. There is almost a limitless number of ways to encourage and help self-development relative to management improvement.

The results of a self-help management improvement program within an organization, either formal or informal, should be the springboard for translating general concepts into practical improvements relative to the problems of the organization. Some individuals will be able to make this translation without assistance. Others will need help. If staff were available, this would seem to be the logical source of assistance. Some small organizations can justify having their own staff for these activities. Others feel that this is a luxury beyond their means. However, some form of staff assistance is available to every small organization, if they know how to take advantage of their opportunities.

MANAGEMENT SURVEY

One technique frequently used by management consultants, which can be used very effectively by management themselves, is the management survey. This approach attempts to evaluate the strengths and weaknesses of all the organization's activities in an impartial and objective manner. When practiced by skilled consultants, expert knowledge and experience is brought to bear upon diagnosing the ills of an organization and bringing to light specific problem areas which merit further analysis and improvement. Where practiced by management, if objectivity is maintained, many problems will also be recognized, and the survey will result in a constructive plan of action for improvement and future development.

A reasonable first step in a self-study management survey would be to briefly write down the history of the organization, who inspired it, how and why it was started, who it serves, its general attitude and policy, etc. This recapitulation should extend to the present time and include a statement of future aims and aspirations. The goals and policies of the organization should be stated and defined as precisely as possible.

A detailed and critical analysis of the workings of the organization should follow the brief outline of its nature and development. This may include an analysis of the organizational structure, the grouping of people and responsibilities, the allocation of effort to each step involved in the operation of the organization (from the initial design of the product or service to the collection for sales), the all important production and service operations, costs and their trends, ratio comparison, sales and marketing, product acceptance, management behavior and development of personnel, labor relations and employee performance, the development and implementation of improvements, reports and their use, the condition and use of plant and facilities, labor utilization, prospects and ability for growth and expansion, etc.

From this analysis, management should be able to isolate the key factors related to improvement and to develop a program for improvement. Comparison of objectives and the ways they are pursued almost always indicates obvious opportunities for improvement and problems to which the solutions are not so obvious. Once recognized, these problems can be approached, and the experience of fellow managers in other organizations as well as professional consultants can be combined with the experience and common sense of the manager in determining a program for improvement. "Staff" help may be indicated.

SOURCES OF STAFF ASSISTANCE

Before discussing the sources of "staff" help the importance of the role of the owner-manager or man-in-charge should again be mentioned. He is the key individual within most small organizations, and he *must* assume the major share of responsibility for improvement activities. If he provides good leadership, the quest for improvement will permeate his entire organization. He must provide the pattern, the leadership, and the necessary support. He must recognize that others cannot entirely solve his problems for him—this must remain his obligation. He must retain the authority and responsibility for the continuing operation and continuing improvement of his organization. However, there are many situations where effective staff help is essential for effective problem solution. Where this is the case, the solution of the problem should be on a partnership basis—the "staff" assisting the "line" by providing an extension of skill, knowledge, experience, and time. The philosophy of the organization should be directed toward an improvement function based upon the concept of dual management responsibilities (to achieve results and to achieve continuing improvement), supported by staff assistance when needed.

Professional staff help is a valuable resource for any organization. This may range from very specific technical help, to very common procedural help (such as legal and accounting advice), to general assistance in improvement programs. This type of assistance and advice may be acquired from salesmen, CPA's, or from a variety of consultants or external "staffs" as well as from staff in the usual sense. It may be free, or costly but economically sound, or cheap but economically very expensive. The variety of staff assistance available to the small organization is great, and the cost and value also varies greatly. The man-in-charge of the small organization usually does not recognize the extensiveness of all the resources at his disposal, nor does he know how to effectively utilize this potentially valuable resource.

COMBINATION OF LINE AND STAFF

Many small organizations have successfully solved their need for staff help by employing an individual with successful staff experience in a combination line and staff capacity. This individual may be an experienced engineer, with or without line experience, hired as plant manager or assistant to the president, with a splitting of his duties between line responsibilities and staff activities. He may be concerned with improvement activities only within his assigned line area, or he may extend his staff services to all facets of the organization.

This approach has worked very successfully for many small organizations (and also for large organizations in the development of a more extensive and formalized improvement function, as presented in Chapter 16). It has much to recommend it. It may be a permanent arrangement, or it may be the prelude to a more extensive staff arrangement—perhaps on a full-time basis. One of its very attractive features is that it allows the development of a staff capability within a small organization with a minimum risk. If the staff services justify expansion on the basis of accomplishments weighed against costs, the staff services can be expanded, either by duplication of the dual arrangement or by creation of a staff position(s). One of the disadvantages of the staff-line arrangement is the competition of line and staff duties, resulting in some cases in conflicts relative to responsibility and time availability.

CONSULTING SERVICES

There are a large number of consulting services available to the small organization, ranging from free services to very costly ones. If a proper perspective is maintained, the free services may be very worthwhile, and the expensive services may also be very economical. The man-in-charge of the small organization should be aware of how he can effectively and economically obtain external staff or consulting services when his problems and improvement activities justify this support, and how he can evaluate which source or sources are most appropriate. Consulting services costing several hundreds of dollars per day may be quite justifiable and economical if the nature of the problem requires specific skills not otherwise available, and if the anticipated results justify the expenditure.

FREE SERVICES

Free consulting services are available to many organizations. Sometimes this occurs because of the needs of a trade association or university for research data or their interest in acquiring specific information. It may also result as a by-product of university courses which require practical experience for their students. Salesmen for office supplies and equipment, materials handling equipment, processing equipment, specific supplies and equipment, etc., frequently will offer some technical or consulting service as a means of demonstrating how their particular wares will benefit the prospective purchaser. Some universities, chambers of commerce, development agencies, trade associations, and government agencies offer technical and consulting services on a limited charge or free basis as a means of encouraging industrial development.

The source of staff assistance without charge to the beneficiary is surprisingly large. Many are very worthwhile—others are very costly when used. All should be carefully evaluated and used with caution. The potential benefits and consequent obligations and costs should be fully considered beforehand. Many of the free services are offered with less than altruistic motives. Even so, many of them are of genuine value to the recipient. When they are offered, they should be carefully evaluated. When they are sought, they should be sought with due consideration to the needs of the organization and an evaluation of the most suitable manner of satisfying these needs. A free service might turn out to be very costly if due caution is not used.

PROFESSIONAL CONSULTANTS

When using professional or consulting help, several cautions should be kept in mind. There are many organizations and individuals available for consulting assignments. Some are competent and honorable—others are not. It would be advisable to avoid those who claim they can solve all the problems of an organization or who can make 100 recommendations for correcting things being done incorrectly for $100. Management should keep in mind that they must continue to operate and live with their organization and must be responsible for the consequences of any errors and misjudgments of the consultant. The most profitable approaches to using consulting services are geared to helping the organization and its people solve their own problems, now and in the future, with occasional assistance from outside sources.

When considering outside help, management should also be wary of the "specialist" or "expert" who is primarily concerned with his own pet approach to problems. Many consultants specialize in a limited approach to the broad area of improvement and attempt to solve all problems with the same approach, regardless of the appropriateness. Small organizations particularly need a "generalist" approach and the systematic determination of what problems within the organization are really important.

This does not mean to depreciate the role of the specialist, but it does mean to encourage caution in the use of the specialist. Someone must determine when and where the specialists are really needed and make sure that they do not overstep their bounds. This general guidance can be provided by a knowledgeable manager-owner or by an *appropriate* professional advisor.

There are many sources of competent consulting help available to every organization. The consultant may be a full-time professional consultant, in individual or firm practice; he may be a "moon-lighter" doing extra work as a supplement to his regular occupation, or he may be a retired manager working part-time. Many professors are expected by their universities to engage in outside professional activity, and they consult on a regular but limited professional basis. Some employed professionals are motivated by their own personal drives (and also encouraged by their employers) to engage in limited moon-light consulting activities during their off hours and vacations. All of these individuals are good potential sources of competent staff help for small organizations. They should be evaluated by management in regard to their competency and integrity before being engaged, and a clear-cut understanding of what is to be done should be reached.

SHARED STAFF

One of the most promising approaches to providing staff assistance to the small organizations is the "rotating" approach. The arrangements may be made by a group of small businessmen, a consultant, or a trade association. The essence of this approach is to develop an arrangement whereby several organizations, which individually perhaps cannot justify hiring their own staffs, cooperatively hire a staff which they share.

An example of this approach is demonstrated by William E. Dykes, a consultant of Marietta, Georgia, who devotes his consulting practice almost exclusively to small business organizations. Typically, he will be working with four organizations at a time. Each will receive a six to twelve week period of concentrated attention during which the consultant acts as the "staff" industrial engineer and management advisor. At the end of this period, the consultant "changes" employers. This continues and the consultant rotates among the four firms. The length of his stay and the scheduling of his return to a given company are arranged on a mutually agreeable basis. If during his assignment at one company a pressing problem arises at another firm, he is available for consultation. The assignments are shared among the firms, as are the expenses.

The general approach of rotating a staff among several small organizations has much to recommend it. It is an approach which has not been seriously considered by small businesses—nor by many consultants. Certainly, there are problems associated with this approach, but there are also substantial benefits which cannot be achieved in other ways.

NONPROFIT ORGANIZATIONS

Nonprofit organizations frequently have additional resources at their disposal which are not normally available to profit-making companies. Many professional organizations, as well as individual professionals, welcome an opportunity to perform a public service. They are anxious to help nonprofit organizations, and many excellent professional services have been donated to community hospitals, libraries, etc. by individuals and professional groups. Management of nonprofit organizations should explore the opportunities for complementing their own skills and resources by enlisting the aid of professional organizations and interested individual professionals.

SUMMARY

Small organizations frequently suffer from an unnecessary inferiority complex relative to improvement activities. The management of improvement has the same validity within a small organization as within medium or large-size ones. The specific approaches to improvement must be tailored to the needs of the organization—but this is true for any organization. A dedication to continuing improvement is essential. Top management (which frequently means the owner-manager in small organizations) must be aware of developments in management and of a wide variety of improvement techniques. Staff assistance *can* be provided to supplement line management improvement endeavors. This might be done by hiring staff-experienced individuals as line managers, by actually developing a staff for improvement activities, by judicious use of consultants, or by a device such as rotating an improvement staff among several organizations.

One might question what skills are desirable for the improvement function staff serving a small organization. A "generalist" rather than a "specialist" is likely to be of more potential value. This does not mean to imply that specialist assistance is not of value, but the specialist approach should be used with caution and only when the talents of the specialist can be exploited relative to the needs of the total organization. In general, such specialties as operations research, computer application, etc., have limited utility within small organizations. However, there are some situations within the confines of small business where these contributions can be of great value. The determination of when this situation exists is the obligation of the generalist and of management.

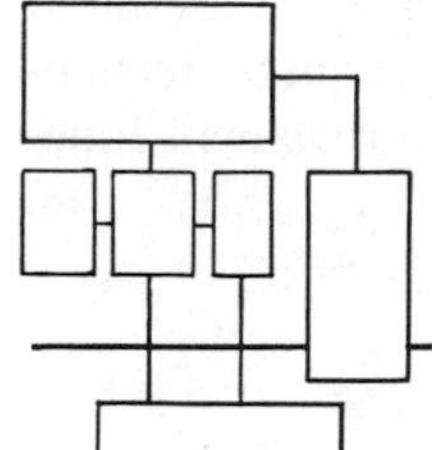

CHAPTER 21

IMPROVEMENT THROUGH FINANCIAL CONTROL—CONTROLLERSHIP

AMERICAN INDUSTRY has long had a healthy respect for the "sharp pencil" boys—the individuals who guide the financial aspects of an organization. Concentration upon accounting, costs, financing, and other financial aspects of operation are of great importance. Formal recognition of the importance of finance goes back at least to the early part of the twentieth century and the work of Harrington Emerson. These early activities have gradually developed into the controllership function of the present day.

The objectives of the controllership function, which are centered around financial aspects of an organization's operation, are to assist top management, and thus the entire organization, in achieving profitable operation. There are some similarities between the broad improvement function and the objectives of the controllership function. Unfortunately, the controllership function in actual practice tends to be much too narrow—it tends to concentrate almost exclusively on financial and cost matters and to shy away from developing a technical capability to enable it to effectively deal with the current technological explosion.

However, some exceptionally valuable contributions to continuing and systematic improvement have developed within this activity. The following presentation is typical of the thinking of more progressive controllers, but unfortunately is not typical of the execution of the controllership function within all organizations.[1] Just as modern industrial engineering becomes the improvement function as it lives up to its stated objectives, modern controllership—when it acquires adequate technological (engineering) capability—also approaches the improvement function as it lives up to its stated objectives.

The Organization of Controllership

by **E. B. COCHRAN***

Manager, Planning Department, Wright Aeronautical Division, Curtiss-Wright Corporation

In the natural development of the industrial engineering function within many organizations, the industrial engineer has assumed many responsibilities of a "controllership" nature. This progression is a natural one, and one that is likely to continue at an accelerated pace as the industrial engineer becomes more proficient with the newer concepts and techniques associated with his field. It is with this thought in mind that we have selected this article for publication. The alert industrial engineer will be aware of the contributions that he may be able to make in the pursuit of the "controllership" function, even though he may be inclined to assume that the function is one of industrial engineering rather than of controllership. There is small profit in arguing titles.

It should be noted that the author does not present a modern view of industrial engineering. He confines the industrial engineering function to shop and manufacturing activity, and does not recognize the emerging role of industrial engineering as an engineer for management—dealing with the systems analysis and design of broad management problems.—ED.

THE controller's function in the enterprise is undergoing considerable change in the direction of becoming the chief planning and control officer for the enterprise.[2] But at present there is frequent misunderstanding of, and lack of sympathy toward, the controller's

* Currently Budget Manager, Rohr Aircraft Corporation.

new role by other executives. This is partly due to fuzzy or outmoded organization theory. But the profession itself can be seriously called to task, since many of those in the position of controller have relied on, and have been trained in, an outmoded and narrow conception of their responsibility. Often this lack of breadth is given protective coloration by verbal obeisance to "modern" controllers' "code," such as the very good one issued by the Controller's Institute.

The powerful need of the enterprise for broader controllership arises from three primary sources:

1. The growing size and complexity of the individual business enterprise.
2. The resulting multiplication of specialists at both the technical and executive levels, with consequent difficulties of coordination and dilution of executive interest in maximizing profits.
3. The trend toward applying the formal planning and control technique, aimed at achieving carefully determined profit objectives, which places intense administrative and analytical loads on top management.

The controller is the natural organization position in which to center the coordination effort now widely recognized as a must for sustained success of the larger enterprise (with, say, $20 million or more sales a year). Consequently his duties may be enunciated broadly under three main headings as follows:

Planning

Supervises the preparation of company short and long-range plans, approving all measures of activity and cost standards contained in them.

Evaluates the company's master plan of operation and investment and recommends action to top management.

Follow-up

Conducts follow-up activity to determine areas of poor performance against the plan and to insure that corrective action is being taken.

Measurement

Supervises statistical activities necessary to properly report on actual and planned activity, and issues financial statements and related data to all requiring them.

Further detail will be found in the job description provided in Table 21-1.

TABLE 21-1 Job Description: Controller

REPORTS TO: The president

BASIC FUNCTION:

To assist the president and his principal executives to obtain maximum profits; spearheads the joint development of realistic operating and investment plans and standards, and administers a system of positive follow-up and controls.

SUPERVISES:

Manager of Controls and Analysis
Manager of Industrial Statistics
Manager of Cost Analysis
Manager of Cost Accounting
Manager of General Accounting
Manager of Procedures and Audits

SPECIFIC DUTIES:

Planning

1. Develops and publishes the ground rules for company short and long-range planning and the general procedure to be followed by each function. Works with department heads to coordinate their planning with company policies and objectives.
2. Reviews and clears all cost standards and measures of activity proposed by departments for use in plans and budgets. Initiates studies of areas where measures are not felt to be reliable.
3. Combines the proposed plans of all departments. Appraises the effects on profit, financial and market position, and the progress anticipated. Evaluates the realism of the proposed plan against general business and industry conditions. Summarizes points of importance for the president and recommends action on the master plan of operations and investment.
4. Issues monthly projections of current operating results for several months ahead, relating changes to the original plan.

Follow-up

5. Develops and insures timely issuance of control reports to the president and his principal executives. Administers a system of supporting reports to underlying levels of supervision.
6. Performs periodic review and appraisal of operations, involving study of performance in all operating areas and determination of factors underlying poor or good results.
7. Conducts a monthly review meeting with the president to bring out significant operating results and action points. Assists the president to prepare for his own follow-up meetings with key operating executives.
8. Works with all levels of supervision to develop understanding of quotas and budgets, the use of control reports, and the technique of holding review meetings on their own performance.

Other

9. Reviews major pricing proposals for maximum profitability and thorough analysis of volume effect.
10. Conducts general accounting, cost estimating, cost accounting, and payroll activities, insuring adequate control over sources of basic data and conformance with government contract requirements. Issues necessary statements, reports, and special statistics.
11. Coordinates the development of, and publishes, all interdepartmental procedures and all manuals and procedures with control significance; audits conformance to such procedures and manuals. Initiates steps to simplify procedures and cut costs.
12. Administers a reports control system covering all recurring reports in the company.

This is certainly a somewhat ambitious set of duties. Therefore this paper will describe in further detail the organization required by a controller who is to perform such tasks.

GENERAL PATTERN OF THE CORPORATE ORGANIZATION

There are, of course, a number of basic approaches to the formal organization of any particular enterprise. Each reflects requirements defined by the industry in which the company operates, its choice of products on which it chooses to compete, the size and location of facilities operated by the company, the particular skills and limitations of the management itself, and so on. Each approach will strongly affect the controller's organization since it will establish the departmental breakdown and interrelations which are the very fabric of any planning and control program to be administered by the controller.

Therefore for the sake of definiteness we shall first take one basic pattern of over-all organization as a framework for this discussion: that of the ordinary medium-sized centralized manufacturing company. With a full complement of normal marketing and product design problems, its manufacturing does not yet involve the organization complexity which accompanies the existence of several sizable and scattered major facilities. A brief organization chart is provided in Fig. 21-1, with major departmental breakdowns indicated for later reference.

It will be noted that the treasury function is shown as separate from the controller. This is not an essential condition since the two easily may be combined, as under a vice-president of finance. The choice to be made here is largely one of individual preference, the emphasis necessary on financing matters, and the qualifications and interests within the top management group itself.

Later, the application of this approach to decentralized organizations will be discussed.

DEPARTMENTS IN THE CONTROLLER'S OFFICE

The controller's group divides itself naturally into three classes, corresponding to main areas of the controller's duties. First will come those who operate predominantly in the planning and follow-up areas. Referring to Fig. 21-1 this covers the controls and analysis and cost analysis departments. Second are the groups which sup-

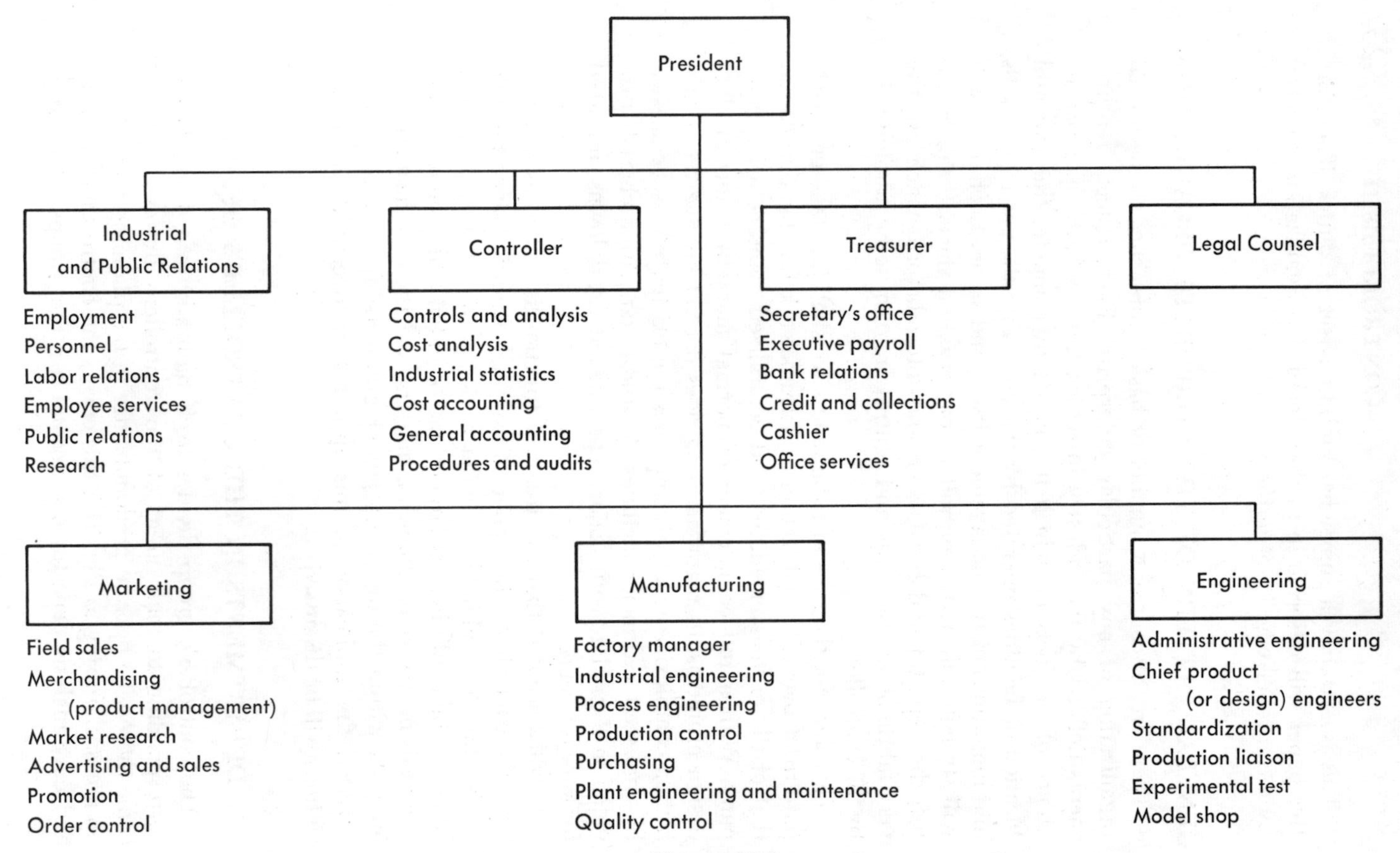
President
Industrial and Public Relations
Employment
Personnel
Labor relations
Employee services
Public relations
Research
Controller
Controls and analysis
Cost analysis
Industrial statistics
Cost accounting
General accounting
Procedures and audits
Treasurer
Secretary's office
Executive payroll
Bank relations
Credit and collections
Cashier
Office services
Legal Counsel
Marketing
Field sales
Merchandising (product management)
Market research
Advertising and sales
Promotion
Order control
Manufacturing
Factory manager
Industrial engineering
Process engineering
Production control
Purchasing
Plant engineering and maintenance
Quality control
Engineering
Administrative engineering
Chief product (or design) engineers
Standardization
Production liaison
Experimental test
Model shop

Figure 21-1

ply the data, statistics and reports necessary to plan operations, measure results and determine the corrective action needed; this covers industrial statistics, cost accounting and general accounting. Third are groups which may be related to one or the other of these two, but which specialize more deeply in one particular phase. In this case there is only one—procedures and audit—but there could be others (such as a tax department).

It may be well to call attention to a key principle of the controller's organization: the consistent joining of planning and follow-up functions. Where a department coordinates planning for an area of operations it also should perform the follow-up activity on that area's performance. The need for this unity is inherent. Planning requires before its completion a reasonably close familiarity with the activity, time and ability to analyze it, effective communication with the line personnel involved (who after all must generate the plans themselves in terms of sound practice or growth), and a capacity to relate each operating area to the others. Follow-up requires exactly the same background and abilities, plus intimate familiarity with the analysis and negotiation which accompanied the submission and approval of operating plans. The two functions therefore must be discharged by the same group for a given area of operations.

Another principle is worth reference here. That is, the separation of statistical from planning and follow-up duties. In many organizations there are several groups within the controller's department which combine these; often a "budget department" is also a central statistical agency, or general accounting prepares company forecasts from the ground up. Such practices often are a necessary interim step towards a sound program of planning and control. But if continued for long they can cause dilution of effort and a poor fit between the tasks to be done and the personnel used on them. The psychology of the two is quite different, and it is dangerous to combine them too closely.

CONTROLS AND ANALYSIS DEPARTMENT

The functions of this department—or some portion of them—may be found residing in groups with a variety of names: "budget department," "statistical control," "planning office," "administrative department," are a few. The important thing is that the functions be performed in an efficient and economical manner. This cannot be the case where they are considered as mere personal duties of the controller himself.

If the controller's office is to contribute as it can to company profits it requires a well-knit group of able, aggressive, imaginative, analytical people. These people must be able to think broadly—as broadly as top management itself—for their assignment is nothing less than to spearhead the profit search which is management's prime objective. The group is responsible for establishment of sound planning procedure, careful evaluation of plans, effective follow-up reports, penetrating analysis of results and a continual training of other departments in the attitudes and action of profit improvement. These responsibilities therefore require isolation from routine and constant exposure to top-level problems and policies.

The department's duties may be more specifically listed as follows:

Planning

1. Recommends over-all planning and control procedures.
2. Issues necessary ground rules and instructions for planning.
3. Assists department heads to prepare plans and forecasts.
4. Analyzes plans and forecasts to locate weak spots and obtain correction.
5. Presents over-all corrected plans to controller and management for approval.
6. Publishes approved plans and forecasts.
7. Reviews all capital appropriation requests for soundness and conformance with company programs.

Follow-up

1. Establishes control reports to all levels of management.
2. Reviews operating performance against plans and forecasts with department heads.
3. Prepares periodic analysis of results, and presents to the controller and management.

Other

1. Reviews major pricing proposals for maximum profitability and thorough analysis of volume effect.

It should be apparent that this group cannot be saddled with the more routine and detailed tasks of statistical work and preparation of standardized reports if it is to perform at its most effective level. For the same reason it should also be freed from the relatively straightforward portion of the task of reviewing results against the plans and other measures established. Once the elements of planning and follow-up procedure are established, other departments (such as cost analysis) can take over a sizable share of the review and follow-up of detailed factory operations, for example.

Accounting groups (general and cost) should therefore service the controls group with financial and operating statements, special tabulations and extensive or detailed calculations as required. The cost analysis group should perform preliminary screening and analysis of detailed operation, product and overhead costs against plans and standards, and pass along only major problems for the deeper analysis and recommendations of the controls group. Cost analysis may similarly review departmental manpower and expense requisitions against approved budgets, referring tough ones to the controls group, and handle the endless review and clearance of new factory cost standards in accordance with the general criteria established by Controls.

Hard and fast rules cannot be stated; the exact delineation of duties will always depend somewhat on the relative strength of the personalities, intellect and experience of the staff comprising each department of the controller's office. But some such division of duties is essential if the full range of activities is to be handled thoroughly and economically without bogging down the controls group.

Organization of the controls group is again dependent on many factors: size of the company; relative importance of the problems faced by the functional areas of marketing, purchasing, manufacturing and inventory control, etc.; relative strength of departments outside the controller's office which deal with planning and control matters in their own areas; strengths, weaknesses and human relations of the personnel currently in the controls office; and so forth. However a basic pattern of organization is useful in most situations and forms a rough yardstick against which alternatives may be measured or at least discussed.

Some five sections or activities are fundamentally involved in the successful functioning of a controls group. Due to their critical importance to the controller's effectiveness each will be discussed briefly.

1. *Operations Analysis* is in a sense the budgetary control group covering operating activities and their costs. This section coordinates the preparation of annual operating budgets and current forecasts to meet company financial objectives as quickly as possible. It estab-

lishes keystones of basic budgeting and forecasting procedure and supervises indoctrination and training programs for operating supervision. It reviews budgets and forecasts of cost and investment in detail and recommends approval or other action. It analyzes details of performance and recommends corrective action where possible. It establishes control reports to operating supervisors and conducts performance reviews with them. Emphasis is on improving product and departmental *cost* matters with some attention to related use of inventory and facilities investment; relations with cost analysis are close as will be seen later.

2. *Product Performance Analysis,* usually a much smaller group, concentrates on the sales side of company performance. It is essential for good profit control that long and short-range product plans be analyzed thoroughly for their sales volume and profit effects. The controller must be in a position quickly to point out fallacies in future plans, relating them to past experience, general industry conditions, profit yield, etc. In this connection the section would review proposed production schedules and sales forecasts. It would also watch sales performance against budgeted volumes, market penetration and product mix, passing along its conclusions to other sections of the Controls Department. Where warranted it would keep a watchful eye over the progress of major new product development programs, insuring that delays or early completion are reflected in financial forecasts and that clear explanations are obtained and corrective action recommended.

   Obviously the work of such a group would have close relations with that of market research, production control and the company economist if there is one. Its justification lies in its interest in the profit consideration and in the development and meeting of product plans which permit the attainment of company budgets and forecasts.

3. *Pricing Analysis* plays a major role in the company's profit control program. This is an area where small apparent differences have major and very tangible consequences in the cash box. The job is a sophisticated one, requiring not only the establishment of sound procedures for drawing up cost studies but also the profit-wise evaluation of major price proposals.

   Many companies fall into the trap of considering pricing to be simply a matter of sales volume or of "cost plus." Both approaches are wrong. The answer lies more in a careful (although not easy) analysis of product specifications, variable, fixed and sunk costs, and profit versus volume relationships—along with the more intangible marketing factors of customers acceptance, effect of promotional programs, restyling, etc. This section by no means usurps the prerogatives of an analytically minded marketing department, where one exists. It simply meets it halfway, applying the cold criterion of profit results and insuring that the best use is made of data available to measure the true profit of pricing proposals and policies. Many companies would see their pricing completely transformed by such a group in the controller's office.

4. *Capital Investment Analysis* handles the detailed review of capital investment proposals and analyzes their subsequent results. The benefits of good sales forecasting, pricing and operating cost control easily can be lost through uneconomic facilities. Or what appeared to be sound investments, and perhaps were, may be turned into veritable ratholes for capital funds as expenditures pile up far beyond the approval level or cost reductions fail to materialize. This section obviously must establish the format and supporting detail required for proposals, as well as the type of follow-up reports to be prepared.

   The personnel involved here should have some acquaintance with manufacturing problems and approaches, for it must work closely with production and industrial engineers if it is to have its proper influence. Their financial bent and access to forward plans and cost targets within the controller's office may often lead them to stimulate new facilities programs from manufacturing and others. Again, if the section is on top of its job, annual preparation of the forward plan for capital investment (which should cover at least five years) should involve simply a summary of programs approved, under active consideration, and known to be required.

5. *Financial Analysis,* in a real sense, has the last word in appraising company performance and helping to formulate programs. For its basic task is the evaluation of results and establishment of goals from the standpoint of maximizing return on capital. This return goal comprises the margin on sales (therefore pricing policy and cost control) and the use of capital (therefore facilities investments and use of working capital items). The group may be small relative to operations analysis or capital investment analysis, but its task is large.

   It will prepare studies of competitors and similar companies to develop realistic standards for sales margin, use of capital components such as plant, cash, inventory, receivables, etc., and return on capital employed, for use in budgets and forecasts. It will analyze over-all operating and investment results periodically, using the results of analysis by the other sections, to measure progress toward over-all financial objectives and locate weaknesses in current operations. It will apply the same approach to proposed budgets and forecasts. It will inevitably become the "special project" section of the controller's office. It probably will also inherit the task of preparing periodic over-all presentations to management on operating results and progress toward broad financial goals.

The key personnel, and even the junior analysts, chosen for the assignments described obviously do not grow on trees. They must have a considerable background in business and economic theory, plus significant experience in work requiring analysis and evaluation of top-level policies and problems. Personal characteristics are just as important. These people must have initiative if they are to ferret out the problems inherent in proposed plans and policies of current operations, or to devise procedures to implement broad management objectives and policies. They must be flexible—broad background and diversity of experience is better than intense training in a narrow area. They must handle people well—their assignments go deep into the plans, professional hopes and personal pride of the company's key personnel. They must be topnotch salesmen to present their conclusions to management in distilled yet interesting and understandable form.

The likelihood that the accounting profession will supply adequate candidates for this activity is quite small.

COST ANALYSIS DEPARTMENT

The functions of the cost analysis department are sometimes hidden within a "budget department," or deep within cost accounting proper. Often they do not appear at all in the controller's office but are performed entirely in the plant, as by an industrial engineering group.

Any of these situations have real disadvantages. In the first instance there is overburdening of the budget or controls group, or dilution of its attention to the really crucial and major problems of profit improvement. In the second case there is a strong tendency to be absorbed by the statistical and reporting activities of cost accounting proper, rather than to stay geared to the cost control aspects of the business and keep close to operating personnel. In the third case, there cannot be the objective and thorough review of cost performance details and operating cost standards only possible when a strong industrial engineering activity is supplemented, cross-checked and coordinated with management goals by an informed group of cost analysts with primary allegiance to the overriding importance of financial consequences.

The duties of the Cost Analysis Department may be listed briefly as follows:

Planning

1. Prepares and issues indexes of past and future cost levels.
2. Helps establish all manufacturing and material cost standards, including variable overhead budgets.
3. Approves all proposed factory cost standards and changes to them.
4. Coordinates preparation of cost estimates and quotations.
5. Reviews appropriation requests, major purchase requisitions and work orders before issuance to insure accuracy, completeness of data and conformance with established procedures.

Follow-up

1. Analyzes variances against cost standards.
2. Evaluates accuracy of factory cost standards.
3. Reviews cost performance with manufacturing and purchasing personnel.
4. Reports actual versus projected savings on capital outlays.

Other

1. Recommends procedures for cost estimating and development of standards.
2. Reviews major cost entries.

The best exposition of this department's activities probably is in terms of its relations to other units in the controller's office and the company.

In relation to Cost Accounting proper, Cost Analysis will prepare special cost statements and analyses from the regular cost data turned out by Cost Accounting. It will also provide Cost Accounting with necessary cost standards for use in variance statements.

In relation to the Operations Analysis Section of the Controls Department, Cost Analysis will locate and summarize all variances against product cost standards and departmental budgets and perform further detailed analysis of cost variances as requested. It will tabulate and review purchase requisitions and proposed work orders against pertinent budgets to insure "precontrol" of expenditures, notifying Operations Analysis of off-standard conditions. It will also evaluate and approve all proposed factory cost standards and changes to them as submitted by industrial engineering, insuring conformance with the policies established by Operations Analysis, and it will coordinate preparation of detailed material cost standards.

In relation to the Pricing Section it prepares an index or indexes of past and future cost levels and coordinates the preparation of cost studies necessary for pricing decisions. For Capital Investment Analysis it reviews appropriation requests for accuracy and suitable detail of cost data, and screens work orders for conformance with approved requests.

Organization of Cost Analysis may be handled by about four main sections:

1. A section to develop operating cost standards and review performance against them. (This may, if warranted, be broken down into separate groups for direct labor, factory overhead, tooling and material handling or warehousing.)
2. A section to perform a similar function for material costs.
3. A cost estimating section, to coordinate preparation of estimates, apply rates and review the results.
4. A special studies group to handle the multitude of special assignments, analyses, preparation of cost procedures, etc.

The key people and creative juniors of this department, as in the case of the controls group, must be chosen to a definite pattern. This pattern is in sharp contrast with that normally presented by cost people. But it is essential to achieve it, for upon this rock many efforts to build modern controllership founder: the usual function of "cost analysis" is quite different from that actually performed by many existing groups with the name, and cannot be handled by the personnel at hand.

Good cost analysis people are a special breed. On the one hand they must obviously know a fair amount about approaches to accounting for costs. But more important, they must be operations-minded, interested in shop and field activities and able to speak the language and understand the thoughts and needs of line personnel. Their systems, techniques and analyses must then be geared to an objective of real service, while guided by principles of sound economics in the light of the profit objective. Men who are trained as industrial engineers are well-suited for this work. Smart ones will learn all the cost accounting needed, that they don't already know instinctively, within a very short time. In contrast, it is practically impossible to train an old line cost *accountant* to be a good cost *analyst*.

INDUSTRIAL STATISTICS DEPARTMENT

This is a function which can vary in importance and stature from a small "chart department" to a full-blown economic analysis group.

The latter is probably the most desirable, since the controller's office is then supplied with a breadth of outlook most helpful to its financial analysis of business decisions and results. Let us list certain major duties:

Planning

1. Projects long-range industry conditions and company market penetration.
2. Reviews details of forecast to insure reasonableness in the light of industry conditions and trends.

Follow-up

1. Reviews company sales results against industry.

Statistical

1. Gathers data on company unit production, sales and prices.
2. Gathers data on industry unit production, sales and prices, and on pertinent economic trends.
3. Gathers data on competitors' financial results and investment.
4. May develop price-volume curves on specific products.

The department might in a smaller organization be combined with the Product Performance section of the Controls Department. But if practical it should be separated so as to keep a fairly abstract view of the economics of the company's industry. Its functions take on critical importance for companies operating in several industrial areas, when close analysis of numerous broader economic factors and trends may spell the difference between failure and prosperity.

The department's responsibilities should not conflict with those of market research. There will be areas of overlap, as is the case for many other pairs of departments, but their emphasis is quite different. The one is interested in the economy and the industry as a whole, the other is concerned with interpreting general conditions in terms of specific product proposals and sales programs.

COST AND GENERAL ACCOUNTING DEPARTMENTS

We now come to two pure accounting groups, which have been purposely separated from the more analytical activities. This is not to say that they are completely insulated from all the considerations discussed, for their work will be strongly influenced by the requirements of the departments previously described. Their personnel should therefore have some understanding of those requirements and the flexibility to meet them without completely upsetting the routine of statements. A listing of duties follows:

COST ACCOUNTING DEPARTMENT

Planning

1. Prepares statements pertinent to cost forecasts and budgets.

Statistical

1. Records costs by product, process and department, as required.
2. Prepares cost of sales statements.
3. Prepares statements of cost variances.
4. Prepares special cost tabulations as required.

Other

1. Recommends improved cost accounting procedures.
2. Manages the taking of physical inventories.

Many details of cost accounting activity have already been touched on and will not be discussed further here.

GENERAL ACCOUNTING DEPARTMENT

Statistical

1. Records data in the general books of account, covering fixed assets, working capital, sales and profit.
2. Issues financial statements and government reports.
3. Prepares special tabulations as required.
4. Bills customers and pays suppliers as directed.
5. Prepares payroll.
6. Reconciles bank balances.
7. Keeps property records.

Planning

1. Prepares and keeps current material for a comprehensive chart and manual of accounts.
2. Prepares statements pertinent to general financial forecasts and budgets.

Other

1. Recommends improved accounting procedures and internal control practices.

To many experts in the financial field it may appear that we have grossly underplayed the contribution and the stature of these two accounting groups. For example, the bulk of discussion to date has concerned the planning and analysis groups. After all, the entire function of controller started from the requirements and uses of general accounting, while cost accountants have developed many techniques of cost control. Furthermore, it may look as if we are writing off the basic importance of accurate records to a company, and the inherent control exercised by them.

Let this be fully granted. And with it let us point out that the bulk of personnel in the controller's office will be in these two departments. But let us not let historical development and the *sine qua non* of accurate records keep us from recognizing the roles which are now pertinent to controllership and needed by top management.

These accounting groups are logically *service* functions, pure and simple. In fact, they usually need considerable re-orienting to be effective in this respect, given the stepped up pace required by a modern control program. It is difficult to change the approach of a long-established group from a self-centered satisfaction with accurate statements as such, to a real concern that these are timely, readable and designed to supply the data that line people really need.

A certain amount of resentment and antagonism is normal during the transition, and not all the "regulars" will make it. The tension may be especially acute in relation to the needs of the controls and cost analysis functions, for the contrast in function between the accounting activity and these two groups awakens a keen sense of the loss of relative status which has occurred, and sometimes a difference in pay scales brings this home. Valuable time can be lost, and valuable men too, if the handling is not skillful and insight into the real potential of each man in accounting activities is less than keen. But the company, which allows sentiment about the change-over to affect its speed of action, is losing far more in profits than it would care to calculate. It must not falter.

In fact, something is gained by the separation, even by those who like it least. For the specialist, accounting, as such, will always offer a pretty wide scope of activities and interests. Accountants are now free to do their job of accounting, with the bulk of special projects and upsetting analysis jobs siphoned off in other directions.

PROCEDURES AND AUDIT DEPARTMENT

Any procedures and audit group is the somewhat unfortunate heir to two absolutely opposed business traditions.

The first involves the need for detailed control over data incorporated into the books of account. Emphasis is on whether bank statements reconcile with receipts and disbursements, whether recorded inventories are really there, whether the books balance and errors are tracked down, etc. This essential and useful function naturally has given rise to the need for detailed prescription of accounting methods and crosschecks, designed to be as nearly foolproof as possible. The nature of accounting procedure, however, is such that these procedures must affect activities in many operating departments such as purchasing, material control and sales. In the course of this, auditors and procedures men frequently may point out obvious simplifications in line operating procedures, often being the only group in a company which looks at detailed methods of operation from a relatively impartial viewpoint. However, in many companies operating personnel have complained that the view of the auditors and procedure writers is narrow and guided more by bookkeeping considerations than by the aim of efficient practical operations. Conflicts between the two points of view are of long standing and considerable bitterness.

The second approach to procedures has been of an entirely different sort. It involves the establishment of a special office or unit at a high level in the organization to review and analyze internal operations from the viewpoint of over-all company efficiency. Since the days of Taylor, the need for such a group has had recurring attention. It has appeared in every conceivable organization spot: the president's office; as part of an industrial engineering or methods department in manufacturing; as part of an administrative vice-president's function; as part of an expanded auditing department; in a department of organization; and so on. The variety of approaches has unavoidably caused confusion as to where such a function should be placed and what separates it from the operating departments whose procedures it affects.

The concept of controllership expounded here carries with it a reasonably clear solution to these conflicting points of view. On the one hand there are many facets of operations which directly affect the books of account and which must be guided by the requirements for accounting control and preservation of assets. This, naturally, calls for controller's approval and audit of basic procedures. On the other hand, the controller's new responsibility for profit planning and control requires him to prepare and keep current a sizable amount of procedural material on that topic, so that the many complex tasks involved may be performed in an orderly manner. As a matter of fact, in a developing installation of planning and control technique it will be found that a large share of time by accounting and analytical personnel (and the controller himself) is on procedural development and discussion. Furthermore, the breadth of this control responsibility will strongly influence the entire procedures activity in the direction of broadening it. This naturally improves the working relationship with line personnel immeasurably. The two approaches to procedures and audits, therefore, may be combined into one as a natural development of the control function, with considerable reduction in conflict and better integration of effort all around. If this is *not* done, the program of planning and control is seriously weakened.

Certain basic points characterize successful operation of a procedures and audit group in this pattern of controllership:

1. Procedures prepared, issued and audited are limited to those with interdepartmental effects or with general planning and control significance. Procedures incident to ordinary internal operation of operating departments do not come within this group's cognizance. After all, a prime factor in supervising a department is to establish sound efficient modes of operation, which are nothing but procedures. And it is essential that line responsibilities not be interfered with. This does not, of course, preclude the possibility of a line department asking for procedures counsel from the controller.
2. To the fullest extent possible, the procedures group does not "write the procedures." It may point out the need for a new one or revision of an old one, but the procedure itself should be drafted in the first instance by the operating department or departments most involved. This approach has many advantages: it insures close attention to the needs of line executives; it harnesses their attention and backing for the procedures as nothing else can; it improves their knowledge and understanding of their own operations and of their connections with other departments; it avoids the buildup of an extensive procedures staff. In short, it recognizes the basic part played by procedures in all managerial activity and encourages better understanding and use of them by line management.

   Naturally the procedures group must review, collate and coordinate a proposed procedure. This may end in major changes in order to fit needs not perceived or understood by the line department heads. But every effort should be made to provide for full participation from the ground up.
3. The activity of auditing is broadened to include review of the degree to which *all* major procedures are working out in practice or

being adhered to by line personnel. This is not a constant detailed review, but a periodic check for each major procedure. To insure objectivity, it should be performed by personnel other than those involved in the writing and issuance of the procedures involved. It will include the usual internal auditing of accounts, and may require the presence of a limited number of accounting audit specialists for use on this phase.

RELATIONSHIPS TO OTHER DEPARTMENTS

It may help give some further sense of the breakaway from traditional concepts of the controller's office if we plot certain relationships between its sections and other departments of the company. This chart brings out clearly the degree to which every other major function in the company—manufacturing, marketing, and engineering—has one or two critical "brain centers," where forward planning and appraisal of results are performed for the head of that function. The flow of ideas and analyses between these groups and the various departments of the controller's office is of key importance to company planning and control. In fact such an interchange, with the resulting effect on company efforts for profit, may be said to *typify* the newer concept of controllership.

For illustration of these relationships, the generation of a recommendation to top management on four basic matters is charted briefly in Table 21-2. This covers:

A. Establishing a manufacturing budget.
B. Determining make or buy on a component.
C. Pricing a product line.
D. Initiating development of a new product.

Thorough study of this chart should be made for a more complete understanding of the dynamics of the controller's organization under conditions of the organization outlined in Fig. 21-1. The illustrations are necessarily brief and may be expanded into much greater detail by the reader.

CONCLUSION

Let us now summarize and give the results of this discussion a wider application.

We have reviewed the general requirements for an organization necessary to implement an advanced concept of controllership, within the framework of a centralized manufacturing structure.

The prime influence in design of this organization is a simple one. It is to focus all company effort on the objective of operating efficiency, as measured by maximum profit results. To secure this, several techniques are useful and even necessary:

1. Planning (or analysis of plans) and follow-up responsibilities are joined rather than placed in separate groups.
2. Planning and follow-up duties are performed by groups separate from those which handle statistical and data-gathering services.
3. A Controls and Analysis group is the keystone of the controller's office, being charged to analyze company programs and results in every area from the profit standpoint. This requires broad understanding of the problems of the business, and exploits accounting and control procedures intensively.
4. Cost Analysis is separated from Cost Accounting proper. This permits better servicing of manufacturing personnel and more concentrated follow-up and analysis of detailed manufacturing standards and results.
5. Cost and General Accounting are separated to insure proper recognition of the two quite different types of accounting services involved.
6. Procedures and Audit functions are broadened and focused directly on planning and control matters. The two are grouped under one head to capitalize on the special knowledge and skills of each, and to encourage a wider concept of auditing.

An attempt has also been made to indicate the dynamics of the controller's office operation. This should demonstrate the relative sterility of an organization which does not face the *operating* problems of its company squarely. But, to do this successfully requires breadth of personnel, an organization structure which frees certain of its key people to perform careful analysis work and an intense desire to serve the company's profit objective.

The foregoing discussion has been entirely in terms of a centralized manufacturing company of medium size without the broad distribution of operating locations which might require a decentralized organization. A few comments are in order on the application of this concept to decentralized situations.

Basically, the major difference consists simply in the placing of

TABLE 21-2

Processing Major Financial Decisions

	Marketing	Manufacturing	Engineering
	A. SETTING MANUFACTURING BUDGETS		
1. Unit Production Schedule	Forecasts sales volume and field stocks by product (merchandising and market research).	Develops rough requirements for direct labor and material by product (process engineering and industrial engineering). Establishes plant capacitiy and work in process requirements (industrial engineering and production control). Develops unit production schedule within plant capacity (production control).	Reviews schedule to insure product availability (administrative engineering).
2. Direct Labor		Develops detailed standards by product and operation (administrative engineering). Projects direct labor hours needed by department and month from standards, schedule, and opening inventories; makes specific allowance for set up, rework, etc. (production control).	Establishes final bill of material for each product (production liaison).

TABLE 21-2 (cont.)

Controls and Analysis	Cost Analysis	Industrial Statistics	Cost Accounting
Appraises proposed price volume relationships and competitive pricing structure (pricing analysis). Reviews sales and field stock forecasts for progress in market penetration, proper mix and conformance with past experience and economic forecasts (product performance analysis).		Forecasts general economic and industry condition.	

TABLE 21-2 (cont.)

Processing Major Financial Decisions

	Marketing	Manufacturing	Engineering
3. Material		Develops detailed standards by product and operation (process engineering). Projects material prices and lot sizes (purchasing and production control).	
4. Overhead and Tools		Develops detailed department standards for indirect labor, supplies, and other overhead cost components—both fixed and variable (industrial engineering).	
5. General Review			

TABLE 21-2 (cont.)

Controls and Analysis	Cost Analysis	Industrial Statistics	Cost Accounting
Establishes general "task" factors to be incorporated in standards, and work centers to be considered (operations analysis).	Reviews and accepts detailed standards in accordance with general criteria from operations analysis. Computes pertinent data on product and department costs.		Prepares necessary tabulations and comparisons of actual costs and variances for use in analyzing and establishing budgets.
Reviews manufacturing cost performance against past experience and operating standards (operations analysis). Appraises manufacturing cost budget against broad standards of return on investment and use of capital (financial analysis).	Prepares over-all statement of manufacturing cost for review and analysis.		

TABLE 21-2 (cont.)

Processing Major Financial Decisions

	Marketing	Manufacturing	Engineering
		B. DETERMINING MAKE OR BUY	
1. Locating Items for Consideration	Suggests manufacture of bought components or subassemblies having new applications with strong potential for growth (market research).	Establishes capacity availability and shortages (production control). Determines bought parts similar to those already made (process engineering). Determines bought items for which satisfactory vendors have not been located (purchasing). Determines made parts on which outside vendors can quote lower costs (purchasing). Determines made parts on which lots are of uneconomic size (production control).	Reviews unsatisfactory vendor parts for design or material simplification or adaptation permitting economic make (production liaison).
2. Analyzing Make and Buy Costs		Develops process charts, equipment needs, and labor, material, and overhead requirements (process engineering and industrial engineering). Obtains necessary further bids from vendors (purchasing).	

TABLE 21-2 (cont.)

Controls and Analysis	Cost Analysis	Industrial Statistics	Cost Accounting
Initiates review of parts on which return on investment is below objective levels (financial analysis and operations analysis).	Reviews data on parts for which costs have been rising or falling relative to others.	Projects trends in pertinent material and capital goods costs.	Tabulates costs on made and bought parts for which costs show a rising or falling trend relative to others.
Evaluates equipment requirements and installation costs and calculates return on investment due to saving in fabrication cost (capital investment analysis). Recommends major policy changes to management (financial analysis).	Prepares final statement of costs.		

TABLE 21-2 (cont.)

Processing Major Financial Decisions

	Marketing	Manufacturing	Engineering
	C. PRICING A PRODUCT LINE		
1. Comparing Products with Competition	Surveys customer opinion. Obtains pertinent competitive data and establishes relative value of product characteristics (market research).	Examines competitive products for differences permitting cost reduction (process engineering). Estimates detailed labor and material requirements for competitive products (industrial engineering).	Examines competitive products for basic design, performance, and materials advantages (chief product or design engineers).
2. Determining Price-Volume Relationships	Estimates effects of price changes in various territories and by major customer classifications (field sales). Estimates effect of specific promotional expenditure changes on volume (Merchandising). Develops correlation studies relating price, promotion expense, and unit volume experience (market research). Projects competitive reaction to price changes (field sales and market research).		
3. Establishing Final Prices	Recommends relationships to hold between company products (merchandising).		

TABLE 21-2 (cont.)

Controls and Analysis	Cost Analysis	Industrial Statistics	Cost Accounting
Develops format for final comparison with competition (pricing analysis).	Prepares necessary comparisons of cost for competitive and proprietary items.		Supplies necessary historical cost data to all concerned.
Reviews Marketing's data and calculations in detail (pricing analysis).	Prepares detailed statements of variable and total costs and profits at various price levels in the format determined by price analysis.	Reviews Marketing's conclusions against broader industry experience and trends.	
Develops proposed pricing structure based on maximizing profit on variable and total costs (pricing analysis and financial analysis), considering investment required.			

TABLE 21-2 (cont.)

Processing Major Financial Decisions

	Marketing	Manufacturing	Engineering
D. INITIATING NEW PRODUCTS			
1. Establishing the market.	Studies needs of potential end users to develop industry and company share (field sales and market research). Develops price-volume relationships (field sales and market research).		Determines general technical feasibility of product proposals. Evaluates performance and specification advantages of proposal versus competition (chief product or design engineers).
2. Estimating Development Costs and Capital Requirements		Evaluates preliminary design and estimates labor and material requirements (process engineering and industrial engineering). Determines general plant and equipment needed for production and experimental fabrication (process engineering).	Prepares preliminary design (chief product or design engineers). Develops detailed plan for development covering: detailed dates for completion of key items; manpower by type; fabrication costs; and testing required (administrative engineering).
3. Evaluation			

TABLE 21-2 (cont.)

Controls and Analysis	Cost Analysis	Industrial Statistics	Cost Accounting
Recommends review of product areas showing declining penetration or profits (product performance analysis and financial analysis). Reviews market forecast and price-volume curve; establishes targeted unit cost (product performance analysis and pricing analysis).		Determines basic economic trends pertinent to a proposed product. Recommends broad product areas for detailed examination by Marketing.	
Reviews development plan for thoroughness and adequacy (product performance analysis). Reviews all plant and equipment (including test facilities) requirements. (capital investment analysis). Develops needs for working capital to support sales volume (financial analysis).	Evaluates projected experimental fabrication costs.		Supplies necessary historical cost data.
Analyzes total investment required and rate of return to be obtained against company objectives for growth and return. Prepares final report for management (financial analysis).	Prepares necessary statements of forward sales, costs and investment.		

certain key functions in a central staff group:

1. Establishing basic accounting, planning and control procedures.
2. Reviewing divisional operating results and forward programs and their compiling into over-all company presentations to top management.
3. Obtaining necessary financing, recommending dividend policy, etc.
4. Approving major capital outlays to insure conformance with previously established budgets or with current top management requirements.
5. Management development—approval or acquisition of key division personnel, insuring proper rotation and training of divisional personnel, etc.

The most immediate need for an operating division is proper coverage of the various record keeping or accounting functions plus necessary expense controls. This has often led to a simple assignment of duties between division and corporate level on this basis, such as the cases where divisions prepare the basic accounting figures and operate simple expense controls while the corporation group performs analysis work, long-range studies and policy recommendations to management. Obviously, this is not an adequate concept if the division is considered a responsible profit center. Consequently, we may even see the other extreme of strong and actually self-sufficient division controller organizations accompanied by a corporation group which merely performs elementary consolidation accounting plus the financial responsibilities mentioned.

To a large extent the distribution of functions obviously depends on the exact philosophy of decentralization held by the corporation's top management and the relative strength of personnel involved.

These brief remarks should help determine the structure of a financial organization for a decentralized corporation, reflecting the principles in this paper.

REFERENCES

1. E. B. Cochran, "The Organization of Controllership," *The Journal of Industrial Engineering*, July–August 1959, p. 268.
2. E. B. Cochran, "What is a Controller," *The Journal of Accountancy*, July 1955.

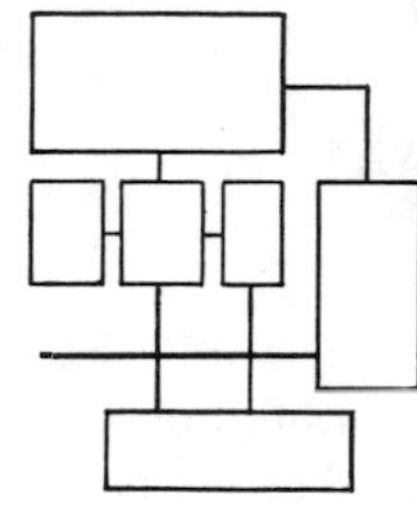

CHAPTER 22

AN EMERGING SCIENCE OF OPERATIONS?

QUESTIONS frequently asked by managers, other engineers, and in particular by engineering education administrators, deal with what industrial engineering is, what are its basic scientific foundations, and how it differs from other areas of engineering and nonengineering endeavor. Although we have discussed these questions in varying detail, they deserve additional consideration. The following material [1] is based upon a presentation by Drs. Schultz and Conway in support of their request for approval to offer a new undergraduate program in industrial engineering at Cornell University. It has been selected for several reasons:

1. It is a good review of points previously presented, although stated in different language.
2. It indicates that some of the so-called irresistible trends in engineering education (that is, the trend toward no specialization in the undergraduate program) are not really irresistible. Cornell University has approved the proposed program for an undergraduate specialty in industrial engineering.
3. The paper suggests an emerging "science of operations" which provides a strong intellectual and academic base upon which modern industrial engineering can build.

Industrial Engineering's Decade of Development

by ASSOC. PROFESSOR RICHARD W. CONWAY
and PROFESSOR ANDREW SCHULTZ, JR.

INDUSTRIAL engineering is a field that has undergone a rather complete revolution in the last decade—a degree of change that is unusual even in an era when rapid change has been commonplace. This means that impressions of industrial engineering acquired before the midfifties require updating.

Both the scope and the methodology of the field have undergone this change, and a concise definition of either that is meaningful or useful cannot be given. A committee of the American Institute of Industrial Engineers defined the field in 1956 to be that of the ". . . design, improvement, or installation of integrated systems of men, materials, and equipment. . . ." Presumably this encompasses manufacturing and service systems, information or procedural systems, and operations control and management systems. In the past, industrial engineers have been traditionally concerned with the design of manufacturing plants, cost or quality control systems, production control systems, materials processing or handling systems, and similar endeavor. These activities are certainly included in the above definition, as are many others. By inference and certainly by past practice, the design of certain elements or subsystems such as individual work centers and production centers is also included in this definition.

This article attempts to provide a brief review of the history of the field, a survey of some of the recent developments that have had a profound effect on its character and role, and a description of the current posture.

HISTORICAL DEVELOPMENT

Industrial engineering began in the latter part of the nineteenth century. The contributions of Frederick W. Taylor and his contemporaries, notably Gantt and later Gilbreth, represented major achievements and provided a foundation for further progress in the field. Taylor's emphasis on analysis, measurement, experimentation, and a fundamental approach to the problems of work design or work planning were most enlightened, especially when one considers the state of development of engineering science at the time. His metal cutting experiments not only were conducted and analyzed in a systematic and orderly manner, but also took place on a scale and produced results of economic and practical importance seldom equaled since, as far as industrial experiments go. Few experiments of such magnitude are performed even today. While the experiments were poorly designed when judged by current criteria for dealing with variations and many variables, they represented a major achievement when judged by the standards of the nineteenth century.

Taylor is of course more famous for his development of an approach to work design measurement. In dealing with these problems he attempted to exercise the same care demonstrated in the metal cutting experiments and was evidently equally devoted to the use of systematic methods of analysis, measurement, and experiment. These areas involve problems in which considerable variation exists after all known causes are accounted for, and in which causal factors not only operate simultaneously but frequently reinforce each other. For these reasons they present problems inherently difficult to analyze, even with today's knowledge and techniques.

It is not hard to comprehend, therefore, why his followers rarely adopted Taylor's underlying philosophy of experiment and analysis and undertook to continue the development he had begun, or why so few of those who did adopt this approach met with much success. Most endeavored to apply his ideas in the industrial arena, applying techniques he had developed without the required underlying research. One result was the outlawing by legislation of all forms of work measurement in governmental establishments. Another was the development of a public image of "the efficiency engineer" which the field has not yet lived down. In fact the term is still occasionally used as a form of opprobrium by writers in various of the "behavioral sciences" who wish to ridicule engineers in general and those dealing with human problems in particular.

Despite these unfortunate developments, by the 1930's there had evolved a fairly clearly defined body of techniques which had been found useful in dealing with practical problems in the design of operating manufacturing systems. These techniques can be included under the following headings:

a. Time study and wage incentive determination
b. Production control
c. Plant layout
d. Work methods design and improvement
e. Job evaluation
f. Equipment selection, tooling and fixture design, engineering economy
g. Paperwork systems or procedures design, cost systems, etc.

Obviously these activities were largely manufacturing-oriented. And they were approached largely from the mechanical or machine production point of view, since most industrial activity was in the area of mechanical-type manufacturing and formal education in industrial engineering often was a part of or an option in mechanical engineering.

A look at formal engineering curricula in industrial engineering during the 1930's would show that most course structures were organized in a fashion similar to the above listing, i.e., oriented toward specific problem areas and related techniques. The methodology used in dealing with these problems was in general of a very practical sort and in large measure empirically derived. Extensive use was made of graphical means of analysis and representation. The process of design of manufacturing or procedural control systems made use of the "questioning viewpoint" and of exhaustive check lists and of "principles" or general rules of good practice. Experimental methods were in most instances rudimentary (and in fact largely remain so). Thus, in arriving at a plant layout, templates or three dimensional models are used in a cut-and-try procedure. Once an apparently acceptable layout is conceived, various forms of graphical analysis may be used to analyze the result. The methods clearly are qualitative and lack the rigor associated with quantitative analysis.

It is interesting to note what the engineer was unable to bring to this activity. His limited tools were not founded upon any organized body of theory of supporting science, as chemical engineering, for example, is founded upon chemistry. The social sciences upon which he was supposed to rely were (and for that matter still are) not well-developed. And experimentation was possible only at the microsystem level. Experimentation *in situ* was all but impossible due to time required, expense involved, and lack of ability to control the experiment. As a result the engineer was limited to observation, rationalization, and cataloging actions in an attempt to summarize and understand experience so that it could be carried to other situations. While the achievements, recognizing these limitations, often were significant, they did not take place against a logical structure. Thus, their formalization, further development, and transmission were inhibited.

NEW DEVELOPMENT

However, during the late 1930's and the 1940's, perhaps accelerated by the national needs associated with the World War II, a number of significant conceptual, scientific, or engineering achievements directly bearing on the field of industrial engineering occurred. It is not intended to catalog all of these here, but certain ones merit special mention. An early factor was the development of an organized theory of statistical control as applied to manufacturing operations by Dr. Walter Shewhart. The applicability of this theory was first demonstrated by the Western Electric Corporation. Thus, a rationale for dealing with the problem of variation was developed to replace the deterministic approach previously implied. From this stemmed further investigation of the application of such abstract mathematical models as those found in the fields of probability and statistics to problems of inspection. This resulted in the development of rational acceptance sampling procedures. Inevitably it was realized that statistical models provided a means of dealing with variation and uncertainty in many other situations.

During the World War II, developments in both mathematical statistics and applied mathematics were accelerated. The Navy as well as Army Ordnance supported research in these areas which was directed toward providing more powerful methods of dealing with complex experimental or operational problems. Attempts to analyze such operations by a quantitative and analytical approach, subsequently termed *operations research,* achieved some substantial success.

After World War II, this research activity continued and applications of various forms of mathematics were developed. Examples are uses of matrix algebra and logic in representing very complex demands on a system, such as a multiproduct, multicomponent mix.

Linear programming provided a means of successfully dealing with one type of multivariable optimization. Work in stochastic processes and probability led to means of dealing with certain impeded flow situations and storage situations through queuing theory. Game theory led to conceptions dealing with decision procedures under conflict.

Concurrently, the development of the modern digital computer had perhaps an even greater potential impact. This tremendous increase in computational ability caused a dramatic shift in the dividing line between mathematical and statistical procedures that can be implemented in a practical way and those which are only of theoretical interest. At the same time it made possible the control of large, complex systems and the synthetic experimentation with numeric models of such systems.

These developments have rather swiftly opened two entirely new methodologies to the industrial engineer. For the first time he has had at least some fragmentary theory upon which to base an understanding of the behavior of complex systems, and for the first time he has had the ability to experiment at least on a representation of complex systems. In total these developments have introduced the industrial engineer to the concept of constructing a symbolic or mathematical model of a physical system and of seeking from this model information which can be usefully applied to the physical system.

INDUSTRIAL ENGINEERING IN TRANSITION

The decade from 1950 to 1960 saw a rather complete reorientation of the field of industrial engineering. The emphasis has shifted from the qualitative to the quantitative aspects of the problem area; academic preparation has become more analytical than descriptive. This change is of course not peculiar to industrial engineering, for the same decade saw a similar increase in emphasis on basic science and a shift in emphasis from design to analysis in nearly every field of engineering. The significant point is that the newly developed mathematical and statistical techniques and the advent of the digital computer permitted industrial engineering to participate in this widespread change. It is also likely that the change was more drastic than in many other fields, for industrial engineering probably began the decade as the least quantitative of all the engineering fields.

Industrial engineering has long suffered, in comparison to the other fields of engineering, from the relatively undeveloped states of the sciences upon which it is based. In effect, there simply did not exist any dominant science upon which industrial engineering could rest. The systems of interest to industrial engineers can perhaps be distinguished from those of interest to other engineers by three characteristics:

1. The emphasis and importance of men in the system.
2. The looseness of coupling between components of the system and the greater variance of response.
3. The actions in the systems tend to be discrete, rather than continuous.

The social sciences, toward which industrial engineering looks for information about the behavior of the human elements of its systems, simply have not been and still are not sufficiently well-developed to support an engineering discipline. The relevant areas of the "science" of mathematics—discrete mathematics and the mathematics of uncertainty—are still not well-developed, but very significant advances have been made in the last twenty years. Perhaps the most promising aspect of all the recent developments is that there seems to be emerging what might be called a *science of operations* which is quite distinct from both mathematics and the social sciences. It appears likely that there can be identified, defined, and described a number of different types of operating systems. These exist completely independently of any area of application. They can be studied in general terms to determine their fundamental properties, which can then be used as the basis for initial analysis and ultimate design of new and more complex systems. Discussion of one or two examples might clarify this point.

As a first example, consider *queuing systems*. In their simplest terms, some examples of applications are airport and airplanes, maintenance man and production machines, telephone system and subscribers, toll booths on expressway and traffic, supermarket checkout counters and customers, and machines and jobs in a manufacturing shop. All of these systems have in common the characteristic that there is a *facility* that provides a *service* to a sequence of arriving *customers*. The customers compete for the service of the facility, and the balance between capacity and demand typically is such that interference situations, in which an arriving customer is served only after some delay, are frequent. The relevant performance characteristics of a queuing system are related to the utilization of the facility, and to the magnitude of the delays experienced by the customers. These characteristics depend upon the pattern in which arrivals occur, the distribution of service times, the structure of the system, and the operating disciplines which are observed. The performance does not depend upon whether the arrivals are men, airplanes, or telephone calls. The performance of a queuing system may be studied abstractly, without direct consideration of the physical phenomena which act as customers and service facilities. Results obtained from such a study—the knowledge of how the system behaves—can then be applied by the industrial engineer in the design of an appropriate service facility, or in the specification of an operating discipline for a facility already in existence. The queuing model is not, of course, an exact description of a real physical system, any more than is any other model, but in many situations a queuing model is a sufficiently good *representation* to provide useful prediction of system performance. It is certain that the queuing model is an important and readily applicable concept in the design of such physical systems as those outlined above, and that it provides an effective and economical way of dealing abstractly and quantitatively with many practical problems.

Another example is provided by the *inventory* system. Examples of such systems are more common and important than one might initially think. In addition to the obvious situations in which a physical item is stocked against a future demand there are many other situations which can be described by the same analytical model. Seats on an airplane, processing capacity of a manufacturing plant, the life of a machine tool can each be considered a form of inventory. All of these situations have one characteristic in common—a *"commodity"* is *stocked* in *anticipation of a demand* whose magnitude is *not completely known* at the time the stocking decision must be made. The performance characteristics of an inventory system are in terms of the costs of securing and holding the inventory and in the level of customer service provided. The inventory model may be used to predict this performance and this information may be used by the engineer to design an inventory system and to specify the rules by which it should operate.

There are many other examples that could be given to emphasize the distinct change in attitude toward the analysis and design of these systems. Abstract modeling in mathematical or symbolic (simulation) terms is involved. Optimization is implied. The result is analysis and evaluation. The implications for the design process of the industrial engineer seem clear. While the result cannot be altogether quantitative any more than design in any other field of engineering is all quantitative, there is now some theoretical basis for many major design decisions. There are now available better means of testing and comparing alternatives and experimenting apart from actual situations. There are now available means of determining the more critical variables and defining the more crucial or sensitive factors involved in the design process. Thus the engineer is potentially able to approach the design problem with a higher order of assurance that the result will be effective, or at least with greater powers of prediction.

A concurrent change of equal importance has taken place in the problem areas to which industrial engineers apply their talents. Prior to 1950, nearly all industrial engineering was practiced in the manufacturing phase of the mechanical goods industries. Today people with this background are practicing, often under names other than industrial engineering, in transportation, distribution, military logistics, weapons systems analysis, finance, public health, and the service industries, as well as in manufacturing and as frequently in the process industries as with the mechanical manufacturing industries.

It is also apparent that the scope of the activity is changing. While traditionally the concern has been with relatively small systems, there is an increasing tendency to broaden the scope of the system under consideration. Current research is concerned with macrosystems, new matriculants to the profession are inclined in this direction, and the emphasis in industrial engineering is shifting away from its former concentration on the design and measurement of individual workplace activities. There are numerous reasons for this shift: for the first time methods are available that make the rational design and analysis of larger systems feasible; technological developments and the previous successful work of industrial engineers has reduced the portion of manufacturing cost attributable to direct labor to such a level that greater opportunities exist elsewhere in the firm.

It should not be inferred that the modern industrial engineer has a complete and rigorous methodology, but he does have an entirely different attitude. While it may be necessary to resort to the same procedure that would have been used a decade ago in order to obtain an immediate and practical answer to a current problem, the industrial engineer has become increasingly aware of the shortcomings of some of these techniques and this awareness has led to increased research and further progress. The actual quantitative methods which are available to the engineer today are still limited and incomplete, but they constitute a significant beginning and there is every indication that the situation will improve. But it is also true that there exists a considerable difference between the best methodology that is available and that which is common practice in the profession. There is very real concern that this difference is increasing rather than decreasing as the rate of innovation accelerates.

It is probable that the next decade will see further advances in industrial engineering, both in basic quantitative techniques and applications to practical situations.

SUMMARY

Drs. Schultz and Conway have implied the emergence of a science of operations during the past decade and have indicated the importance of this development relative to the modernization of industrial engineering. This development is well underway and of great significance to improvement function endeavors. When combined with operations research, management science, and the more traditional aspects of industrial engineering, it does lead to the natural development of what has been called *modern* industrial engineering. Substantial further developments should be anticipated in the fields of mathematics, social-behavioral sciences, engineering and the *engineering* of industrial engineering as well as in the emerging science of operations. These developments will continue to have a marked and beneficial influence upon modern industrial engineering and improvement function activity. These developments do provide a sound intellectual and academic basis for much needed practical application. Educational programs and professional practice have been substantially influenced. The growing recognition of the importance of a concerted and contrived quest for continual improvement within all organizations has sparked academic and research interest.

REFERENCE

1. Richard W. Conway and Andrew Schultz, Jr., "Industrial Engineering's Decade of Development," *The Cornell Engineer,* January 1963, p. 2.

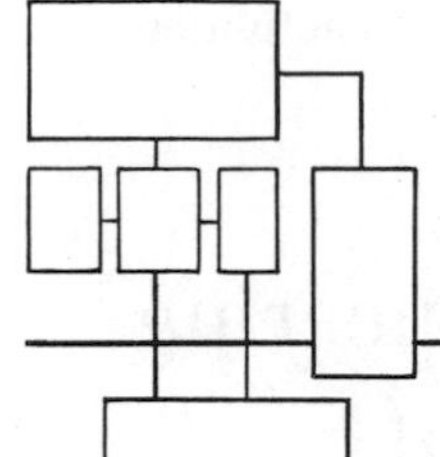

CHAPTER 23

EDUCATIONAL APPROACHES

FROM CONSIDERATION of the previous materials, one might be curious as to what educational preparation is most appropriate for individuals who will successfully participate as specialists in the development of broad-scale improvement functions. While the final answer cannot be given at the present time, there are several academic approaches which seem to have merit. Predominate among these are programs in *modern* industrial engineering and programs of management and administration built upon a technical (or engineering) foundation.

Three education programs have been selected for presentation in this chapter. These cannot be regarded as typical programs, but as representative of some of the current academic approaches related to improvement function endeavors. One is a modern industrial engineering program from Northwestern University.[1] The second represents the approach and philosophy of the Graduate School of Industrial Administration of Carnegie Institute of Technology.[2] The third is the administration engineering program of Kieo University of Tokyo, Japan and has been selected to provide some indication of international developments.

The modern industrial engineering program of Northwestern University has been selected for presentation because it is the one I know best, for I was responsible for organizing the department and the programs. The opportunity to do so came at a time when it was appropriate to make drastic departures from past educational patterns. The program is not presented as an ideal pattern for others to follow, but it does represent one workable approach to the modern treatment of the field, and one which has had some influence in stimulating and encouraging other educators to undertake a more modern, yet strongly engineering-based, approach to preparing individuals for improvement function activities.

Exploiting Science and Engineering As Aids to Management: A Modern Industrial Engineering Approach

by **ROBERT N. LEHRER**

Professor and Chairman, Department of Industrial Engineering, The Technological Institute, Northwestern University, Evanston, Illinois

THERE is little doubt that a revolution in management is currently underway in the United States and throughout much of the world. This revolution has been sparked, in part, by an exploding technology. Science and engineering are having a pervasive influence upon the problems of management in both manufacturing and non-manufacturing organizations. The problems of exploiting science and engineering, both relative to the processes of managing and various processes for producing (not confined to manufacturing, but encompassing goal-directed activities in general) have not been adequately solved.

In addition to the revolution caused by our expanding technical knowledge, science and engineering are becoming increasingly important to management due to advances in understanding human behavior relative to the processes of managing and producing, and also relative to the much broader role of man and society.

Various approaches to solving management education problems were outlined and discussed in an earlier issue of this publication.[3] However, this earlier discussion fails to recognize the significance of engineering-based educational programs, and the impact they are bound to have on management practice in the years ahead. The objective of this paper is to present some thoughts on the importance of engineering and science as they can be used to assist management, and to outline an educational program designed to prepare men—not for management *per se,* but—to serve as staff specialists dealing with various aspects of problem solving and the design of management systems and systems for producing. This program might have been called "management science" or a variety of other names. We decided to name it industrial engineering, for *it is* an engineering program and tends to reflect some of the best features of modern industrial engineering practice and theory.[4] It is my strong conviction that programs of this type are an essential part of the eventual solution to the problems of effective management and effective management education. Business administration and the various management or administration programs can solve only a part of the total problem.

In January 1958 a department of industrial engineering was established at the Technological Institute of Northwestern University, and a new curricular program was adopted. Although the program represented a radical departure from established education patterns and created an entirely new image of industrial engineering education, the concepts upon which the program is based are simple and straightforward. They are, in essence, a reflection of what we think industrial engineering should be at the present time.* The program has received much interest from educators as well as from business and industry. Although the program was viewed with some reservations concerning its implementation, it is now completely operational and it is well-received.

BASIC CONCEPTS

The organization of a new educational venture naturally reflects the organizer's evaluation of the objectives for the program, and the environment within which the program and the products of the program will operate. It was our conviction that a new program in industrial engineering should have substantial "scientific" content, should treat engineering in a fundamental way, should prepare the

* I hesitate to say "should be" for I do not want to imply that we feel our approach is the only answer to the problems of industrial engineering education, even though we are quite satisfied that it is an appropriate answer for our institution. The appropriate programs for other educational institutions should reflect their individual aspirations as well as their interpretations of engineering, education, and industrial engineering.

student for broad intellectual growth throughout his life, and should provide a professional preparation geared to an increasingly rapid rate of change in technology, business, and industry.

The objectives of our program were strongly influenced by our conviction that industrial engineering involves effective and efficient problem-solving within a framework of techno-economic-social systems, and that the true mission of industrial engineering will eventually center around management advisory services, problem solving, and the design, improvement, and installation of systems for "producing" and for "managing."

The specific criteria used in designing our curriculum were:

1. It must be strong in basic engineering.
2. It must reflect the "general education" philosophy of our university.
3. It must be oriented toward principles, systems, and creative engineering work.
4. It should take full advantage of the recent developments in the areas often referred to as operations research, management sciences, behavioral sciences, computers and systems engineering.
5. It should prepare students to effectively deal with new and unusual problems without reliance upon specific and restricted "techniques."
6. It should prepare the student to exploit "traditional" industrial engineering without requiring more than an absolute minimum of formal instruction in these subject areas.*
7. It should take full advantage of the educational opportunities provided by our cooperative "work-study" program.

In summary, it was our objective to provide our students with an educational experience that would prepare them for effectively dealing with new and unusual problems in a manner that would enable them to make a maximum contribution to the efficient operation and management of the organizations with which they would eventually become associated. It is our firm conviction that the industrial engineer of the future must be problem oriented to the extent that he can systematically determine the problem areas where industrial engineering will have its maximum contribution to the total organization, and be able to define the problem within the

* The "traditional" industrial engineering areas are usually thought of as time study, wage incentives, methods improvement, plant layout, production control, job evaluation, etc. We do not feel that these areas are totally lacking in value—however, they do tend to be restrictive in terms of preoccupation with techniques and limited problem areas. Much of the essence of these subjects can be learned as a by-product of formal work of a much more basic and broad nature. Most of the techniques can be readily acquired on-the-job, if and when they are needed.

total system environment with sufficient precision that the need for analytical and problem-solving techniques will become quite apparent. At this point we expect the industrial engineer to draw upon his broad background of engineering, mathematical, and scientific knowledge (both physical and behavioral) to devise an efficient approach to solving his problems. In many cases he will recognize his need for specific techniques with which he is familiar, or that he can acquire by reference to current and past practices, and in other cases he will recognize that he should attempt to supplement his skills and knowledge by enlisting the aid of other professionals. The essence of our philosophy is "do not rely upon techniques, but rely upon a broad and basic education and upon adequately defining the problems."

We have fully recognized that there are several different types of careers to which our students may aspire, and these have been considered in the design of our program. Most industrial engineering programs aspire to training individuals as engineers in general, and also for eventual management responsibilities. These two objectives are partially considered in our program, but we have elected to concentrate more fully upon the preparation for careers in the profession of industrial engineering as we visualize it can be, at both the practicing level and at the research and teaching levels.

UNDERGRADUATE CURRICULUM

An option program offered by the Mechanical Engineering Department had been in operation for a number of years prior to the establishment of the Department of Industrial Engineering in January 1958. The option program was a combination of some engineering courses with work offered by the business school. The general flavor was very much along the lines of "business and engineering," with a scattering of courses in the functional business administration areas. When the new department was organized we felt it would be desirable to make all changes required to have a truly modern program. We recognized that some of these changes might be quite drastic, but we did want to take full advantage of the developments of the last ten or so years as they influenced industrial engineering. The resulting program departed very substantially from the past patterns of industrial engineering education. This is evident from the attached curriculum display (Fig. 23-1), which shows the 194 credit units in groupings of courses in industrial en-

Industrial Engineering Curriculum—Northwestern University, Technological Institute, Evanston, Illinois (1961–62)

	FRESHMAN Fall	FRESHMAN Winter	FRESHMAN Spring	SOPHOMORE Fall	SOPHOMORE Winter	SOPHOMORE Spring	JUNIOR Fall	JUNIOR Winter	JUNIOR Spring	SENIOR Fall	SENIOR Winter	SENIOR Spring
Industrial Engineering (36)				Production Eng. I IE-B10	Production Eng. II IE-B11		Intro. to I.E. IE-C10	Indus. Eng. Analys. I IE-C21	Indus. Eng. Analys. II IE-C22	Indus. Eng. Design I IE-C31	Indus. Eng. Design II IE-C32	Indus. Eng. Design III IE-C33
									(Industrial Engineering-9 Courses)			Case Problems IE-C40
Basic Sciences (60)							Eng. Statistics ES-C02	Quant. Methods in I.E. I IE-C11	Quant. Methods in I.E. II IE-C12	(Mathematics and Applied Mathematics-9 Courses)		
	ANALYTICAL GEOMETRY AND CALCULUS Math. A15	Math. B16	Math. B17	Math. B18	Math. B19	Eng. Math. I Math. C14						
	GENERAL CHEMISTRY I Chem. A-20	II Chem. A30	III or A40	(Chemistry-3 Courses)								
			PRINCIPLES OF PHYSICS I Phys. A50	II Phys. A51	III Phys. A52	(Physics-3 Courses)						
Engineering Sciences and Engineering (46)	Analytic Graphics ES-A20	(Graphics-1 Course)		Mechan. I CE-B10	Mechan. II CE-B11	Mechan. of Mat'ls. CE-B16	Fluid Mechanics CE-B41	Circuits I EE-B11	Electrical Eng. Selection	Feedback Systems EE-C48	(Engineering Sciences-10 Courses)	
						Thermodynamics ME-B20				Machine Design ME-B15		
						Princ. of Mat'ls. ES-B01			(Psychology-Sociology-Economics-6 Courses)			
Social Science and General Education (52)	COMPOSITION AND ENGLISH LITERATURE Eng. A10-1	Eng. A10-2	Eng. A10-3				Elective or Psych.	Psych.	Economics or Accounting		Sociology	Sociology
		Approved Elective									Economics Econ. B03	
(194)	(Physical Education or NROTC)									Gen. Ed. Elective	Gen. Ed. Elective	Gen. Ed. Elective
	16	16	16	16	16	16	16	17	16	17	16	16

Figure 23-1

gineering (36 credits), basic sciences (60 credits), engineering and engineering sciences (46 credits), and general education (52 credits).

Freshman Year. The first year is the same as the programs in the other fields of engineering, consisting of mathematics, chemistry, English, analytic graphics, an approved elective, and the first quarter of the physics sequence.

Sophomore Year. The second year is the same as in the other engineering programs with the exception of a two course sequence in production engineering. Mathematics is continued through differential equations, the physics sequence is completed, and the engineering science courses are started. The group of engineering science courses consists of Mechanics I, Mechanics II, Mechanics of Materials, Thermodynamics, and Principles of the Properties of Materials.

The production engineering courses are intended to introduce the industrial engineering student to the broad area of production and to serve as the background for the later and more analytical industrial engineering courses. The first course is devoted to "operations" and to productive activities that are primarily centered around these operations in a manufacturing process. The intent is to have a very broad coverage of a variety of systems "components." At the present time the course work is largely centered around metal-processing activities, but we are in the process of broadening the coverage to include a wide range of fundamental "operations" extending well beyond metal-working and manufacturing. The second production engineering course is primarily concerned with more generalized systems and processing concepts. A general conceptual framework for understanding and analyzing processing activities is developed, analytical models are introduced as tools for process and systems analysis, the theory of measurement is presented, and the students are brought into direct contact with our small-scale computer (LGP-30).

Junior Year. The third year of the program contains an industrial engineering-sequence of courses, an "applied mathematics" sequence, a sequence in engineering science, and a sequence in general education.

The industrial engineering courses include Introduction to Industrial Engineering and two quarters of Industrial Engineering Analysis. The introductory course is intended to provide a broad perspective of modern industrial engineering and to introduce the student to a broad range of topics dealing with the relationships between management and engineering and the use of "science" as an aid to serving management. One of the basic objectives of this course is to develop a professional orientation on the part of the student. However, the course is also taken by engineering students from other departments as a general introduction to the field.

The two courses in Industrial Engineering Analysis are primarily devoted to the methodology of locating problem areas within an organization, determining the exact nature of these problems and defining them, developing a course of action for adequately solving the problems in light of the total organization system, and developing a means for implementing solutions to the problems. The first course deals with activities that are primarily of a production nature (but not confined to manufacturing nor factory work), while the second course is primarily concerned with problems dealing with information systems. Both of these courses are intentionally oriented away from techniques, although consideration of specific techniques always arises in conjunction with the outside project required for each of the courses. The projects are an important part of these courses.

The "applied mathematics" sequence consists of Engineering Statistics and two quarters of Quantitative Methods in Industrial Engineering. These three courses involve the development of mathematical concepts and the immediate application of these concepts to problems of concern to the engineer and the industrial engineer. Each of these courses involves a laboratory activity used for developing further understanding of the utility of mathematical concepts as problem-solving devices. The statistics course covers the general area of probability and statistics up to the analysis of variance and an introduction to the design of experiments.

The Quantitative Methods courses include an assortment of mathematical topics of particular utility in systems analysis and design. The intent is to introduce the student to the wealth of useful mathematical notions and techniques not covered in the usual mathematics and engineering courses. Topics include symbolic logic, set theory, algebra, vector spaces and linear transformations, constrained extrema methods, transform methods and stochastic processes.

The engineering science courses include fluid mechanics, an electrical engineering circuits course, and an electrical engineering selection.

The social science-general education courses include an elective or psychology course, a psychology course, and a course in economics or accounting. The majority of our students take two psychology courses. We are currently negotiating with the Economics Department to offer a theory of the firm type course to take the place of the course indicated as "Economics or Accounting." When this is achieved, we will have two economics courses in our program. The first one will be the introductory economics course and the second one will be the theory of the firm course. This may eventually develop into a managerial economics sequence.

Senior Year. The senior year includes a sequence designated as Industrial Engineering Design, Case Problems in Industrial Engineering, Feedback Systems, Machine Design, a three-quarter sequence in General Education (electives), two quarters of sociology, and one course in economics.

The Industrial Engineering Design courses deal with various aspect of systems design, starting with optimization techniques and progressing to more complex total systems problems. The Industrial Engineering Analysis courses and the Statistics-Quantitative Methods courses are prerequisites. The first design course is devoted principally to the techniques and methodology of operations research from a systems design point of view. The techniques are presented in a rigorous but perceptive manner, and limitations and important underlying assumptions are stressed. The second and third design courses are to an even greater extent problem oriented. The second one deals with an assortment of productive and management control systems problems. Additional concepts and techniques, including simulation and general experimentation procedures, are introduced in conjunction with these problems. The third course provides an opportunity for the student to become thoroughly entangled with several more complex systems design problems—problems of the scope of designing and testing a production, inventory and distribution control system, or designing a transportation system for an urban community. Although these are not field problems, the practical aspects of problem formulation, data collection and implementation are carefully considered.

The Case Problems in Industrial Engineering course is a four-credit course of which three credits are devoted to organization theory and the fourth credit to a series of seminar type presentations by individuals who have been doing outstanding work in various aspects of modern industrial engineering (including activities such as operations research, management science, data processing, economic analysis, management research, etc.). Representatives from leading business and industrial organizations present details of their programs, accomplishments, aspirations, difficulties, management reactions, etc., and then discuss these with the students.

The Feedback Systems course is an electrical engineering course devoted to control theory from the electrical engineering point of view. Although this is an excellent course, we anticipate that eventually we will have a more generalized control theory course, possibly oriented more directly to control implications within "managing" and "producing" systems. This course is a prerequisite for the Industrial Engineering Design II course.

The Machine Design course is basically a mechanical engineering design course. It is hoped that eventually we will have a mechanical "systems" type design course.

The general education elective sequence is part of the university program in general education and allows for selections from a wide variety of liberal arts offerings.

The two courses in sociology are selected from the broad offerings of the sociology department. The two courses in psychology, in conjunction with the two courses in sociology, are intended to provide a background in these facets of the behavioral sciences for our students.

Summary of Curriculum. The industrial engineering program includes the basic material associated with all of our engineering programs (mathematics, chemistry, physics, graphics, and the engineering sciences); nine courses in industrial engineering; an additional three courses in the quantitative methods-applied mathematics area (which can rightly be classified as industrial engineering courses); additional engineering courses (feedback systems and machine design); and six courses in the general area of psychology, sociology, and economics.

The industrial engineering courses are grouped into five segments (or six if we classify the statistics and quantitative methods work as industrial engineering courses):

1. Two courses in production engineering (IE-B 10, B 11 "Production Engineering I, II")
2. One orientation course (IE-C 10 "Introduction to Industrial Engineering")
3. Two courses dealing with problem-solving methodology (IE-C21, C22 "Industrial Engineering Analysis I, II")

4. Three courses dealing with progressively more complex aspects of systems design (IE-C31, C32, C33 "Industrial Engineering Design I, II, III)
5. One course dealing with organization theory and related problems associated with the implementation of modern industrial engineering activities (IE-C40 "Case Problems in Industrial Engineering").

The three-course sequence in Statistics and Quantitative Methods in Industrial Engineering is intended to be "industrial engineering" from the standpoint of teaching more than just the mathematical concepts. The examples, exercises and problems are a means of illustrating the utility and the limitations of mathematical concept in both the newer and the more traditional areas of industrial engineering activity. We view these courses as being very important from the standpoint of developing a feeling for "context" as well as for understanding and skill with mathematical techniques.

We recognize that our undergraduate program is not ideal. Several deficiencies have already been mentioned, and there have been problems associated with implementation. Even so, we have been very pleased with the results already obtained. One of the most undesirable aspects is the lack of flexibility in free electives. There is some flexibility in the selection of psychology, sociology and general education electives. We wish we could allow at least the same amount of freedom of choice in the other areas, but it seems impossible to do this within the four year (12 quarter) program limitation. We are continuing to explore possibilities for improving the coverage of the material in the basic areas in hopes of devising more efficient ways to accomplish our end objectives. If we can further improve the effectiveness of coverage, perhaps we will eventually be able to include some electives in our program.

Implementation. Ninety-six undergraduate students and two graduate students were enrolled in the option program just prior to the establishment of the industrial engineering department. The majority of these students elected to transfer to the industrial engineering program, and to shift over to the new curriculum. A few students did transfer to other programs within the university, and a few students transferred to the new program from other engineering departments. The net result was that during the first quarter the department was in operation the undergraduate enrollment was 88 and the graduate enrollment was 1. Within the three year period to January 1961 the undergraduate enrollment gradually increased to 93, while the graduate enrollment grew more rapidly to 29. The graduate enrollment for the Fall quarter 1961 is 36, of which 18 are at the Ph.D. level.

The new course work was offered as rapidly as possible consistent with the student's preparation and the acquisition of faculty, and we completed the implementation of the entire program during the 1960–61 school year.

The Cooperative Program. The cooperative program has been a feature of our engineering programs at the Technological Institute of Northwestern University since its original organization. This program allows the students to spend alternate quarters in school and in industry starting with the third quarter of their sophomore year. The program results in twelve quarters in school (the same total number required by a four-year noncooperative program) and six quarters in industry. The cooperative program extends the student's work to a total of five years.

Even though the majority of the faculty and the students strongly endorse the cooperative program, it was made optional two years ago. This action seemed desirable in order to allow some students with aspirations for the Ph.D. degree to start their engineering program with the assurance that they would not be obliged to spend 18 months in industry during their academic program. It was our anticipation that many of the undecided students would learn of the value of the cooperative program from association with the upper class students during their first year and a half on campus, and would therefore choose the cooperative program. Over 80% of our students do elect the cooperative program.

The co-op assignments for industrial engineering students vary widely, and provide an excellent opportunity to supplement course work with valuable practical experience in both the traditional and the modern aspects of industrial engineering.

FACULTY

Innovation in educational programs presents numerous problems. The two that have been most difficult to overcome are lack of adequate text material and faculty. Of these two, faculty is by far the more difficult obstacle to overcome, and when it is overcome the text problem tends to become less severe. Well-qualified faculty for any discipline are in short supply, but they are even in shorter supply for the type of new program that we undertook. We have been very fortunate in obtaining faculty with excellent qualifications and with a sympathetic attitude toward the new educational venture involved in our program.

The faculty members are all engineers, either by basic education or by inclination and point of view. They all hold earned doctoral degrees, and are keenly interested in the educational, research, and professional problems associated with our field. Three of the men are strongly oriented toward mathematical work, three are strongly interested in behavioral, organizational and innovative problems (one man has his Ph.D. in psychology), and one faculty member is primarily concerned with productive processes. We anticipate expanding our faculty by adding one more man to concentrate his attention toward the "systems" aspects of producing or goal-oriented systems. All of the faculty devote approximately one half of their time to formal academic matters (teaching and working with students). The balance of their time is devoted to research, scholarly activity, and professional services.

THE GRADUATE PROGRAM

Although the undergraduate program reflects no specialization in terms of areas within industrial engineering, the graduate program allows specialization in one or more of five areas. These are:

1. Operations research and management science.
2. Organization theory.
3. Information systems analysis and design.
4. Work study.
5. Processing and automation.

All five of these areas are closely interrelated and have a "systems" orientation. Of the five, we find that the majority of our students initially select the first area, but some of them eventually tend toward specialization in one of the other areas in conjunction with the first.

Our graduate program is directed primarily toward the Ph.D. program, but we also do have a master's program. Our first Ph.D. degree was awarded during the summer of 1960, and two more men completed their programs during the spring and summer of 1961. The students come from many other schools and include faculty on leave from their own institutions. Our goal is a graduate student group of about fifty, all aiming toward the Ph.D.

It should be specifically mentioned that we do not consider "industry" in its narrow sense as the only "customers" for our product.

Many of our graduates pursue advanced degrees (almost 70% of the 1960 and 1961 graduating classes did so), and many are employed by nonmanufacturing organizations and education-research organizations. Also, it should be specifically mentioned that our interpretation of "industrial engineering" is broader than used by many other organizations. The industrial engineering area of operation extends well beyond just manufacturing.

WHY "INDUSTRIAL ENGINEERING" AS A NAME?

We are frequently questioned as to why we have retained the name industrial engineering for our program and our department. Although our interpretation of modern industrial engineering differs substantially from the more traditional type of industrial engineering, it has been our belief that we can make our maximum contribution by judiciously combining the better aspects of traditional industrial engineering with the newer developments associated with such things as operations research, management science, computers, systems engineering, etc. Our orientation is toward solving problems of a systems nature—particularly in the design, improvement and installation of systems for producing and systems for managing. We are aiming toward a role of "management adviser" and "problem solver" for the industrial engineer. We believe that "industrial" is a broad term, extending well beyond manufacturing, including all goal-oriented activity. We also believe "engineering" to be descriptive, for we are vitally concerned with practical application of knowledge in devising ways to better utilize the resources of nature, and of human nature, for the benefit of man. Frankly, we carefully considered other names when organizing our department, and we are still giving occasional thought to the matter. But, we have concluded that the alternative terminology has limitations equally as severe as the limitations usually associated with the name industrial engineering. At this point we are attempting to help industrial engineering live up to the aspirations implicit in the official AIIE definition of the profession.* It is our hope that we will help demonstrate what the AIIE definition attempts to define.

* The definition adopted by the American Institute of Industrial Engineers is: Industrial engineering is concerned with the design, improvement, and installation of integrated systems of men, materials, and equipment; drawing upon specialized knowledge and skill in the mathematical, physical, and social sciences together with the principles and methods of engineering analysis and design, to specify, predict, and evaluate the results to be obtained from such systems.

BUSINESS ADMINISTRATION VERSUS MODERN INDUSTRIAL ENGINEERING

The program in modern industrial engineering that has been discussed should not be considered as entirely typical of educational approaches in the United States. Many universities have had academically weak programs, and many of these have been strengthened in a variety of ways. Typically, this strengthening has included more rigorous coverage of the engineering sciences, more mathematical work, additional coverage of the behavioral and social sciences, and a more modern and analytical treatment of the traditional industrial engineering courses. Some programs deal almost entirely with "manufacturing" problems while others have extended their areas to encompass producing and controlling systems of all sorts. A few programs, such as the one at Northwestern, have made a drastic departure from the compartmentalized-technique-problem area structure in favor of a more fundamental approach. These programs are in a sense quite similar in objectives to some of the more progressive business administration programs. The desire to exploit "science" (in particular, the use of analytical tools and the social-behavioral sciences) is common to both. However, there are vast differences. The industrial engineering programs retain "engineering" and tend to point toward a systems engineering treatment of both the producing system and the related management system. Further, it is believed that the design, improvement, and installation of integrated system of men, materials, and equipment is in itself an engineering activity. The engineering methodology associated with these design activities is still in the embryo stage, but it is being developed by engineers. It is doubtful that the business school setting will ever fully allow a similar development. It would seem most reasonable to expect the substantial contributions for engineering design relative to systems of producing and managing to come from an engineering environment. Not only is it important to have a general science and engineering background, but the orientation must be one of useful exploitation of science, engineering, and management technology relative to fully integrated systems of men, materials, and equipment, not confined to the usual interpretation of production or manufacturing.

Speaking relative to our own program, we do not believe it is possible to teach management as a science, nor do we attempt to do this. However, we are convinced that we can teach a great deal about the use of "science" for effectively solving some management problems. The science that is involved covers a very broad spectrum, and is best used in conjunction with knowledge that is not strictly "science." We attempt to blend these ingredients by means of the general problem-solving orientation permeating our entire program. Engineering has much to offer along these lines. We are convinced that undergraduate and graduate students can be effectively educated along these lines.

Our program has been organized on the basis of intentionally slighting "technique" types of courses. Techniques frequently become obsolete very rapidly, but fundamental knowledge and approaches to problems do not. Further, we feel that techniques can be readily acquired by our students if they are properly motivated and if they develop an appreciation for effectively combining "technique" with their knowledge of fundamentals.

Our experience in this matter has been very gratifying. The cooperative program provides an excellent opportunity for practical experience and also a background for developing an adequate appreciation of the effectiveness of combining technique and fundamental knowledge.

We do not feel that our mission is to train managers *per se*. Our objective is to educate engineers. The graduate may pursue a career in engineering in general, a career concentrating on the modern aspects of industrial engineering, or he may eventually end up in a management position. It is significant that if our graduate aspires to a career within the technical areas of modern industrial engineering, he will be well equipped to do this. He will be a management adviser and a problem solver with an ability to exploit both the newer aspects of modern industrial engineering and also the more traditional areas of industrial engineering.

We are not attempting to *train* our graduate to have maximum effectiveness upon graduation, but to provide him with a background which will allow him to become increasingly effective throughout his professional career.* We are hopeful that our educational approach will allow the individual, by virtue of continual growth throughout his career, to avoid becoming technologically

* Even though we do not attempt to train our students to be of maximum benefit to their employers on their first assignments, we have observed that most of them perform quite well. Part of their success is due to the co-op experience and part is due to their inclination to treat problems in fundamental terms. Working skills are acquired very rapidly when these skills are needed.

obsolete. The problem of technological obsolescence is one that has been of increasing frustration to many management personnel as well as to many practicing industrial engineers. We are hopeful that our graduates will not be frustrated by such problems, for one part of our program philosophy is to develop an ability to cope with changing situations and frustrations.

The main differentiation between the modern industrial engineer and the business administration graduate centers around the engineering that should be involved in an industrial engineering program. This includes the so-called basic engineering sciences, and the engineering involved in industrial engineering courses of analysis and design. This background in engineering prepares the student to deal with complex problems as an engineer, drawing upon his background of mathematical, physical and social sciences, and fully utilizing the principles and methods of engineering analysis and design. It is our feeling that there are substantial reasons for retaining the engineering involved in industrial engineering in order to prepare men to deal with increasingly complex technology as it is involved in the operation of business and industry. Further, we feel that many problems that are not intrinsically technical require engineering knowledge and skill for proper analysis and solution.

Schools of business have been very severely criticized for their lack of actively exploiting mathematical analysis and the behavioral sciences in their programs. Several schools of business (some of them labeled business administration, some of them industrial administration, some of them labeled industrial management) have done outstandingly good work in correcting these deficiencies. Products of these educational programs have had some exceptionally fine opportunities to prepare for careers that will parallel modern industrial engineering. However, mathematics alone is not sufficient. Most business school programs still suffer from the lack of the rigor of engineering and their graduates find it extremely difficult to use mathematics to the full extent of its power as a problem-solving tool along with other tools and techniques associated with the engineering methods of analysis and design.

It should be noted that some business schools are in fact training engineers in some aspects of industrial engineering. For example, The Graduate School of Industrial Administration of Carnegie Institute of Technology requires the B.S. in engineering (or its general equivalent) as a prerequisite for admission.[2] The "engineering" aspect of the instruction could be questioned, and it should be noted that the faculty of this school do not claim to be teaching engineering. But, it is my opinion that much of their work actually is engineering.

There are other "business" schools doing excellent work also. It is our opinion that we perhaps have more in common with these schools than we do with some of the industrial engineering schools. We do not believe that the designation "engineering" or "business" is as important as the substance of the educational program and the orientation of the faculty. Adequate solution to many of the most significant problems facing management requires a strong background in mathematics and science concepts, and the full exploitation of these in conjunction with the methodology usually associated with engineering. If preparation for working with these areas can be provided within any educational organization, more power to them. The industrial engineering profession is working toward a reactivation and a strengthening of their professional capabilities. The eventual results should have a substantial effect upon management, and should greatly facilitate the effective exploitation of engineering and science on behalf of management in general.

SUMMARY

Although industrial engineering is not well understood by industry relative to its modern capabilities, there are a growing number of companies who do take advantage of its full power for exploiting science and engineering as aids to more effective management. These companies have learned that modern industrial engineering is very effective, but requires a strong academic preparation for best results. Progressive educational programs have been enthusiastically supported by many business and industrial organizations. The details of the modern industrial engineering programs in American universities vary considerably. The program at the Technological Institute, Northwestern University has been discussed in detail, both from the point of view of the underlying concepts and the organization of education details. This program has been in operation since 1958, and results clearly indicate that the educational objectives have been achieved.

ACKNOWLEDGMENTS

Although I am responsible for the initial organization of the program, its actual implementation and the philosophy that has been presented in this paper reflect the individual and collective thinking of the entire faculty of the Department of Industrial Engineering at Northwestern University. Each individual has made substantial and unique contributions. I am pleased to acknowledge these, and to express appreciation to Bruce McK. Johnson, Gilbert K. Krulee, Ray S. Lindenmeyer, Loring G. Mitten, Albert H. Rubenstein, C. M. Shetty, and Sidney Singer.

As mentioned in the foregoing article, science and technology have had a substantial influence upon education within business administration schools. The problems of improving management through more effective educational programs has been the subject of extensive study in recent years. Two very penetrating analyses were sponsored by the Ford Foundation[5] and by the Carnegie Corporation.[6] The general conclusion of these studies can be briefly summarized as follows:

> With the increasing complexity of business operations and management problems, further improvement in the effectiveness of the process of management must come from more extensive use of science-based knowledge, judiciously combined with the more empirical knowledge typically associated with the art of management.

These reports have caused widespread interest in the further development and use of mathematical analysis and the behavioral sciences as aids for the solution of managerial problems. They have also provided further encouragement for the development of management science as an educational and professional specialty, and they have had a healthy influence on the improvement of management education in schools of business administration, industrial management, and industrial administration.

The following material presents the philosophy and program of the Graduate School of Industrial Administration of Carnegie Institute of Technology. The development of the program preceded the critical appraisal of business and management education previously mentioned and perhaps had some influence on the conclusion of these studies. This program cannot be regarded as a typical approach. It is unique and very progressive, and it has provided a measure of leadership for schools of management and business administration. The primary objective of the program is to prepare individuals for eventual responsibility at high managerial levels. Many of these persons will probably make substantial direct and indirect contributions to improvement function activities. The Northwestern University approach to modern industrial engineering and the Carnegie Tech approach to graduate education in industrial administration represent two quite different approaches to achieving somewhat similar objectives.

Industrial Administration: Education for 1980*

by **G. L. BACH**

Dean, Graduate School of Industrial Administration, Carnegie Institute of Technology

Over the past decade, it seems clear that two significant changes are occurring in industrial engineering. First, it has become less descriptive and how-to-do-it oriented, and more fundamentally analytical. This has involved greater introduction of statistics and modern mathematics, and many of the tools of "operations research." Second, it has introduced more of a management viewpoint, especially in the production and manufacturing area, but extending beyond this.

Over the same period, major modifications have been introduced at leading graduate business schools. These, too, have involved increasing emphasis on analysis in contrast to descriptive, how-to-do-it approaches. They, too, have looked increasingly toward fundamental training for management, in contrast to narrow specialization in the particular functional fields of business.

At a few universities, a new approach, often called "industrial administration" or "industrial management," has been taken. It begins without the ties to the past of either industrial engineering or business administration, and builds directly on the presumption that the major goal is to train men for managerial responsibilities in the world of 1980—where the role of careful, rational analysis will bulk large, where management will increasingly need to utilize effectively modern technology, and where managerial problems will be ever changing, and far different from those we recognize today.

My purpose is to present the rationale underlying one such new program in industrial administration—the Graduate School of In-

* Based upon a presentation to the industrial engineering section of the American Society for Engineering Education in June, 1959.

dustrial Administration at Carnegie Tech—and briefly the educational approach to which it has led. I do not wish to imply, of course, that this is "the" kind of education for the future. But, I venture to hope that it may be of some interest to you, particularly as it relates to the changing nature of industrial engineering.

TRAINING FOR CHANGE

My first proposition is that the universities are training men for the world of the 1980's, and that we ought to face up to this fact. In 1980, most present college students will be only about 40, with over half of their professional lives still before them. To train men primarily for the 1960's is to miss most of the problem. To focus even on the 1970's is to concentrate on the first quarter of our students' professional careers. The world of the 1980's—terrifyingly far away as it may seem—thus provides a goal only about midway through the careers of our present students.

When our school of industrial administration was established in 1949, we spent a year trying to face up to this fact. We talked to everyone we could find, we looked at professional education in widely differing fields, and we read. What were our conclusions?

First, although no one knows what the industrial world of 1980 will look like, I am sure of one thing. It, and the rest of the world, will change greatly over the next quarter of a century. Edward Teller, the famous physicist, has stated recently that in the century since 1850 man has roughly doubled his knowledge of the world and of mankind in the world. While any such observation must be extremely rough, it suggests the enormous accumulation of knowledge that has been taking place in the last three centuries. If Teller is right, in knowledge of human behavior we will learn more about man and his behavior in the next century than in all previous history. Today's newspaper accounts of fantastic space age developments make this prediction increasingly believable. What most people don't realize is that a similar explosion may be underway in our knowledge of man and his managerial behavior.

Given the certainty of change and the uncertainty of its direction and outcome, it seems to me clear that we must place central importance on our university training—for administration in industry, as elsewhere—on students' thought processes and not on particularized subject matter. In such a world, surely anything we can do to develop flexibility of mind, openness and receptivity to new and changing ideas, habitual skills in learning for oneself, and other such mental characteristics, must promise more usefulness to the individual and to society over the quarter century of change ahead, than would comparable attention to descriptive information about today's institutions and today's best industrial practice. It suggests equally that we must emphasize fundamental analytical tools, reaching for those of broad and general applicability, with emphasis on how to use them effectively in widely varying situations, rather than on detailed particular skills and techniques.

DIRECTIONS OF CHANGE

This is the main conclusion we reached. But beyond this, I suggest that we do have a good deal of evidence about some of the major directions of change. What are some of these?

1. Management will become ever more rational and analytical, and the role of "hunch" and even "informed judgment" will become steadily smaller as the years go by. Mathematical programming, queueing theory, statistical decision theory, and other such tools will be commonplace in the industry of 1980, and the effective manager will have to know how to use them, just as he must now know how to use the contributions of modern engineering and science. To focus too heavily on particular analytical approaches would be a mistake, however. The critical change will be the increase in the clarification of the variables that need to be considered in making industrial decisions, the increase in the use of carefully obtained quantitative information as to these variables, and the increase in the use of rigorous analysis in weighting and combining the variables involved. We all know that in some vague intuitive way this is what we must be doing when we make decisions now. The change I am predicting is, therefore, one of clarifying and bringing to the surface the variables and implicit logical models our minds must now be using in decision making, plus a big improvement in the logic of the models and their methods.

   I want to emphasize that I am not referring merely to decisions in the production and manufacturing areas, where such methods have thus far been most generally applied. One of the biggest advances is, I believe, going to be the extension of such thinking throughout the entire range of management decision making.
2. Increased emphasis will be placed on the job of management, or administration, *per se*, especially in the bigger companies. Management must make decisions, and it must get the decisions (plans and policies) carried out effectively. The need for effective adminis-

tration, *per se,* has been emphasized many times in recent years, and there is no need to labor it here. It is related to the growing size and complexity of business in all of its elements, to the greater need for conscious planning and control, to the growing difficulties of communication in large and complex organizations, and so on. It means less and less willingness to assume that good managers are just born and that there is nothing to do about it except let them develop as they will.

3. The social responsibility of the corporation and of the businessmen in it will bulk ever larger in the day-to-day life of most business firms. Explicit interest in the public good as a legitimate and important immediate goal of business behavior will continue to grow, in contrast to any simple emphasis on short-run profit maximization. Business will participate in a conscious fashion to an increasing extent in the social-economic processes of our democratic society. Business will be judged by the community increasingly on the way in which it participates in these processes, as well as on the older criteria of production and price. The role of the manager, therefore, will increasingly be that of a man with many masters, and it will behoove him to be sensitive to the pulse of the whole community, not merely to what goes on inside his factory walls. He will become increasingly a coordinator of diverse interests and "pulls" in the modern firm and in modern society—in contrast to simply being "the boss," responsible merely to a small group of stockholders.

EDUCATIONAL OBJECTIVES

To us, this analysis pointed strongly toward educational focus on the development of individual abilities to think, to adjust, and to learn independently in a world of change, after leaving the campus. It emphasized, certainly for men who will rise to managerial positions, the importance of becoming prepared to make and implement decisions on unknown problems, with unknown, yet-to-be-developed analytical tools. Our basic educational objective, we said, would therefore be to help each student acquire for himself:

1. *Competence in the orderly, analytical exploration and handling of problems.* Ability to identify, to size up, and to deal effectively with problems wherever they arise is the mark of the able professional man in any field. Development of an habitually orderly, rational approach to problems, in whatever area they arise, is a major goal of our educational program. This competence does not come automatically; it can be taught.

2. *Thorough and integrated understanding of fundamental knowledge in industrial administration.* The educational program emphasizes thorough knowledge, and effective use of that relatively small amount of fundamental knowledge which has *general* usefulness and applicability. This approach emphasizes the job of using basic concepts and principles in defining and handling problems—in contrast to trying to memorize "answers," detailed techniques, and rules of thumb, which are apt to be of little value when new problems arise in the future. These fundamental tools should be drawn from wherever they are available—mathematics, engineering, business, economics, the behavioral sciences. In a world of rapid change, unless the administrator has a firm grasp of fundamental knowledge, concepts, and principles, to serve as a framework in analyzing and handling diverse problems, he will be lost in a maze of facts and details.
3. *The habit of learning from experience, including habitual receptiveness to new ideas and new ways of doing things.* No school can teach more than a small portion of what the successful professional man must know; the rest he must learn for himself through life. In the modern world of rapid change, the man who does not continue to learn and grow is soon consigned to routine tasks. To grow he must observe, listen, and read widely and perceptively, constantly adjusting his thinking and practices in the light of what he learns.
4. *A basis for dealing effectively with other people, both in person and through written communication.* In modern industry, as in every other phase of modern life, ability to work effectively with other people is perhaps the most crucial of all skills. Administrative policy is made and carried out by individuals, working as parts of groups. Thorough understanding of human nature and of individual motivation in group relationships is increasingly essential for successful formation and execution of administrative policies.
5. *Thorough understanding of the economic, political, and social system in which he lives and in which industry operates.* As a man moves upward in industry, he becomes increasingly concerned with the relations between his business and the outside world. Business cycles, labor unions, political developments, taxes—such forces exercise powerful influence on him and on his firm. On grounds of both professional administrative training and responsible citizenship, genuine understanding of the over-all economic and social system is essential, parallel to the training for internal management of industrial affairs.
6. *Independence of thought and maturity of character.* For future managerial growth and for responsible citizenship, each man must develop an ability to reach conclusions *for himself* on a carefully

reasoned basis. As a foundation he must develop his own set of moral and ethical values, and he must recognize the need for working constructively with others who hold different sets of values. Only such a set of personal and social values can provide the foundation on which true independence of thought and maturity of judgment can rest.

It will be clear that this list of fundamental objectives could, with little change, be applied to most other areas of professional education, and this is as it should be. But the fundamental analytical tools developed, and the problem areas investigated, differentiate training for industrial administration from that in other professional fields.

EDUCATIONAL PROGRAM

What kind of educational program can develop these abilities? Carnegie's Graduate School of Industrial Administration provides a two year M.S. program in industrial administration specifically for men with undergraduate backgrounds in science, engineering, and mathematics. Each year we accept about fifty such men, mainly headed for managerial careers in industry, where combined training in engineering-science and in management is increasingly in demand. For this group, we have designed the following program. Remember, in this description of specific course areas, that overriding emphasis is placed on the six fundamental objectives indicated previously. Decision-making and getting decisions carried out effectively, plus the tools needed to achieve these goals, provide the organizing focus for the curriculum.

FIRST-YEAR PROGRAM

The first-year program contains three foundation stems and the beginning of application to the functional areas of business.

1. *A foundation stem—"the administrative process and human behavior"* (*the behavioral sciences*). This stem looks in detail at the firm as a going organization, and at the behavior of human beings as individuals and as groups in it. It draws heavily on the analytical concepts and approaches of the "behavioral sciences," as well as upon what we are beginning to build up in the theory of administration, in understanding these processes. It is concerned not primarily with the traditional descriptive aspects of business firms, but with analytical tools designed to help understand influence processes, motivation, communication processes, and so on in the organi-

zation. It is basically a tool stem, but there is heavy emphasis on getting students to apply these tools for themselves in analyzing business situations of all sorts. Unfortunately, the behavioral sciences as they now stand do not provide a large reservoir of immediately useful analytical concepts and models. But there is much there, and more every year. There is still a big job ahead in reforging many of the tools and in building new ones, cooperatively with behavioral scientists, to develop this stem from the modest level at which it must now operate to the crucial position it will surely have as the years go by.

2. *A foundation stem—"quantitative methods and mathematics."* This stem deals with the use of figures in business decision-making and control. It provides new tools of modern mathematics to the extent they are needed, and builds heavily on the available tools of accounting and statistics. The emphasis is not on training accountants or statisticians or mathematicians. Rather it is on the use of these disciplines to help make good managerial decisions and to implement them effectively. With the backgrounds our students have in engineering and science, it is possible to move rapidly in these areas and to make use of many of the modern developments which would not be feasible for regular business school groups. Here, as with the behavioral science foundation stem, there is much work to be done in shaping up the tools of modern quantitative methods so they will be most effective for managerial decision purposes.
3. *A foundation stem—"economic analysis and the environment of business."* Here intensive attention is given to the analytical tools of both micro- and macro-economics. Again, the goal is not to train men as professional economists, but to see that they have a good grasp of the central analytical concepts of modern economics in both areas—the behavior of the business firm as an individual unit in the market economy, and the over-all processes of economic growth and fluctuations. Attention is focused both on managerial applications of these tools and on understanding the functioning of the entire economic system. Repeatedly, for example, on the problem of investment decisions, students are placed in a position of looking at the same situation from a managerial decision-making point of view and from the point of view of its relationship to over-all economic development.
4. *The functional fields of business.* About three-fourths of the time in the first year is devoted to the three stems above. But students cannot learn to use analytical tools effectively without using them. In business, the so-called "functional fields" (production, marketing, and finance) provide the major problem areas for the exercise of decision-making and tool-using ability. Our conception is that these fields are essentially applied problem areas.

Take the production area as one example. Here we want the students to get a good exposure to the major types of problems faced by modern business in the whole area of production. In looking at these problems, we expect him to pick up a good bit of information about the modern world, but this is not the primary objective. Mainly he is asked to analyze problems in the subareas of the production function, bringing to bear the tools he is learning throughout the rest of the curriculum. There is not yet in the production area a cohesive discipline of analysis and organized knowledge, and we believe that many of the analytical tools needed can be provided by the three foundation stems above. For example, the modern developments in inventory control and production go back to mathematics and central concepts of economic theory. Getting satisfactory work levels out of production employees is much the same problem as for any other class of employees—here the tools of the behavioral sciences can help in understanding human motivation and response to different types of incentives and pressures. Good analysis of a plant layout problem requires understanding of engineering considerations, economic considerations, and of human considerations, and in all of them information comes largely in quantitative form. An optimal plant location decision requires, again, analysis using all the above tool areas, unless one is prepared to go by the old "hunch" procedure.

We approach the functional areas of marketing and finance in much the same way. But a reminder: in the first year, all these three functional areas together get only about a quarter of the total time —about the equivalent of a one-semester course in each, if you want to chop it up that way.

In summary, the first year is devoted mainly to foundation building, with a strong introduction to the methods of orderly problem-solving behavior; and to an introduction to the major functional areas in business largely through repetitive problem solving involving integrated use of the analytical tools and methods being learned concurrently.

SECOND-YEAR PROGRAM

The second-year program is built directly on the foundation of the first. About one-half the program is required, the rest elective.

1. A *required full-year course—"advanced business and engineering economics."* In this course we make heavy use of the strong quanti-

tative and engineering backgrounds of the men in the program. This is largely a problem-oriented course, with stress on both learning some of the new analytical approaches and actually using them in handling problems. All students learn to program and use the digital computer on managerial applications. Linear programming, quadratic decision rules, and some advanced managerial economics are customarily included, although the exact course coverage varies from year to year. Further mathematics, for example, some set theory, is taught as the students need it to handle the problems they are given. A major problem in the course each year involves going out into industry to handle a "real world" situation.

2. *A required full-year course—"administration and business policy."* This is what the title implies—an integrating, problem-oriented approach to a wide variety of business policy problems, mainly at the upper management level. The first half of the course is devoted to the modern theory of organizations and administration, building especially on the behavioral science stem of the first year. This is followed by intensive use of business policy cases, designed to integrate the various functional fields of business in making company-wide decisions and getting them carried out effectively. It also includes a new complex "business game," developed at Carnegie, which the students play through the entire semester, using the computer. In this, competitive teams must handle the subproblems within the production, marketing, and financial areas of the firm underlying the decisions made in the game, as well as the simple quick decisions ordinarily called for by currently used "business games."
3. *A required half- or full-year course—"ideas and social change."* This course stems from the propositions above concerning the likely future role of business and the businessman in a rapidly changing democratic society. Its goal is to provide perspective on the entire process of social change and of the shifting role of business in that process. Some semesters the course is focused on periods where modern business is intimately involved; other times, entirely different periods of change are analyzed. In all cases, the hope is that the student will begin to understand these processes and to improve his ability to live and lead effectively in tomorrow's world of rapid change.
4. *The rest of the second-year curriculum is elective.* Two comments.

   First, there is a restriction that no student can take more than one full year of advanced work in any of the special functional areas—production, marketing, and finance. This much specialization (about a year and a half of course work in a special area) seems to us to be enough to get the man well prepared to do good work when he takes a specific job on leaving the school. Most of his time in graduate school can be better spent building more fundamental tools than in accumulating more particularized knowledge, which I suggest is the main result when more time than this is spent in any one of the functional areas.

Second, in the elective courses available, we are placing stress on what we hope will be fundamental tools—analysis of small group behavior, advanced statistical analysis, modern mathematics, managerial economics, modern data processing, and so on.

At the end of the second year, our hope is that the graduate has a thorough foundation for long range advancement in management, and also a sound foundation to take on a job and do it well promptly on entering industry. *Most important, we hope he has the tools and the frame of mind to learn for himself as the world changes and as he faces different problems from field to field and from firm to firm.*

RELATIONSHIP OF I.A. TO I.E.

What is the relation of industrial administration, so conceived, to industrial engineering?

First, industrial engineering is frequently focused on a particular functional area of business (the one we call production), while industrial administration, at least as we conceive it, is essentially training for general management combined with training for engineering or science. This means that industrial administration, in our conception, is essentially a graduate program which presumes that the man already has a sound foundation in engineering-science. Parenthetically, we find that students from good industrial engineering undergraduate programs are well ahead of the game in the production area, and thus have more time free to push ahead either at a more advanced level in production or in other areas. But they are not usually much farther along than other strong engineering and science students in the other foundation areas.

This difference in breadth of objective and of background is the major difference between I.E. and I.A. as we see it. I should suppose the difference would stand out more strongly in comparing our graduate I.A. program with a graduate program in I.E., where there tends to be increasing depth in one special area of production. We believe—though of course we may be wrong—that the foundation a man gets in the I.A. program is about optimal for his going into the various jobs in industry that point toward management, in contrast to technician-type jobs. If a man wants to have a career in, say, operations research, we advise him to go on to the Ph.D. program, where he can push more deeply into the technical aspects of operations research in application to industrial problems.

How do we make use of the special abilities of men from mathematics, science, and engineering? In much the same way as a strong program in industrial engineering might do:

1. Throughout, we capitalize on the strong aptitude of the men in quantitative method and their ability in abstract thinking. In the quantitative methods area, we put major stress on modern statistical analysis, especially statistical decision theory.
2. We use their mathematics, and build in some further training in mathematics that would be completely out of the question for non-engineering-science-oriented people—some modern algebra, matrices, advanced calculus—and stress the *use* of these mathematical concepts in managerial analysis.
3. All students learn to use our digital computer, and we expect them to actually use it, including programming it independently, on some project.
4. In the production and managerial economics areas especially, we push the men faster and further than would be feasible in a business school graduate program.
5. All students are thoroughly exposed to the modern techniques that are often called "operations research"—mathematical programming, game theory, queueing theory, and so on, especially in the required second-year course in "Advanced Business and Engineering Economics." There is a chance for those who want to go on further to do so.
6. We make increasing use of "business games" as teaching devices, especially in the business policy area but also in the functional areas of business. For example, students in the advanced production courses have developed a complete business game of their own, which has forced them to clarify and quantify all the major interrelationships in the decision-making process in the production area.

The differences between industrial administration and industrial engineering may be substantial. But they surely shade into one another, and they have much in common.

CONCLUSIONS

Does the development of industrial administration programs at the graduate level, for engineering graduates, have useful implications for undergraduate teaching? Though I do so with humility, since I am not an engineer, I suggest that much of what I have argued above is applicable to undergraduate teaching in industrial engineering or in a special program designed to combine training for management and engineering. Increasingly, industrial engineers will need to understand the total management problem to do a good job, as they move from narrower tasks like time and motion study and plant layout to broader tasks such as decision rules for entire production processes. Modern research has demonstrated conclusively that optimum inventory control and production scheduling policies can only be arrived at with full understanding of demand and marketing conditions. Much can be accomplished by suboptimizing, but eventually managerial decisions must take into account the interrelations among the many functions and activities of the business. As this occurs, the case for broader training for industrial engineers, encompassing an integrated approach to management education something like the one above, will become increasingly relevant and important.

At the undergraduate level it is clear that the pace would have to be much slower than I have implied above, and that more stress would have to be placed on helping the student to learn and apply the analytical tools he uses. Clearly, the less mature man, even though he is of high ability, has a harder job using abstractions and seeing how they can be utilized in handling real world problems.

But two other criticisms must be faced, if one takes seriously the kind of teaching implied above for undergraduates.

First, is the typical undergraduate high enough in ability to benefit from such general, problem-solving education? Even if we recognize that the typical undergraduate is unlikely ever to be president of General Motors or of anything else, the rate of obsolescence of particularized knowledge and particularized training is so great that the more fundamental type of training still seems clearly better for him—even though he gets less out of it than would the more advanced, higher quality student. Why should we fill his head with knowledge that will be largely out of date in a few years, and of which, from all the studies we have, he will remember very little indeed in a few years anyhow? Worse, if he does remember it, the answers he has memorized today are likely to be wrong for the different problems of tomorrow, whether they be answers on how to schedule production, how to organize an accounting department, or how to set market quotas. After scaling down final performance aspirations drastically from the graduate level, my own conclusion is that if we cannot count on the average student's getting more out of a reasonably fundamental program than out of a detailed descriptive program, we should re-examine our entire concept of university education in the scheme of things.

Second, the related criticism that a typical undergraduate will probably be a specialist all his life and ought to be trained thoroughly in some specialty so at least he can do that well. It certainly is true that many of our undergraduates will not even achieve middle management positions, although I am doubtful that we can always pick out which ones will move up and which ones will not. But assume that a man probably will remain a specialized person. First, the evidence is clear that he is likely to end up being a specialist in a different area than the one he picked for specialization in college. This casts doubt upon highly specialized training.

More fundamental is the main point made above that highly-specialized training is not the most useful training even for the specialist. To check this point, go back and read the industrial engineering textbooks of twenty-five years ago, and see how much that is there you would want a good industrial engineer to use as his main set of tools today. At that level of detail, it may well be that today's best industrial engineering practice will do as much harm as good if it is used exactly twenty-five years from today. In conclusion, I suggest that a careful look backward and ahead provides an overwhelming testimonial to fundamental and generalized, as contrasted to highly specialized, college training in industrial engineering, and in industrial administration.

EDUCATIONAL APPROACHES IN OTHER COUNTRIES

Academic preparation for improvement function activities has been largely an American activity until recently. This situation is gradually changing, for many other countries are making extensive use of operations research, management science, and industrial engineering—both in its traditional and in its modern scope. Academic programs have been started in many countries as a natural response to the emerging need of business and industry for individuals with specialized education to deal with improvement function activities.

As an example of this development the program in administration engineering of Kieo University, Tokyo, Japan has been selected.* This program, which is geared to the needs of Japan, is illustrative of the natural development of educational resources in response to the needs of a country. The same general factors are in operation in many other countries—and the academic response is somewhat similar. Specialized educational programs are being started. They usually have some similarity one to another, but they also have differences reflecting the varying specific needs and abilities of the local situations.

THE UNIVERSITY

Founded in 1858, Kieo University is a well-established and highly respected university in Tokyo, which has the usual university colleges and programs. Engineering was started in 1939 and developed along the traditional lines of specialization in mechanical, electrical, and chemical technologies. A recognition of the growing need for new engineering specialties became evident in the mid-1950's. Subsequently the Department of Instrumentation Engineering was organized, in order to keep up with the demands of the coming era of automation. A Department of Administration Engineering was established in 1959 in response to the growing needs for specialization in the wedding of technology and management. The instrumentation engineering program is primarily technical in orientation and concentrates upon control technology as related to various manufacturing processes. The administration engineering program concentrates upon the combining of technology and management, with less emphasis on automation and control technology and more stress on managerial planning and control. The two programs represent a very powerful approach to modern industrial engineering and preparation for improvement function endeavors. For the sake of brevity, only the administration engineering activities will be discussed.

The objective of the administration engineering program is to prepare future technical management leadership and staff specialists to deal with problems of combining technology and management. The basic concept of the program is to combine engineering and administration, stressing a unification of control concepts and techniques as they can be used to achieve greater efficiency in managerial and production activities.

* Information concerning the administration engineering program of Kieo University was obtained from Dr. Ziro Yamauti, head professor of the department and from personal contact with the faculty.

THE PROGRAM

The administration engineering program first requires the student to achieve a high degree of proficiency in the fundamentals of engineering and mathematics and then to take required and elective courses in work study, operations research, electronic computers, and general management.

Work study places emphasis on the productive and administrative techniques for analyzing production and clerical work based upon the fundamentals of mechanical, electrical, and chemical engineering as well as on the technology of motion and time study and other traditional industrial engineering subjects. Specialization in this area is intended to prepare the student for assignments in the traditional areas of industrial engineering.

Operations research requires study of statistics, probability, modern mathematics, operations research techniques, production planning, and managerial control. Specialization in this area prepares the student for work with quality control, design of experiments, operations research, statistical research, management planning and research, and similar activities.

Specialization in the electronic computer area stresses both the design of information and control systems and the use of electronic computers for business and scientific-engineering purposes.

The area of general management includes study in economic analysis, managerial control, accounting control, cost control, profit planning and control, and related subjects. Stress is placed upon control procedures, synthesis, and the integration of engineering and administration.

The faculty of the new department is composed of well-qualified individuals with academic and professional experience not only in engineering but also in economics, psychology, mathematics, physical sciences, and commerce. Close contacts are maintained with industry and with the other faculties of the university. A thesis is required of all students, which may be theoretical or practical, and may be developed from an industrial setting.

Other manifestations of close university-industry relationships are: sponsored research, an arrangement for industrial personnel to associate with the department as special researchers to pursue specific projects from an academic base, a "special student" arrangement allowing study in various areas by industrial people, and a series of seminars and short-courses sponsored by the department. Seminar topics include applied statistics, human engineering, motion and time study, cost control, operations research, and managerial mathematics.

Although the department was organized in early 1959, progress in development and acceptance has been rapid. Twenty students were graduated in 1962, almost 50 in 1963, and by 1965 the graduating classes will reach the planned level of 80 to 120 per year. Graduate programs at both the M.S. and Ph.D. levels were placed in operation in April, 1963.

It is the author's observation that the program is one of quality, and that the faculty is indeed very well qualified. The results already achieved lead me to conclude that the program will have a substantial influence upon improvement function activities in Japan.

SUMMARY

Requirements for educational programs dealing with improvement function activities have been undergoing an expansion in the United States and other countries. Although no really uniform pattern has emerged, the most promising approaches seem to stress an engineering or technological base. Three representative educational approaches have been presented. Many other variations exist.

REFERENCES

1. Robert N. Lehrer, "Exploiting Science and Engineering as Aids to Management: A Modern Industrial Engineering Approach," *Management International,* Vol. 2, No. 2, 1962, p. 3.
2. G. L. Bach, "Industrial Administration: Education for 1980," *The Journal of Industrial Engineering*, September–October 1959, p. 390.
3. Adolph E. Grunewald, "Management Education in Ferment," *Management International,* No. 2, March–April 1961, p. 73.
4. Further information on the changing nature of industrial engineering can be found in the following:
   Austin Weston (ed.), "The Emerging Role of Industrial Engineering," *The Journal of Industrial Engineering,* Special Issue Vol. XII, No. 2, Part 2, March–April 1961.
   R. N. Lehrer, "Changing Industrial Engineering Practices in the United States," *Work Study and Industrial Engineering,* April 1959, p. 112.
   The PERT system, developed in conjunction with the research and development management of the Polaris missile system, is another example of high level *modern* industrial engineering effort. For some details see:
   D. G. Malcolm, et al., "Application of a Technique for R & D Evaluation," *Operations Research,* September–October 1959.

D. G. Malcolm and Alan J. Rowe (eds.), *Management Control Systems*, Wiley, New York, 1960.

5. Robert A. Gordon and James E. Howell, *Higher Education for Business*, Harper, New York, 1959.
6. Frank C. Pierson, *The Education of American Businessmen*, McGraw-Hill, New York, 1959.

Additional information on industrial engineering programs can be found in the September–October 1962 issue of *The Journal of Industrial Engineering* (Vol. XII, No. 5), which is devoted to educational programs accredited by the Engineer's Council for Professional Development.

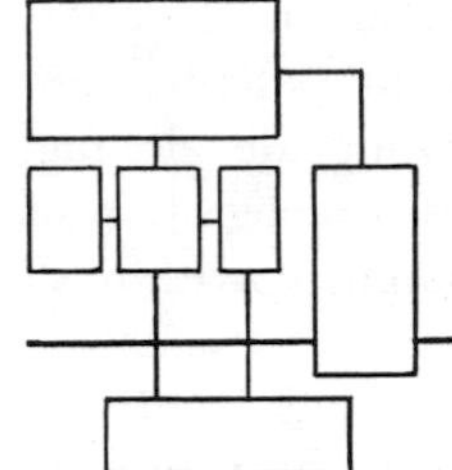

CHAPTER 24

WHERE DO WE GO FROM HERE?

THE MAIN OBJECTIVES of this book have been to draw attention to various processes of improvement within organizations and to develop the concept that improvement can be systematically and continually pursued and achieved within all organizations.

An improvement function has been advocated as an approach to systematic pursuit of improvement. This function deserves to be recognized as a major functional activity, with the responsibility for unifying and giving support to all improvement activities within the organization. It should not disrupt what is being done on behalf of improvement, but make existing improvement efforts more effective and add breadth and depth to an organization-wide quest for continual improvement.

Within many organizations it may be appropriate to recognize the improvement function in a formal way, by the establishment of a corporate position with primary responsibility for improvement activities. This may involve the creation of a "vice-president of improvement" position (or a similarly designated top management position) with responsibility for the organization, implementation, execution, and coordination of organization-wide improvement activities. Within other companies these responsibilities perhaps can be discharged within the present organizational structure. In either case, it is of considerable importance that the quest for continual improvement—the pursuit of betterment and efficiency—be overtly recognized as a major responsibility, and that plans for achieving needed improvement be formulated and discharged with recognition not only of the need for improvement, but also of the many resources of common sense, science, and technology that can be used and exploited for the benefit of the organization. This requires an awareness of the vast range of these resources, a systematic analysis and assessment of opportunities for service to management and opportunities for potential improvement, and a dynamic set of strategies for cultivating, developing, and implementing improvements. Above all, it requires a recognition of the respectability of efficiency and a desire for its attainment within all facets of an organization.

In developing the above points, a variety of materials has been presented. Some have been a collection of concepts. Some have been inspirational in nature. Some have drawn upon experiences and case examples. Some of these experiences have been critically analyzed while others have been presented for analysis by the reader. A limited amount of "how-to-do-it" suggestions has also been presented. Out of these varied materials, it is hoped that the reader will develop his own thoughts and concepts of the management of improvement endeavors and a conviction that the process of improvement can be systematically managed.

Even though many topics have been presented, many others of importance have not. The specific tools or techniques for developing improvements have been omitted. This has been intentional, for these materials are readily available from many sources. The techniques for systematically analyzing the needs and opportunities for improvement—the various diagnostic tools—have also been omitted. These deserve a separate presentation. Additional examples of improvement function activities would also be desirable. However, the present volume does provide the background concepts and guides which will allow interested individuals to either initiate an improvement function activity or to unify and broaden existing improvement endeavors to approach the scope and depth of a true organization-wide improvement function.

Where do we go from here? It is hoped that we go toward the development and implementation of broad-gage and organization-wide improvement function activities as a means of continually striving for and achieving improvement within the many production and service organizations so vital to our social and economic well being. To do those things which we as individuals and as a people would like to do, it is imperative that we continue to effect improvements in all facets of our activities, and that we improve the rate with which improvement is achieved. This is the challenge. We have the concepts. We have many examples of successful organization for such activities from which we can gain understanding about how we should proceed. And we have considerable information about strategic and tactical considerations which should help assure success. True, we have need for further development of understanding and approaches to recognizing, evaluating, and solving our problems of improvement, but we do now have a reasonably solid theoretical base upon which to build improvement function activities.

As a summary review, some of the guiding thoughts presented in earlier pages are again presented. The underlying philosophy of the book has been:

1. Approaches to improvement should serve the entire organization, as a whole and in all its parts as related to the whole.
2. Improvement is a management responsibility. In a sense all individuals within an organization are managers. However, the heaviest obligations for improvements efforts are at the top.
3. Improvement can be achieved by:
   management improvement
   better systems for managing
   better systems relative to those being managed, including
      improved design of products and services
      improved design of operations
      improved design of processes
      improved design of systems of operation
4. Improvement can be achieved by management helping themselves.
5. Improvement can be achieved by staff support and assistance.
6. Improvement can be achieved by exploitation of science and technology —and experience and common sense—in the areas of:
   systems being managed
   systems for managing
   the "art" of managing
7. The efficiency of the process of improvement can be improved by:
   retaining those aspects of existing approaches which have proven to be of value
   improving the effectiveness and utility of available approaches by modification and adaption
   devising new, broader, and more effective approaches
8. Any organization can increase its rate of improvement by establishing "improvement function" responsibilities as one of the basic functional parts of the organization. This function is charged with the responsibility for assisting, guiding, and supporting the quest for improvement by:
   helping to determine what areas within the organization need improvement
   helping to devise strategies and tactics for achieving the desired improvements
   helping to achieve useful and lasting application of improvement

providing strong guidance for the continual and systematic quest for and achievement of improvement throughout the organization.

There have been attempts to develop a broad improvement function within many organizations. Some of these have been outstandingly successful. Many have failed. The successes have been greatly influenced by the presence of key factors. The failures have been greatly influenced by their lack. These factors are:

1. Management support and vision relative to the improvement function—usually originating with top management and then spreading enthusiastically to all other levels.
2. A dynamic, flexible, and responsive function—proceeding according to the needs of the organization and the serving of these needs at the appropriate time.
3. Keen awareness of the strategy of improvement endeavors—using appropriate strategies for detecting needs, and for satisfying them. These strategies require a breadth of vision and competency, and also a narrowness and depth within a wide variety of specialized activities.
4. Personnel participating in the improvement function with technical competency in both the broad and the narrow problem areas, and a nontechnical competency to achieve harmonious endeavors in pursuit of improvement.
5. A dual approach: (a) strengthening of the manager's position and the line organization, and (b) effective staff supports to further strengthen the manager's position by extending and expanding the skills at his disposal.
6. An exploitation of science and technology for management's use.
7. Practice of the concept of dual management responsibility: (a) to accomplish results from the activity for which responsible, and (b) to continually pursue and achieve improvement in achieving these results.

APPENDIX

APPROACHES TO TEACHING MANAGEMENT OF IMPROVEMENT

Although the main theme of this book may not seem to be oriented directly in scope nor in presentation to text usage, its use as a text for university courses has been a primary consideration in its preparation. There are a number of ways in which it can be used as the main text for a variety of courses. The most obvious areas (other than those which deal directly with the management of improvement) are introductory programs in industrial engineering, management, business administration, and operations research—courses organized to provide the student with an introduction to and a broad view of their intended field of specialization. This type of course is also of considerable value to students from other programs, as an elective or required course to supplement their specialized studies and to provide a better appreciation of how their future endeavors are likely to relate to the operation of an organization. Similar courses are also found at the graduate level, often provided as a transition to orient students to a graduate field differing from their undergraduate specialization.

The organization of these courses and the ways in which this book can be used as a text should be individual—tailored to the specific needs. To illustrate how this can be done and to relate some of the author's experience in using the text material, the following general comments are made. (The author would be pleased to correspond directly with individuals desiring more detailed information.)

DIFFERING APPROACHES

This book can be used as the only text material, with assignments, lectures, and discussion following the chapter sequence, or the instructor may select the sequence of materials he desires. The author's personal preference is to use the book along with supplementary materials. Some of the various approaches to doing this are:

1. To provide explanation of and expansion upon the various terminology and concepts encountered in each chapter. This can be done by lecture or by a combination of lecture and class discussion.
2. To require the students to search out appropriate library materials for all new terminology and concepts as they are encountered in the assigned text material. Written reports or class discussion, monitored and guided by the instructor, can be used to clarify and consolidate comprehension of these materials.
3. To supplement the text and lecture materials with movies and visual aids.
4. To use simulation exercises as a supplementary, and a very intriguing, learning-teaching device.
5. To use project and problem assignments as a complement to the assigned reading and to the class discussion and lectures.
6. To supplement the text with assigned reading materials, and with additional topical material introduced by the instructor.

The most satisfactory approach in the author's experience and opinion is to combine elements of the above—to use the book as the main text with the supplementary material introduced as follows:

1. Terminology and concepts: Each student is required to identify, define, and briefly describe all new terminology and concepts encountered in the assigned reading. This is done by independent library research, with written reports submitted periodically during the term, graded, and then discussed in class.
2. Movies: Many excellent movies illustrating various facets of management and improvement activities are available. An effective approach to using movies requires them to be considered by the instructor and students as an important teaching-learning device and not as a pleasant diversion. This can be done by proper integration of the movies with the main topics of the course, adequate introduction of the movies before showing, and evaluation and consolidation of the "message" of the movie after it has been shown. The author has found it to be effective to use one to

two page outlines summarizing the highlights of each movie. After the general subject matter of the movie has been introduced to the class, the outlines are distributed for the students to read, the movie is shown (with some illumination in the room so that notes can be made on the outline), and then after the showing the main points of the movie are discussed with the class. The students are expected to thoroughly comprehend the materials of the movie and are responsible for and tested on these matters. A sample outline of one movie is presentd in Table A-1.

Selection from among available movies should be with full consideration of the specific objectives of the course and a careful evaluation of the content and value of the individual movies. The author has used the set of visual aids listed in Table A-2 in an undergraduate course Introduction to Industrial Engineering. New movies are continually being evaluated, some of them added to the list, and others removed.

3. Simulation: There are many simulation exercises which can be used as motivational techniques to encourage student learning. One that has been very effective in the author's experience, used in conjunction with the text, is the UCLA top management simulation exercise. This is a competitive simulation exercise, which allows students to develop some appreciation for the complexity of managerial decision-making and the role of staff support in the operation of an enterprise. There is some question about how much is actually learned about real life decision-making from such an experience, but there is little question about the student motivation to learn more about the real life processes. With some encouragement and guidance from the instructor, even the average students perform exceptionally well in independent study and learning.

   The simulation exercise is usually started the second or third week of the term, after the concepts of simulation and the operation of a corporation have been briefly introduced. The class is divided into company teams of about four students. The companies formulate their basic business policies, undergo a trial simulation period, analyze what is happening, and then start the simulation exercise in earnest. Decisions are made approximately every other class meeting, and the simulation results are returned to the teams during the intervening meetings. A period of two to three years operation is simulated during the term. Each team is guided by their own policy statements, analyzes the results, formulates their decisions, re-evaluates their policies, and maintains a running summary of the "corporate" experiences. A final report summarizing and critically analyzing the simulation experience is required toward the end of the term. The instructor encourages the students to search out library materials which will help them understand the analysis of performance data and the decision-making process. Little class time is devoted to the simulation exercise other than an occasional five or ten minutes spent in discussing results and raising questions which will stimulate and guide students in their independent study.

TABLE A-1

Simulogs (The Rand Corporation)

To keep alert and progressive a modern organization must constantly improve its administration and decision-making ability. Systems simulation is one new tool for improving these management practices. This film illustrates simulation in terms of the Air Force logistics system.

I. Logistics is the art of getting what is needed, where it is needed, when it is needed, from where it is manufactured and stored.

II. To study this complex problem the Air Force established a logistics simulation laboratory. Such simulation has as its purpose:
   - A. To study and analyze the organizational and functional interactions between segments of the system, and therefore lead to suggested changes and improvements.
   - B. To develop new policies and to thoroughly test them without disrupting the existing organization.

III. A systems simulation is set up and conducted by:
   - A. Using known operating features of the existing organization to set up the "first" simulated system.
   - B. Using the established simulation system as a reference point to design new simulations that will test new and alternative policies.
   - C. Operating the simulated systems simultaneously under controlled and identical laboratory conditions.

IV. As an example the Air Force established two simulated logistics systems (LS 1 and LS 2) to test new procurement policies, namely:
   - A. Hi-value procurement using deferred buying during "Phase-in" periods.
   - B. Low-value procurement for class 2 and 3 supplies considering such factors as:
     1. Warehouse and paper work costs
     2. Cost of the item
     3. Transportation costs
     4. Shortage risks
     5. Demand rates

     (This often results in purchasing larger quantities of low cost items.)
   - C. Relying heavily on automatic computing equipment for routine decisions.

V. The real world data used in the simulation are of prime importance in insuring the reality and validity of the simulation.

VI. Computers help model and scale down the real world. They:
   - A. Record and store all simulation data.
   - B. Prepare daily and quarterly status reports on the simulated operation.
   - C. Simulate daily operations including the coordination of simulated decisions with operating data.
   - D. Act as an automatic source of minor decision making.
   - E. Are used extensively in summarizing and analyzing test results.

VII. In summary, simulation can:
   - A. Be a considerable time saver in testing new policies—in the Air Force simulation three years of logistics operations were condensed into three months.
   - B. Test procedures and policies under situations of realistic stress and crisis.
   - C. Allow several people to operate the entire organization without disrupting existing operating conditions.

TABLE A-2

List of Films and Film Strips

Management Concepts for Depot Maintenance
  USAF Film SFP 480
McGraw-Hill Industrial Management Series Films
  Internal Organization
  Risk and Forecasting
  Product Development
  Physical Facilities
  Materials Control
  Production Control
  Production Control II
  Job Evaluation
  Quality Control
  Methods Analysis
McGraw-Hill Nature of Work Series Films
  The Clerk
  The Man on the Assembly Line
  The Skilled Worker
  The General Foreman
  The Department Manager
  The Vice President
Electronics for Accounting and Business
  Arthur Anderson Co.
This is Automation
  General Electric Co.
Numerical Control
  Boeing Airplane Co.
Production 5118
  Film No. 588, Modern Talking Picture Service, Inc.
American Management Association O.R. Film Strip Series
  Operations Research: What It Is
  Operations Research: How It Works
  Operations Research: Scope and Limitations
Simulogs
  The Rand Corporation
Breakthrough
  U.S. Navy
A Matter of Degree (Film Strip)
  Crown Zellerbach Corp.
The Information Machine
  International Business Machines Corp.
Systems and Data Services (SdS) (Film Strip)
  International Harvester Co.
The Tyranny of Large Numbers
  Western Electric Co.

4. Projects: A variety of projects can be used to supplement and extend the materials covered in class and in assigned reading. One project which has proven to be effective requires each student to select or hypothesize a product to be used as the basis for starting a business and to outline in chronological order all considerations and decisions which would confront him in his first five years of business. Execution of the project is done independently, using any appropriate library materials. A report is required about midterm.
5. Additional topics: The presentation of additional topics by demonstration and lecture is desirable in many cases. These may be selected to meet the needs for rounding out the course and may include such things as:
   - presentation of project summaries from research and consulting experiences of the instructor
   - summary of work presented in periodical publications, selected to illustrate specific problem situations or analytical tools and approaches
   - presentations summarizing the highlights of subsequent courses in the academic program.

The possible approaches to course organization are infinite. The above suggestions have been made to indicate a few ways in which the book *Management of Improvement: Concepts, Organization and Strategy* can be used. They reflect the author's experience and should not be regarded as the only effective approaches.

INDEX